Introduction to

MICROORGANISMS

By LaVERNE RUTH THOMPSON
R.N., M.A., M.S. in Public Health
ASSOCIATE PROFESSOR OF NURSING EDUCATION,
TEACHERS COLLEGE, COLUMBIA UNIVERSITY

Third Edition – Illustrated

PHILADELPHIA – LONDON – 1954

W. B. SAUNDERS COMPANY

PREFACE TO THE THIRD EDITION

THE third edition of INTRODUCTION TO MICROORGANISMS has been written for the student whose chief interest lies in the field of health and welfare instead of in bacteriology per se. This book, therefore, places emphasis on those life activities of microorganisms which influence man and his environment. The content throughout has been selected in terms of public health implications to help the student develop an understanding of and an interest in the control and prevention of disease. Since the student is not required to recognize and identify microorganisms, relatively little space is devoted to the minute details of structure and chemistry which differentiate one from another. Instead the attention is directed to such questions as: *Where does this parasite live? How does it enter the body? How does it produce disease? How does the host respond? How does it affect the welfare of man? Can the disease which it causes be prevented? Does this organism respond to antibiotics?* These and similar questions make up the core of the book.

The first chapters have been written in terms so simple that they can be understood by persons with no previous knowledge of the subject. Then as new concepts are developed, they are incorporated into the succeeding chapters of the book. As a result, the vocabulary of Unit IV is much more difficult than that of Unit I; it is assumed that the student will acquire essential terms as the course progresses. (It is also assumed that the student will have had some introduction to chemistry.) In order to give reality to the subject, the author refers to the general experience of the student and to observations which can be made in the laboratory. Suitable laboratory exercises will be found at the end of Units I, II, III, and IV. Current research is mentioned to promote an awareness and an appreciation of the contribution of research to the ever-developing body of knowledge. Experimental evidence, too, is presented from time to time to help the student acquire the critical attitude which demands and considers the evidence before accepting a new concept or revising an old, established idea.

Although the general pattern of the book remains essentially unchanged, each chapter has been revised in the light of current research. The book has been enlarged by the addition of a more detailed discussion of the physiology of bacteria and new chapters on the ecology of microorganisms and on parasites as stress agents.

The book is divided into five units: I. Fundamentals of Microbiology, II. Bacteria and Environment, III. Parasites and the Host, IV. The Pathogens, and V. Man against Parasites. Unit I deals with the common forms of microorganisms, their characteristics and activities, and their relation to each other and to higher forms of life.

Unit II deals with the effect of environmental factors on microorganisms with special consideration of those variables which determine the success or failure of disinfection and sterilization procedures. Unit III considers parasitism, infection, immunity, chemotherapy, environmental sanitation, and hospital sanitation. Emphasis is placed on the relation of life activities of microorganisms to methods of control. The aim has been to develop a unified understanding of host-parasite relationships by stressing similarities in parasites rather than their differences. This approach is supported by extensive investigations which indicate that harmful parasites, be they large or small, tend to injure living cells and that body response to such injury usually includes inflammation, hypersensitivity, and antibody formation. A chapter, *Parasites as Stress Agents,* has been included to aid the student to gain perspective on the relation of pathogenic microorganisms to human disease. The voluminous research of the last decade has demonstrated that illness is commonly due to multiple stresses and that the role of microorganisms is often secondary. Also important is the evidence that inapparent or subclinical infections are common in some infectious diseases. This does not mean that microorganisms are unimportant. It does mean that in viewing health problems one must consider not only microorganisms but also the other stresses which impinge upon human beings. Unit IV presents the common pathogens and the infections which they cause. The parasites have been grouped according to their mode of entry to aid the student in learning methods of control and prevention. These are listed according to their biological classification at the head of each chapter. Unit V traces man's efforts to control disease by the establishment of local, national, and international agencies.

As in previous editions, both primary and secondary sources have been used. The bibliography at the end of each chapter lists the sources used in the revision and retains some of the more important older references. The photographs used in the text have been borrowed from various sources, including the Journal of Bacteriology, Archives of Pathology, Journal of Immunology, Journal of Pathology and Bacteriology, American Review of Tuberculosis, Journal of Experimental Medicine, and Public Health Reports. The origin of each picture is indicated in the descriptive title. Drawings have been contributed by the following artists: Mrs. Peggy C. James, Daisy Stillwell, and Hakola Studios. The author is indebted to the friends who have read parts of the book while it was in preparation, and especially to Mrs. Gertrude MacFarland, Mrs. Edythe Leddy, and Miss Ruth Garvey who gave invaluable assistance with the manuscript.

LA VERNE THOMPSON

New York City

CONTENTS

Unit II   *BACTERIA AND ENVIRONMENT*

Unit IV   THE PATHOGENS

Unit I   FUNDAMENTALS OF MICROBIOLOGY

CHAPTER 1   *Introduction*

MICROBIOLOGY is the study of living things so minute they cannot be seen with the unaided eye. These tiny bodies are a constant and intimate part of man's environment. They abound in the earth he walks upon, in the air he breathes, in the food he eats; they live between the teeth, in the sweat glands, in the crypts of the tonsils, and in the intestines. In fact, they are everywhere. The reader may well ask, How do we know that microorganisms exist? If they do exist, how can one study the unseen? Can anything so small be important? What, if any, is their relation to man and his welfare? The following pages are directed toward answering these questions.

Man's survival and welfare depend upon the presence of plants and animals—visible and invisible. The benefits conferred by edible plants and animals are self-evident as are the dangers from lions, tigers, rattlesnakes, and poison ivy. Less obvious is the role of microscopic animals and plants. Many microorganisms increase the fertility of the soil thus

1

insuring a constant food supply for man and animals. Some cause economic loss by spoiling food or deteriorating fibers, while others bring about desirable changes and are therefore useful in the processing of fabrics, leather, cheeses, and alcoholic beverages. In brief, microorganisms are constantly at work changing our external environment.

Man's internal environment too may be influenced by a variety of small plants and animals which have adapted themselves to life on the surface or within body tissues. Such organisms often cause injury, and interfere with the normal function of the body, thus producing disease. In like manner, certain organisms cause disease in plants and animals. Indeed, the nuisance value of this group is so high that one tends to forget the many essential benefits derived from the activities of other microorganisms. A knowledge of the behavior and habits of these organisms is essential if one is to direct and utilize those organisms which produce desirable changes or to exercise some degree of control over those which produce disease.

SCOPE OF STUDY

There are thousands of species of microorganisms—far too many for thorough study. This volume will devote some space to the organisms which change the external environment, but the major interest will be centered on those which cause disease in man, with emphasis on the characteristics which make possible the prevention or control of disease. Disease-producing organisms vary greatly in their size and complexity. Some are so small that each consists of a single microscopic unit called a *cell*. Others consist of many cells and may even be large enough to see without the aid of a microscope. The larger forms are exemplified by a large variety of flat and round worms. Many of the microscopic forms interesting to health workers are simple in structure. In fact, some are so simple that it is difficult to tell whether they are plants or animals. As would be expected, microorganisms exhibit significant differences in appearance, life activities, and the places they inhabit. For convenience they may be assigned to one of three groups:

1. Those resembling plants: the *algae* (contain chlorophyll) and microscopic *fungi*
(without chlorophyll), *molds,*
yeasts, and *bacteria*
2. Those resembling animals: the *protozoa*
3. Those without distinctive
plant or animal
characteristics: the *viruses* and *rickettsias*

The viruses and rickettsias are disease-producing organisms
which live within the cells of plants or animals. The protozoa
are one-celled animals. The plantlike organisms include two
groups: the algae which produce chlorophyll and the fungi
which lack chlorophyll. Such a classification is arbitrary and
does not always fit the facts. In reality many microorganisms
resemble both plant and animal cells. For example, certain
protozoa contain chlorophyll (plant characteristic) while
many microscopic fungi require complex food materials (animal characteristic). But even with its limitations this grouping
of organisms is useful and will be followed. This book will
include discussions of the microscopic organisms which grow
in the dark: the fungi, the protozoa, and the viruses and
rickettsias. The algae will be omitted because they do not
grow in the absence of light and, furthermore, are incapable
of producing disease.

Microorganisms have many characteristics which are common to living organisms as a whole. For example, all are composed of protoplasm and all must carry out similar functions
in order to survive. For convenience, therefore, in this book the
activities of bacterial cells will be considered in some detail
and this description will be used as a basis for understanding
the life processes of other types of cells. A consideration of
cell substance or protoplasm and of its fundamental characteristics is now in order.

COMPOSITION AND BASIC CHARACTERISTICS OF MICROORGANISMS

Like other living things, microorganisms are composed of
definite organized masses of *protoplasm* called *cells.* Many
exist as single cells—each unit capable of independent life.

Protoplasm is a clear, sticky gel composed of water, dissolved salts and globules or granules of fats, carbohydrates, and proteins. This gel has a fibrous, stringy texture thought to be due to the arrangement of amino acids in long polypeptide chains. Water is an essential part of all protoplasm because it constitutes the important solvent of the cell and of the surrounding medium. Water also takes an active part in such chemical reactions as hydrolysis and synthesis. Protoplasm is remarkable for its ability to release and utilize energy and to transform nonliving materials (foods) into living protoplasm. Another characteristic of all protoplasm is its ability to respond to stimuli—that is, *irritability*. In microorganisms, irritability is often manifested by changes in the rate of growth, reproduction, or chemical reactions, and sometimes by movement.

One might question the ability of any microscopic mass of protoplasm to produce significant effects. Microorganisms as a group have, however, remarkable ability for rapid multiplication; so they tend not to exist long as solitary units. For example, a single colon bacterium (*Escherichia coli*) introduced into a suitable fluid containing foods may, if conditions are favorable, give rise to over a million new bacteria in a period of five or six hours. Each new cell, like its predecessor, is a unit capable of preparing and using material for growth and for securing energy to do its work. Thus in this short time a single cell has initiated processes which have removed from the environment enough raw materials to build a million cells and has returned detectable quantities of waste products.

IMPORTANCE OF MICROORGANISMS

Everyone is familiar with some of the changes produced by microorganisms, as, for example, the souring of milk, the spoiling of food, and the decomposition of plant and animal matter. One sees that microorganisms must be considered very effective agents of change. Man's concern is to encourage some changes and to discourage or stop others. Sanitation procedures are designed to remove, kill, or exclude disease-producing organisms. Food preservation consists of processes that change the food or the environment to prevent the action of microorganisms. In contrast, whole industries are concerned with growing microorganisms to obtain some desirable product. The following are typical examples of processes utilizing the chemical activities of microorganisms for the benefit of human beings.

Agriculture   Tilling the soil is really a process of growing microorganisms in order to grow plants. Fertile top soil, sometimes called the "living soil," contains a large and varied population. A gram (less than a teaspoonful) of rich well-cultivated soil may contain 20,000,000 bacteria; 20,000,000 actinomycetes; 1,000,000 molds; 1,000,000 protozoa; and perhaps 800,000 algae. These are essential for the growth of crops. Fertilizer (in the form of manure, green plants, leaves, and often of inorganic salts) supplies food and a suitable growth medium for bacteria and other microorganisms which in turn supply nitrates and other essential compounds essential for plant growth. Digging in the soil provides the needed oxygen. In the case of the nitrogen-fixing bacteria, the microorganisms are often planted with the seeds of peas, beans, and alfalfa; otherwise, they are provided by the soil itself or by the fertilizer.

Alcoholic Fermentation   Long before microorganisms were known to exist, they were used in making fermented drinks. The juice of grapes or other fruits was allowed to stand until yeasts normally present on the skins of the fruit produced enzymes that changed the sugars to alcohol and carbon dioxide. Beer was produced by the action of yeasts on malt and hops. Success in beer or wine making depends upon encouraging certain yeasts and in keeping out other microorganisms which spoil the taste of the product.

To make bread, yeast is introduced into the dough and allowed to grow and to form enzymes that ferment sugars, until the dough is filled with bubbles of carbon dioxide. The gas makes the loaf light and porous before it is baked. The alcohol is, of course, vaporized during baking.

Acetic and Lactic Acid Fermentation   Vinegar is made by the acetic acid bacteria, which have the ability to oxidize the alcohol contained in wine or hard cider. The various kinds of sour milk are the result of fermentation of lactose by lactic acid bacteria. The same type of reaction produces sauerkraut from chopped cabbage, and ensilage from chopped green corn or hay. The acid content of these foods makes them relatively resistant to further bacterial action. In warm countries where milk spoils quickly, the natives preserve it by inoculating it with sour milk containing lactic acid bacteria.

Cheese   Cheese is the by-product of molds or bacteria growing upon milk curd. The cheesemaker sets up conditions favorable to the growth of fungi that will give the desired flavor and consistency. The soft cheeses, Camembert and Brie, are ripened by molds; Limburger and Liederkranz are matured by bacteria. Hard cheeses may be the product of either bacteria or molds. The green mold which ripened Gorgonzola, Roquefort, or blue cheese is visible in these cheeses. Bacteria that form acid and gas (carbon dioxide) account for the flavor and the holes of Swiss and Parmesan cheeses. Edam and Cheddar cheeses, which contain no holes, are the product of bacteria that do not form gas.

Tea, Coffee, and Cocoa   The characteristic flavors of these beverages are developed by exposing the green leaves of the tea and the berries of the coffee and cocoa plants to fermentation by bacteria and yeasts.

Linen and Leather   The "retting" of flax from which linen is made is accomplished by bacterial enzymes. The plants are soaked in water until bacteria have dissolved the carbohydrate pectin which binds the fibers together. In leather manufacture, bacteria are used to dissolve the undesirable portions of the hides.

Antibiotics   Some microorganisms (bacteria, molds, and actinomycetes) produce substances which inhibit the growth of disease-producing organisms. For example, penicillin is obtained by growing huge quantities of the mold *Penicillium notatum,* from which the active agent is extracted. These useful substances, called *antibiotics,* will be discussed in Chapter 18.

Vitamin Assay   Certain protozoa, bacteria, and yeasts are useful in determining the vitamin concentration in any food or commercial product. An organism which requires the vitamin in question is grown in a series of cultures containing known quantities of the vitamin. At the same time, it is inoculated into a vitamin-free medium to which varying quantities of the test product have been added. After a period of growth, the two series can be compared in terms of detectable changes, such as the cloudiness of the medium, the rate at which oxygen disappears, or the rate at which carbon dioxide or acid is formed. By comparing the "unknowns" with the tubes containing known quantities of vitamin, the presence of vitamin can be detected and the amount estimated. Figure 22, page 121, shows the influence of varying quantities of thiamine on the growth of yeast.

MATERIALS FOR GROWTH OF MICROORGANISMS

All microorganisms utilize materials from the environment to build cell substance. To support microbial life an environment must provide a variety of inorganic salts* and suitable sources of nitrogen, carbon, and elements or compounds which will release energy. Microorganisms differ markedly in the types of environments and nutrients required for growth. The least demanding microbes (a group of primitive bacteria) can synthesize cell protoplasm from ammonium or nitrate salts and carbon dioxide. Energy for this process is obtained by oxidizing sulfur, iron, or nitrate or, in the case of the purple sulfur bacteria, from the sun. Organisms which can utilize inorganic salts as sources of energy and growth materials are said to be *autotrophic*. These organisms are relatively self-sufficient since, like plants, they can build protoplasm from inorganic materials. Most bacteria and other microorganisms are *heterotrophic*—that is, they are more or less dependent upon products formed by other living organisms. They obtain carbon from organic compounds and nitrogen from either organic or inorganic sources. Energy for growth and synthesis is obtained by fermenting energy-rich organic materials. Heterotrophic microorganisms resemble animals in that they utilize complex compounds as nutrients.

These differences in food requirements reflect great differences in synthetic or building ability on the part of various

* The chlorides, sulfates and carbonates of sodium, calcium, potassium, copper, ammonium, and some other metals in trace amounts.

microorganisms. At one end of the scale are the autotrophs which can synthesize everything they need from simple compounds of inorganic elements. At the other end one finds the parasitic organisms which lack the ability to synthesize various essential compounds and are therefore dependent upon the host to supply them ready for use. Even less synthetic ability is shown or needed by organisms which habitually live within functioning host cells, as, for example, the viruses. Organisms which depend upon other living cells as sources of nutrients and energy have been called *hypotrophic*. Their life activities and influence will be discussed in Chapter 12. The structural characteristics of common bacteria will be described in Chapter 2; the physiology of bacterial cells, in Chapter 3.

SUMMARY

1. Microorganisms produce significant changes in their environment. These changes are beneficial when they contribute to the fertility of the soil or the processing of foods or fibers. They are harmful or undesirable when they cause disease, spoil foods, or deteriorate fibers.

2. Microorganisms exhibit many characteristics which are common to all living cells. Microorganisms differ markedly in structure and life activities. On the basis of these differences, they have been placed into arbitrary groups: algae, yeasts, molds, protozoa, bacteria, rickettsias, and viruses.

SUPPLEMENTARY READINGS

Burrows, W.: Jordan-Burrows Textbook of Bacteriology. 15th ed. Philadelphia, W. B. Saunders Co., 1949.

Dubos, R. J.: Bacterial and Mycotic Infections of Man. 2nd ed. Philadelphia, J. B. Lippincott Co., 1952.

Frobisher, M.: Fundamentals of Bacteriology. 5th ed. Philadelphia, W. B. Saunders Co., 1953.

Henrici, A. T.: Biology of Bacteria. 3d ed. New York, D. C. Heath & Co., 1948.

Porter, J. R.: Bacterial Chemistry and Physiology. New York, John Wiley & Sons, 1946.

Salle, A. J.: Fundamental Principles of Bacteriology. 3d ed. New York, McGraw-Hill Book Co., 1948.

Smith, D. T., and Conant, N. F.: Zinsser's Textbook of Bacteriology. 10th ed. New York, Appleton-Century-Crofts, Inc., 1952.

Werkman, C. H., and Wilson, P. W.: Bacterial Physiology. New York, Academic Press, Inc., 1951.

CHAPTER 2

Bacteria—Cell Structure and Microscopy

CELL STRUCTURE

THE MOST important of all microorganisms, from a human viewpoint, are the plantlike single cells called bacteria. Bacteria vary greatly in size but all are so small that they can be seen only through a compound microscope at a magnification of greater than 100. As a rule they are stained with aniline dyes to make them readily visible. Careful scrutiny of a bacterial cell magnified 1000 times reveals a tiny sphere or cylinder of undifferentiated protoplasm. One sees no well-defined nucleus or cell wall. In this respect, bacteria appear to differ from typical plant and animal cells. The difference, however, is more apparent than real, since the minute size of the bacterial cell makes observation difficult. Furthermore, the staining methods commonly used are not suitable for revealing cell structure. Special stains and pictures taken with the electron microscope (magnification 10,000 times) reveal that the bacterial cell is a mass of protoplasm surrounded by three layers: the cytoplasmic membrane, the cell wall, and the capsule, or slime layer.

Cytoplasmic Membrane The cytoplasmic membrane is a thin, semipermeable layer closely attached to the body of the cell. It is thought to be composed of compounds of fat and protein (lipoproteins) which stain readily. In stained preparations, one usually sees the cell mass and the cytoplasmic membrane as a single unit. Normally this membrane lies in close contact with the cell wall but it can be separated by exposing the cell to the action of strong salt solutions (plasmolysis). The cytoplasmic membrane undoubtedly plays an important part in regulating cell permeability.

Cell Wall The cell wall is a relatively thick, rigid, supporting layer which confines and protects the internal cell structure and in some measure controls permeability. There is no general agreement regarding its composition. Some authorities report that it varies from species to species and may consist of mucins, cellulose, or hemicellulose. Since it resists staining, it is usually not seen. It is clearly revealed, however, in pictures taken with the electron microscope. (See Figure 4C, page 15.)

Slime Layer, or Capsule   Most bacteria secrete a complex gummy substance which diffuses into the surrounding medium or remains around the cell. When this material remains concentrated around the cell, it is called a *slime layer* or *capsule*. (See Figure 5.) In some species, this coat is dense and thick, and is therefore easily visible to the average observer. It is usually composed of a starchlike polysaccharide, but may consist of protein in the form of polypeptides or even an inorganic jelly. Since it stains with difficulty, it is usually observed as a clear halo around one or more bacterial cells. Bacteria showing well-developed capsules are said to be *encapsulated*. (See Figure 5, page 17.) Although the ability to produce capsular material is hereditary it may be stimulated or depressed by various environmental conditions.

Some free-living bacteria show capsules only when grown on a medium that is rich in carbohydrate. Certain parasitic bacteria develop large capsules when growing in the animal body, but tend to lose this ability when growing on artificial media for long periods. Capsules can be removed from bacteria by washing them in water or by subjecting them to the action of suitable enzymes. Cells thus deprived of their capsules will grow readily on suitable nutrient media and will produce descendants with typical capsules. Encapsulated bacteria are more capable of producing disease than the non-encapsulated organisms of the same species. Apparently the capsule protects the cell against the secretions and cells of the animal body. The pneumococcus, the organism which often causes pneumonia, forms large well-defined capsules that have been studied in detail by scientists. These gummy structures consist of various complex carbohydrates (polysaccharides). The polysaccharides which compose the capsule differ not only for distinct species but also for members of the same species. This is the basis for dividing pneumococci into more than seventy different types.

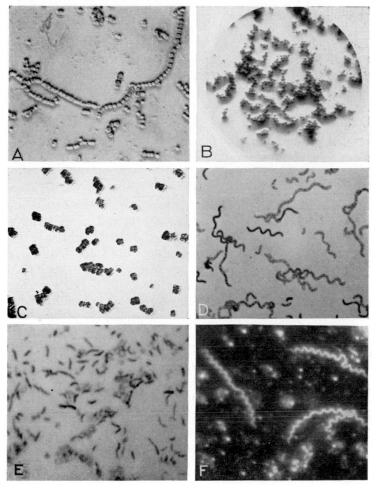

Figure 1   Photomicrographs of bacteria. *A*, Spheres in chains (Streptococci), (× 1250); *B*, Spheres in clusters (Micrococci), (× 600); *C*, Spheres in packets (Sarcinae), (× 550); *D*, Rigid spirals (spirilla), (× 1000); *E*, Curved rods (vibriones), (× 1200); *F*, Flexible spirals (spirochetes), (× 2150). (Courtesy General Biological Supply House.)

Internal Structure   Nuclei   The cell proper when observed with the compound microscope appears to consist of a clear semiliquid (cytoplasm). Special stains and the electron microscope reveal that certain bacteria contain opaque bodies thought to be nuclei. This assumption is strengthened by the fact that these bodies apparently divide during cell division and also enter spore formation. (See Figures 4 and 7.) These findings suggest that bacteria are typical cells equipped with nuclei which control metabolic activities and carry the hereditary characteristics of the cell. During cell division these nuclei divide by a process that appears to be similar to mitosis. Granules may sometimes be seen in the cytoplasm but nuclei are not visible in the common stained preparations. To the average student, bacteria appear as minute, transparent, colorless bodies staining evenly when treated with basic dyes.

GRANULES   When suitable methods of preparation and examination are used, large numbers of granules can be observed in the cytoplasm of young bacterial cells. In older cells the granules are less prominent. It is thought that they are reserves stored during periods of high activity for use when food supplies are less adequate. A small number of disease-producing bacteria characteristically form large conspicuous granules. The presence of granules is an aid in identifying the organisms that cause diphtheria (*Corynebacterium diphtheriae*) and plague (*Pasturella pestis*).

Special Structures   The search for unique and distinguishing features in the structure of bacteria is often fruitless. Frequently their structure is apparently as simple as their physiology is complex. Certain species may, however, form flagella, spores, or both.

FLAGELLA   Motile bacteria are capable of changing their position by a creeping or swimming movement. Swimming bacteria usually possess long threadlike filaments called *flagella* which may appear at the end of the cell (terminal flagella) or on the lateral surfaces (lateral flagella). Flagella are not visible in ordinary stained or unstained preparations, but they can be demonstrated by the electron microscope, special stains, or by darkfield examination of living organisms mounted in a viscous fluid. (See Figure 2.) Flagella are associated with motion since they are commonly present on motile bacteria (spirilla and some rods) and are only infrequently found on nonmotile organisms (cocci and other rods). For many years, bacterial flagella were considered organs of locomotion which

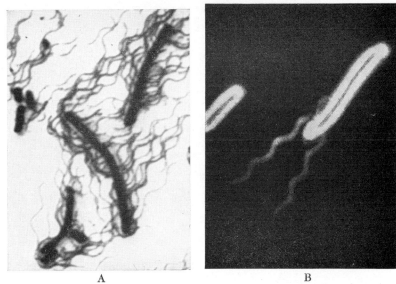

A   B

Figure 2 *A,* Photomicrograph of bacteria (*Salmonella typhosa*) stained to show numerous flagella ($\times$ 2900). *B,* Photomicrographs of living unstained *Salmonella typhosa* showing flagella (methylcellulose preparation on a dark field). Note that the unstained organism shows only two flagella. (*A,* Courtesy General Biological Supply House, *B,* Pijper, A.: J. Bact., 53.)

propelled bacteria through the medium. Today, this concept is being challenged. It is thought by some scientists that all motile bacteria propel themselves through fluid by means of twisting movements of their bodies. It has been suggested that flagella are threads of polysaccharide (from the slime layer) twisted off as wavy tails and are, therefore, the result, and not the cause of motion. If this concept of motion is correct, it seems likely that the organisms which are now considered as motile rods are really spirals instead of cylinders. Photomicrographs of bacteria treated to slow their motion show "tails" composed of two or more twisted flagella. (See Figure 2.) There is no general agreement regarding the origin of flagella. Some bacteriologists claim that they arise from the cell wall or cytoplasmic membrane.

SPORES Some bacilli when faced with starvation develop within the cell a single resistant resting body called a *spore.*

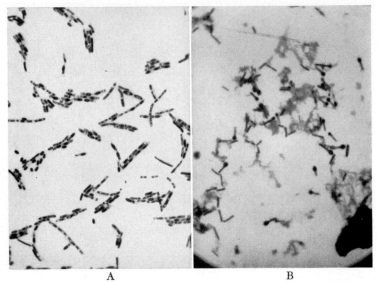

A   B

Figure 3   A, Bacilli showing central spores (× 1260). B, Bacilli showing some terminal spores (× 1350).

During spore formation, a portion of the cell (containing chromatin-like nuclear material) encloses itself within a membranous sac. This mass of protoplasm develops into a dense, inactive body. In the meantime, the remainder of the cell disintegrates and finally disappears, leaving only the resistant spore surrounded by tough protecting membranes which are relatively impermeable. (See Figure 4.) Spore formation does not increase the number of cells, since one vegetative cell forms one spore.

Because of its inactivity, the spore is very resistant to drying, to temperature changes, and to dyes and disinfectants. For this reason, bacilli in the spore stage are hard to kill and are capable of surviving unfavorable conditions for long periods of time. In fact, bacterial spores have been known to remain alive for twenty years, and to survive very unfavorable conditions. Some but not all rods (bacilli) form spores; in general, the cocci do not form spores.

When favorable conditions develop, the spore absorbs water and develops into a typical vegetative cell capable of repro-

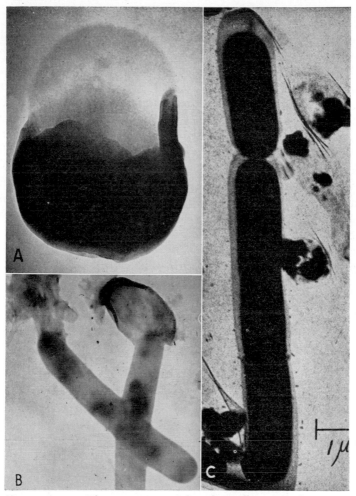

Figure 4   Electron micrographs of *Bacillus mycoides*. *A,* Germinating spore from a culture two hours old grown at 35° C. on nutrient agar. The two coats which surround the spore protoplasm are visible in the lower right section of the micrograph. *B,* Further development of vegetative cells in a culture grown at room temperature for sixteen hours. The large opaque bodies within the nearly transparent protoplasm are thought to be nuclei. (From a study, with the high voltage electron microscope, of the endospore and life cycle of *Bacillus mycoides* reported by Knaysi, G., Baker, R. F., and Hillier, J.: J. Bact., 53.) *C,* Electron micrograph of *Bacillus subtilis* (× 12,200). Note the continuous cell wall with thin column of cytoplasm extending from one cell to the other. Note the place in the lower cell where there is a slight indentation and thickening suggestive of the place where cell division may occur. (Mudd, Polevitsky, Anderson, and Chambers: J. Bact., 42.)

duction. These vegetative cells are no more resistant than other active cells.

In unstained preparations, a spore appears as a round or oval shining mass; in stained preparations, it is seen as a colorless body surrounded by more or less stained protoplasm. In old spores, sometimes only the membrane stains; then the spore appears as an unstained mass surrounded by a thin, colored line. Spores may appear in one of three positions in the rod: in the center (*central*), off center (*excentric* or *subterminal*), and at one end (*terminal*). Cells which contain a small spore may retain their normal contour, while those containing large spores take on a swollen or bulging appearance. (See Figure 3.)

Shape   Bacterial cells maintain a definite and fairly constant shape. On this basis, they fall into three groups:

1. The sphere—*coccus* (pl. *cocci*)
2. Spiral forms:
     a. curved rod—*vibrio* (pl. *vibriones*)
     b. rigid corkscrew—*spirillum* (pl. *spirilla*)
     c. flexible corkscrew—*spirochete* (pl. *spirochetes*)
3. The cylinder or straight rod—*bacillus* (pl. *bacilli*) or *bacterium* (pl. *bacteria*)

The terms "bacillus" and "bacterium" are often used interchangeably to refer to a rod-shaped organism. However, correct usage would restrict the word "bacillus" to spore-forming organisms and the term "bacterium" to those rods which form no spores.

Arrangement   When bacteria are examined under the microscope they often present a characteristic arrangement. After division, the cell walls of the organisms may remain attached. Therefore, rods often appear either singly or in short or long chains. Curved rods may take an S or spiral form. Cocci present even more varied arrangements because they can divide in one, two, or three planes. When division occurs in one plane, cocci may appear singly, in pairs, or in chains. Cleavage in two or three planes accounts for groups of fours, cubes, packets, or irregular masses. (See Figure 1.) The following names are applied to the cocci which have a tendency to appear in characteristic patterns:

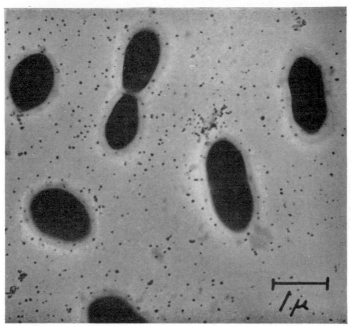

Figure 5 Electron micrograph of diplococci (*Diplococcus pneumoniae*) in various stages of cell division. Observe that all the cocci are surrounded by capsules. (Mudd, Heimets, and Anderson: J. Exper. Med., 78.)

THE ARRANGEMENT OF SPHERES	NAME
Singly or in clusters	Micrococci
Pairs	Diplococci
Chains	Streptococci
Fours	Tetrads
Packets	Sarcinae

The student must not expect that all the bacteria in view will conform to one of these patterns. A part of this arrangement is purely accidental; consequently, one sees some organisms alone, some in small groups, and some in large masses. If, after examining several microscopic fields, one observes cocci in chains, he will tentatively call them streptococci; if they are in irregular masses, he may consider them micrococci. The final identification can seldom be made by microscopic study alone.

Size Bacteria are so very small that they require a

special unit of measure called the *micromillimeter* or *micron*. A micron is $\frac{1}{1000}$ of a millimeter, or approximately $\frac{1}{25,000}$ of an inch. The symbol μ is often used in place of the word micron. Custom dictates that the size of organisms be reported by recording first the length, then the width. For instance, the size of the organisms which cause anthrax, typhoid fever, and whooping cough would be listed in this way:

MICROORGANISMS	SIZE
Bacillus anthracis	4.5–10 $\times$ 1–1.5 μ
Salmonella typhosa	3–4 $\times$ 0.5–0.8 μ
Hemophilus pertussis	0.5 $\times$ 0.2 μ

Most common bacteria range in size from 0.2 to 10 microns in length, although some soil bacteria may be as large as 50 or 60 microns. The microorganisms that are too minute to be seen when they are magnified one or two thousand times are usually classified with the viruses and will be discussed in Chapter 12.

MICROSCOPIC EXAMINATION

There are two common ways to prepare bacteria for microscopic study: the hanging-drop preparation, and the stained smear.

Hanging-Drop Preparation   The hanging drop, a temporary device for studying bacteria, is like a miniature aquarium. (See Figure 6.) As the name indicates, a drop of culture actually hangs from a coverglass supported by a concave slide. (For method of preparation, see page 110.) Here bacteria can be seen as small colorless bodies of definite and characteristic shape and size. Some bacterial cells are motile, and in young cultures can be seen moving from place to place. Others are characteristically nonmotile, and exhibit only a quivering or vibratory motion called *Brownian* movement. Such vibratory motion is characteristic of all small bodies when they are suspended in a liquid or gaseous medium, and is the result of molecular bombardment.

The more common method of examining bacteria is by the stained smear. (Most of the photographs of the preceding section were taken of bacteria prepared by this method.)

Stained Smears   A smear is a permanent preparation made by spreading a drop of culture on a glass slide. After

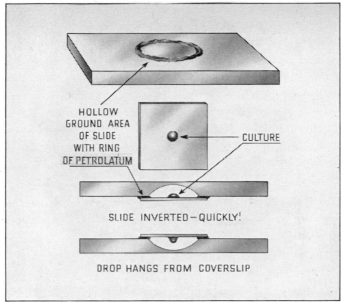

HOLLOW
GROUND AREA
OF SLIDE
WITH RING
OF PETROLATUM

CULTURE

SLIDE INVERTED—QUICKLY!

DROP HANGS FROM COVERSLIP

Figure 6   Hanging-drop preparation.

drying, the smear is attached to the slide or *fixed* by gentle heating and is then stained by covering the slide with an aniline dye such as methylene blue or safranin. These are basic dyes which combine with the acidic constituents (nucleic acids) of the cell protoplasm, causing them to take on the color of the dye. Under the microscope, therefore, one sees dead cells that have been colored and somewhat distorted by the staining process.

Staining by Gram's method is a more complicated procedure, but it is generally more useful. In this procedure the smear (previously dried and fixed) is subjected first to crystal or gentian violet, then to iodine, then to alcohol, and finally to a counterstain. How these stains function is indicated below:

GRAM'S STAIN

STAINING SOLUTION	ACTION
1. Gentian violet	All organisms take the stain by forming an ionic bond between a basic group of the dye and an acidic group of the cell with the result that all cells acquire the purple color of the stain.

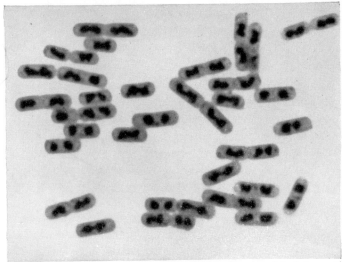

Figure 7   Bacterial cells stained to show nuclei (chromatinic structures) in *Bacillus cereus*. Fixed with osmium vapor, stained by acid Giemsa. Photographed mounted in water. Magnified 3000 times. (C. Robinow.)

GRAM'S STAIN (*Continued*)

STAINING SOLUTION	ACTION
2. Iodine solution	Iodine (mordant) enters all cells and forms a precipitate.
3. Alcohol (a solvent)	*In gram-negative organisms:* alcohol enters the cells freely washing away the iodine dye precipitate leaving the cells colorless. *In gram-positive organisms:* alcohol or alcohol iodine solution does not pass the cell membrane or passes with difficulty. As a result the dye is retained and the cell appears purple.
4. Counterstain (safranin, bismarck brown)	Counterstain unites with colorless (gram-negative) organisms which take the color of the counterstain.

This method of staining is a significant aid to the bacteriologist. By its use bacteria can be classified into two groups: the *gram-positive*, those that retain the purple dye; and the *gram-negative*, those that are decolorized by alcohol and take the color of the counterstain. These two responses to one staining process undoubtedly denote chemical differences in the composition of the bacteria and *probably,* more important, differences in cell permeability. In general, gram-positive bacteria differ from gram-negative in their ability to resist the destructive action of chemical agents and dyes. This is well illustrated by the response of various organisms to penicillin. Gram-positive organisms (micrococci, streptococci, and pneumococci) are readily inhibited by it, while the gram-negative organisms (*Escherichia coli, Salmonella typhosa*) are very resistant to its action.

Gram-positive organisms can be rendered gram negative by prolonged decolorization with alcohol and by removing various constituents of the bacterial cell such as magnesium ribonucleate, lipids, polysaccharides, fatty acids, and nucleoproteins. Treating cells with water, ribonuclease, lysozyme, fat solvents, acids, or alkalies will also change the reaction of an organism from gram positive to negative. There is reason to believe that these procedures change the permeability of the cell and that this is a major factor in determining the gram reaction, although some authorities believe that the protoplasm of gram-positive organisms is more acid than that of gram-negative and that this may account for the ability to form stable compounds with basic gentian violet and iodine. Gram-negative organisms do not show this variability; they remain always gram negative.

It is well to remember that old cultures of gram-positive organisms tend to become gram negative; therefore, to be certain of the gram reaction, it is necessary to use cultures that are not more than twenty-four hours old. In addition to the age of the culture, environmental factors such as the pH of the medium may cause a change in the gram reaction. Then, too, certain strains of organisms usually considered as gram positive are really gram variable in that they retain little purple stain.

The gram-staining process was named for the originator, Christian Gram, who introduced it in 1884. Some modification of the gram stain is used in practically every bacteriology laboratory, because the morphology (structure) of the organisms and the gram reaction give the first clue to the identity of the organism. (See Table 1.)

Table 1   CLASSIFICATION OF SOME COMMON BACTERIA
ACCORDING TO THE GRAM'S STAIN

GRAM POSITIVE	GRAM NEGATIVE
	Parasitic organisms
1. All spore-forming rods	1. Many intestinal bacteria
Examples:	Examples:
Bacillus subtilis	Escherichia coli
Bacillus anthracis	Salmonella typhosa
	Proteus vulgaris
2. Most of the cocci	2. Other parasitic rods
Examples:	Examples:
Streptococcus	Brucella
Pneumococcus	Pasteurella
Micrococcus	
	3. Few cocci
	Examples:
	Gonococcus
	Meningococcus
	Neisseria catarrhalis
	Free-living organisms
	1. Pigment-producing rods
	Examples:
	Serratia
	Chromobacteria

SUMMARY

1. The structure of bacterial cells can be observed by examining living or dead organisms with the aid of a compound microscope. Bacteria may be examined in a hanging drop or in a smear that has been dried and stained with simple aniline dyes or with a differential stain.

2. Bacterial cells, though apparently simple in structure, often differ from one another in shape, size, or arrangement of cells. Certain organisms are distinguished by the possession of special structures such as spores or flagella.

SUPPLEMENTARY READINGS

BOOKS:

Bissct, K. A.: The Cytology and Life History of Bacteria. Baltimore, Williams & Wilkins Co., 1950.

Braun, W.: Bacterial Genetics. Philadelphia, W. B. Saunders Co., 1953.

Burrows, W.: Jordan-Burrows Textbook of Bacteriology. 15th ed. Philadelphia, W. B. Saunders Co., 1949.

Henrici, A. T.: The Biology of Bacteria. 3d ed. New York, D. C. Heath & Co., 1948.

Knaysi, G.: Elements of Bacterial Cytology. 2nd ed. Ithaca, N. Y., Comstock Publishing Co., 1951.

Smith, D. T., and Conant, N. F.: Zinsser's Textbook of Bacteriology. 10th ed. New York, Appleton-Century-Crofts, Inc., 1952.

PERIODICAL:

Bartholomew, J. W., and Mittwer, T.: The Gram Stain. Bact. Rev., *16:* 1–29, 1952.

CHAPTER 3

Bacteria—Enzymes and Identification

ENZYMES

BACTERIA like other living cells consist of organized masses of protoplasm which are capable of duplicating themselves from materials available in the environment. They carry on the complex reactions of cell building, respiration, and digestion by means of active secretions called enzymes.

An enzyme is a protein cell product capable of transforming other substances by increasing or slowing chemical reactions that are already in progress. Enzymes act as catalysts that influence the rate of chemical change and are not used up in the process. They carry on the complicated chemistry of life, namely, breathing, digesting food, and building cell substance and new cells. Enzymes are manufactured by the cell to do the work of the cell; that is, to produce changes. Not all cells secrete the same enzymes, hence there may be differences in the types of food used or the products formed. Some enzymes function within the cell, while others are excreted from the cell and act upon the medium. The secretions which prepare foods for the use of the cell are of the latter type.

The chemical composition of enzymes is not completely known. Those which have been isolated in pure state are protein in character, and some are crystalline. Like other proteins, most are denatured or destroyed by temperatures of 70° C. (158° F.) or above, and are precipitated by reaction with salts of heavy metals. Cold inhibits their action, but causes no permanent change. Enzymes are specific in their actions. For example, the enzyme lactase causes the sugar lactose to react with water and break up into two simpler molecules (hydrolysis), but it does not induce any such reaction in the sugars maltose and sucrose; lipases split fats but do not change carbohydrates or proteins. Not only are enzyme actions specific, but they may also be reversible. For example, the enzymes which hydrolyze food protein may also assist in the synthesis

24

of cell protein. Like the enzymes in the human digestive organs, they are sensitive to the reaction of the surrounding medium; some function only in a weak acid, some in a neutral medium, and still others require a weak alkaline medium.

Enzymes are known by what they do. For instance, if the

Table 2   SOME COMMON ENZYMES AND THEIR ACTION

ENZYMES	REACTION CATALYZED
HYDROLYTIC AND COAGULATING ENZYMES—insignificant energy changes	
Protein-coagulating enzymes	
Coagulase	Coagulation of blood serum
Rennin	Coagulation of milk
Proteolytic enzymes	*Hydrolysis or synthesis of proteins*
Gelatinase	Hydrolysis of gelatin
Peptidase	Hydrolysis of peptides
Amidase	Hydrolysis of certain amino acids
Esterases	*Hydrolysis or synthesis of esters*
Lipase	Hydrolysis of fats
Phosphatase	Hydrolysis of organic phosphates
Carbohydrases	*Hydrolysis or synthesis of carbohydrates*
Amylase	Hydrolysis of starch
Cellulase	Hydrolysis of cellulose
Pectinase	Hydrolysis of pectin
Lactase	Hydrolysis of lactose
Maltase	Hydrolysis of maltose
Sucrase	Hydrolysis of sucrose
RESPIRATORY ENZYMES—release energy for cell use	
Oxidases	Combination of oxygen with substrate
Dehydrogenases	Transfer hydrogen from substrate to hydrogen acceptor (often oxygen)
Reductases	Favor reduction reactions
Catalases	Transform hydrogen peroxide to water and oxygen
Peroxidases	Oxidation of substrate by hydrogen peroxide
Carboxylases	Remove carbon dioxide from organic acids

secretions of living cells cause gelatin to change from a solid to a liquid (at 20° C. [68° F.]), one may conclude that the fluid contains a gelatin-digesting enzyme, *gelatinase*. Many enzymes are named by adding the letters "ase" to the name of the chemical reaction or to the name of the substance affected by the enzyme. For example, an enzyme which hydrolyzes cellulose is called *cellulase,* and one that reduces nitrates may be called *nitrate reductase.* However, these names are seldom used; one implies their présence and activity by saying that the bacteria "ferment lactose and dextrose" or that they "liquefy gelatin." As the enzyme equipment of bacterial cells is fairly constant, the chemical changes produced by them can be used as one means of identifying microorganisms. Table 2 summarizes some of the common chemical changes and the enzymes that are responsible for them. Most of these enzymes serve the cells that produce them by making possible the reactions which provide energy or prepare food materials or synthesize cell proteins, carbohydrates, or fats. The reactions are conveniently divided into two classes (as in Table 2): those which release only insignificant amounts of energy (hydrolysis and coagulation) and those whose chief function is supplying energy for the cell. More consideration will be given to these reactions in Chapter 4.

The preceding discussions have pointed out that bacteria produce enzymes which enable them to utilize simple or complex foods in their natural environment. It is possible to provide conditions which resemble those found in nature as a means of growing bacteria for study.

GROWTH OF BACTERIA FOR STUDY

The problem of growing bacteria is essentially one of supplying suitable conditions for cell activity and the materials for cell building. Different kinds of bacteria differ markedly in the enzymes produced as well as in the materials required for growth. (See page 52.) Hence no one environment is suitable for all bacteria. In nature or in the laboratory a particular organism will thrive in any habitat which meets its needs. Most bacteria can be grown in the laboratory if suitable conditions are provided.

Cotton-stoppered test tubes containing food constitute a satisfactory place in which to grow microorganisms. The cotton stoppers* permit the entrance of air and prevent the introduc-

---

* Nonabsorbent cotton is preferred because it does not readily become wet. A damp plug may act as a carrier and transfer bacteria in either direction.

tion of foreign bacteria. Covered glass dishes, called *petri dishes,* are also useful for growing bacteria. Test tubes and petri dishes, together with the food within them, must first be rendered free from living forms (*sterilized*) to rid them of competing microorganisms.

Before discussing food for microorganisms, it will be necessary to introduce a few new terms. A glass tube used for growing bacteria is called a *culture tube.* The food material in or upon which the bacteria grow is called a *culture medium* (pl. *media*). A medium that contains living bacteria is a *culture.* When only one species or type of cell is present, it is known as a *pure culture.* A medium that contains more than one species is called a *mixed culture.*

Nutrient Medium The type of food to be used depends upon the organism to be grown. Media are of two types: synthetic and nonsynthetic. Synthetic media are those in which the exact chemical composition is known. They commonly consist of ammonium and other inorganic salts* with or without specific amino acids or vitamins. Nonsynthetic media, in contrast, are those in which the exact composition is unknown. Many common media are of this variety. Some bacteria grow readily in a medium which provides water, inorganic salts, and one or more carbon and nitrogen compounds. Others will fail to grow unless the medium is enriched by the addition of specific nutrients such as blood, amino acids, or vitamins. (See Chapter 5.)

Nutrient broth is a common and useful medium containing meat extract, peptone, salt, and water. It can be used plain or modified by the addition of other substances such as agar, gelatin, sugar, or blood. This medium supplies proteins of varying complexity (peptones, amino acids), which are important in building cell substances. It also supplies traces of

---

* The composition of one such medium is:

	GRAMS PER LITER
Glucose	1
KH_2PO_4	2
K_2HPO_4	7
Na citrate·$5H_2O$	0.5
$MgSO_4$·$7H_2O$	0.1
$(NH_4)_2SO_4$	1.0

muscle sugar (glucose or glycogen) and many salts, as well as the growth-promoting vitamins of the B-complex group (thiamine, riboflavin, pantothenic acid, nicotinic acid, biotin, pyridoxine, folic acid, and *p*-aminobenzoic acid, all of which are derived from beef extract). Because it supplies a variety of food materials, it meets the needs of many common bacteria. Since living cells are sensitive to acids and bases, the reaction of the medium must be adjusted to make it approximately neutral.

Broth can be converted into the solid medium, *nutrient agar,* by adding 1.5 per cent of agar-agar.* This medium is a firm jelly which can be melted by boiling and which becomes solid at approximately body temperature. A layer of agar in a test tube or petri dish is a suitable moist surface on which to grow bacteria.

By definition, media are substances that will support bacterial growth. In the preparation of media, microorganisms which were present in the ingredients, in the air, and on the utensils become a part of the medium. If other conditions are as favorable as the water and food supply, there will soon be a thriving culture of bacteria. These organisms can be killed by subjecting them to heat. Nutrient broth and agar are rendered free from bacteria (*sterilized*) by applying steam under pressure at a temperature of 121° C. (250° F.) for fifteen minutes. Media containing foods that are changed by high temperatures may be treated by *fractional sterilization;* i.e., by heating the material at from 100° to 110° C. (212° to 230° F.) for thirty minutes on each of three successive days. (For details of sterilization, see Chapter 10.)

Growing Aerobic Bacteria   Many bacteria are capable of using oxygen from the air. These are called *aerobes* or *aerobic* bacteria, in contrast to the anaerobes that do not thrive in the presence of oxygen. (See pages 43 and 49.) The methods described in this chapter are suitable for growing aerobic bacteria.

Transplanting Bacteria   A bacterial culture represents a tremendous population of living cells competing for a

* A dried seaweed without food value for most bacteria.

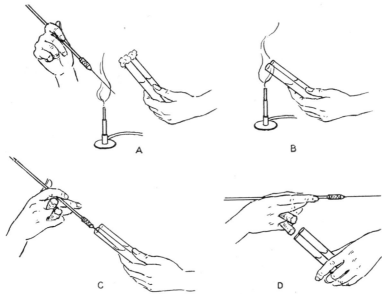

Figure 8   The method of inoculation. A medium is inoculated by transferring a small amount of culture to a sterile medium using a sterile inoculating needle. The steps include: *A*, The flaming of the needle and the removal of stoppers. *B*, The flaming of the mouths of the tubes. *C*, The transfer of bacteria from the culture to new medium. *D*, The flaming of the tubes and the replacing of stoppers.

limited food supply. The accumulation of waste products from the growth of many individual organisms, together with the diminishing food supply, produces conditions that check further growth. To have young, vigorous specimens for study, it is necessary to transfer a few cells from the culture to a sterile medium. This process is called *inoculation*.

Inoculation must be done with care in order to avoid the introduction of bacteria from the needle, the air, or hands, thus contaminating the culture. Care must also be taken to avoid transferring any of the culture to the working surface or the hands. It is well to remember that the culture tube, properly used, serves to keep the cultivated bacteria within its walls and to exclude all other organisms. Some of the steps in this procedure are shown in Figure 8. Observe (1) that the tubes and cotton plugs are held in such a way as to facilitate handling, (2) that unnecessary contact with air and hands is avoided, and (3) that the transfer needle is flamed before and after the material is carried from one tube to the other.

Figure 9   Streak plates—prepared by streaking a culture of bacteria over the surface of sterile agar plates. The white areas represent colonies, each consisting of innumerable bacterial cells. By streaking a number of plates in succession, it is possible to obtain widely scattered colonies containing organisms of a single type. Isolated colonies may be used to obtain organisms in pure culture.

Bacterial Growth   ·   After the new culture has been labeled, it is usually placed at body temperature (37° C. [98.6° F.]) for twenty-four hours or at room temperature (20° to 22° C. [68° to 71.6° F.]) for forty-eight hours. During this time, rapid growth takes place, resulting in the development of countless cells, which make the broth look cloudy. Although most organisms grow uniformly in all parts of the broth, a few varieties grow chiefly on the surface or on the bottom, leaving the rest of the liquid transparent. The change in the appearance of the medium is easily detected if the tube is compared with one containing sterile broth. On an agar *slant,* the bacterial population accumulates until it forms a visible mass consisting of innumerable individual cells. Sometimes this surface growth displays color, but more frequently it is gray or white. When a clump of organisms is placed on an isolated area of a nutrient agar plate the organisms tend to form a more or less circular mass of visible growth. This mass is called a *colony.* (See Figure 9.) Colonies vary markedly in size and shape. For example, some of the bacteria found in the human throat form pinpoint colonies while organisms taken from the air tend to form relatively large colonies.

Obtaining Pure Cultures   Most of the materials that are brought to the laboratory for study contain many kinds of bacteria. Such mixed cultures can be separated in the laboratory by special techniques. The following method is an exam-

A   B

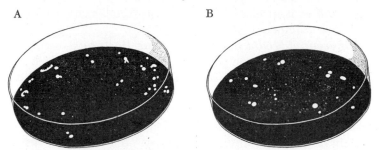

Figure 10   Dilution plates—Plate A was inoculated with a more
concentrated culture than was used for Plate B.

ple of the simplest of these techniques. Melted agar is first
poured into sterile petri dishes. These are called *agar plates*.
When the agar becomes solidified, it is inoculated by streaking
it with the mixture in such a way that the organisms will be
widely separated on the plate. Such a preparation is called a
streak plate. (See Figures 9 and 10.) A second method of separation, which is really only a modification of the first, is by means
of *dilution plates*. (See Figure 10.) A series of tubes of melted
agar are inoculated by introducing appropriate quantities of the
bacterial culture into the melted agar, and the mixture is
poured into sterile petri dishes, allowed to harden, and incubated. In twenty-four hours, the progeny of the organisms
transferred to the agar plates will be large enough to form
visible colonies. After incubation, an agar plate that was
seeded with a mixed culture may reveal several types of
colonies, such as large, rough, white colonies; small, smooth,
white colonies; and small, smooth, yellow colonies. To obtain
a pure culture of any one of these bacteria, it will be necessary
to transfer a small amount of material from one of the isolated
colonies to a tube of sterile broth.

The methods just described are commonly used in isolating
bacteria from natural sources. When the organisms sought are
easily grown and have distinctive characteristics, nutrient agar
plates are suitable for their cultivation. Enriched media such
as blood agar will be required for isolating organisms which
require more complex nutrients. Differential media are useful
both for the identification of bacteria and for their isolation,
particularly when the organisms sought are few in number or

when different species of bacteria with similar characteristics are found together.

Differential Media Used in Isolating Bacteria   A differential medium is one which contains substances which can be changed by some organisms but not by others, or substances which discourage the growth of certain bacteria. In addition to their most common use, i.e., for the identification of bacteria, differential media may be helpful in the isolation of certain bacteria that are not easily separated from their neighbors. Separation is especially difficult when few bacteria of one kind are accompanied by large numbers of other organisms with similar characteristics. One procedure for discovering and isolating the less numerous bacteria is to add to the nutrient medium an agent (dye or antibiotic) which prevents the growth of the unwanted bacteria. For example, the addition of suitable quantities of brilliant green dye will prevent the growth of the colon bacterium (*Escherichia coli*) without interfering with the growth of the typhoid organism. Likewise the addition of penicillin to nutrient blood agar will prevent the growth of most gram-positive organisms and thus favor the growth of any gram-negative organism which may be present. Other differential media are made by adding substances which can be changed by bacterial enzymes.

Sometimes the problem of isolation is made difficult by the similarities in appearance of colonies of different bacteria. For example, the typhoid organisms (*Salmonella typhosa*) closely resemble the colon bacteria (*Escherichia coli*) in that both are small gram-negative rods which form small white colonies when grown on nutrient agar. When the presence of both these organisms is suspected a medium composed of nutrient agar, lactose, and an acid-base indicator solves the problem of separation by providing a sugar which is fermented by *Escherichia coli* but not by the typhoid organisms. On this medium, lactose-fermenting organisms (*Escherichia coli*) grow as colored colonies while the organisms which do not ferment lactose form white colonies.

As a rule, differential media used for isolating bacteria are complex in composition since they usually contain a variety of buffer salts, dyes and various sugars in addition to the usual nutrients.

IDENTIFICATION OF BACTERIA

Bacteria can be identified by finding characteristics which distinguish one type of organism from all others. (See page 37.) Distinguishing characteristics include the appearance of the bacterial cell and colony, staining reactions, motility, temperature and food requirements, and the products formed during growth. The latter are especially important since many bacteria look alike but differ in the enzymes they produce and in the changes which occur in their environment.

Differential Media Used to Identify Bacteria Environmental changes can be detected by growing the organisms to be identified in pure culture in a variety of differential media. Media used to detect enzyme production are usually relatively simple in composition. The common simple differential media include: nutrient gelatin, litmus milk, nutrient sugar media, peptone broth, and nitrate broth.

NUTRIENT GELATIN   Gelatin is prepared by adding 15 per cent gelatin to nutrient broth and is, therefore, essentially a jellied broth enriched by gelatin. Some bacteria form enzymes which digest and liquefy gelatin, while other bacteria are unable to attack this food but use the other nutrients contained in broth. Thus all bacteria growing on this medium can be divided into two groups: those that liquefy gelatin, and those that do not. (See page 36.)

LITMUS MILK   Milk is an excellent food for bacteria—it contains fats, carbohydrates, proteins, and salts. In fresh milk, the carbohydrate is present in the form of milk sugar (*lactose*). The heat of sterilization often changes a small amount of lactose to the simple sugars glucose and galactose. Sterile milk, therefore, contains a small amount of glucose and a large amount of lactose. Some bacteria can use neither of these sugars; some use both glucose and lactose; and others use only glucose. Bacterial action on sugars results in the formation of acids or acids and gases. (See page 48 for discussion of chemical changes involved.) The organisms using both sugars may form enough acid to curdle the milk. The natural souring of milk is due to the growth of lactose-fermenting organisms. Since the supply of glucose is limited, the acid produced from that sugar alone may not be sufficient to change the appearance of the milk unless an indicator is added. Litmus is often added to milk to show changes in the reaction of the medium. Litmus milk, which is pale lavender in color, turns pink when acids are formed and changes to a deep blue or purple when the liquid becomes alkaline.

Milk also contains two proteins: *lactalbumin* (milk albumin), and *casein* (the milk solid used for cheese). Bacterial action on lactalbumin results in the formation of basic amines and ammonia. The presence of ammonia is indicated by a deep blue or purple in the medium. Casein, a finely suspended solid, may be coagulated by acids or cell secretions, or it may be digested. The process that changes the solid casein to simpler soluble proteins (peptones and amino acids) is called *peptonization.** Peptonization of milk causes it to take on the appearance of dirty water. (See page 36.)

NUTRIENT SUGAR MEDIA   Sugar agar is made by adding 1 per cent dextrose, lactose, mannite, or other sugar to nutrient agar. An indicator which will change color in the presence of acid is usually added, so that changes in reaction may be easily detected. For instance, on a litmus-lactose-agar plate, acid-forming colonies change the medium from blue to pink, those that form no acid leave the medium unchanged.

Sugar broths are made by adding a sugar and an indicator to nutrient broth. An inverted vial is often placed in the tube of broth to collect any gases that may be formed. Organisms growing in a sugar broth may be divided into two groups: those that use the sugar, as shown by the formation of acids or of acids and gas; and those that leave the sugar unchanged.

SPECIAL MEDIA   Some bacteria are so fastidious in their food requirements that they grow with reluctance or not at all on the media described above. To grow these, it is necessary

* This process is essentially a hydrolysis catalyzed by bacterial enzymes and is similar to the reactions which occur in the human digestive tract.

to provide special enriched media. Some of the less hardy varieties, which ordinarily live in or on the human body, grow readily if blood or body fluids are added to broth or agar. Blood serum or whole blood can be used for this purpose. Blood broth is prepared by adding a small amount (0.1 to 1 cc.) of sterile blood to a tube of sterile broth containing 0.85 per cent sodium chloride. Blood agar is made by adding from 1 to 2 cc. of sterile blood to a tube containing melted agar. After the blood and agar are mixed, the tube can be slanted, or the contents poured into a petri dish to make an enriched agar plate. Blood agar can be used as a differential medium, since bacteria that grow on it fall into one of three classes: those that produce no change in the medium (*nonhemolytic*); those that dissolve red blood cells, leaving transparent areas around the colonies (*hemolytic*); and those that change the blood pigment (*hemoglobin*) from red to green, causing a brownish-green halo to appear around the colony (*viridans* or green-forming bacteria). Certain other bacteria, the blood-loving, or *hemophilic,* group, require hemoglobin for growth.

The reactions observable in some of the common differential media are listed in Table 3.

Distinguishing Characteristics of Bacteria   The characteristics which distinguish one kind of organism from another may relate either to behavior or to structure. That relating to behavior due to difference in enzyme production and its effect on differential media has just been discussed. Organisms may be distinguished by their natural habitat, requirements for food and oxygen, and their ability to survive unfavorable conditions or their ability to produce disease. In addition, bacterial cells may differ in size, shape, arrangement, motility, and staining reactions. Colonies too may present characteristic sizes, shapes, and colors although many are small, white, and circular. Table 4 shows some of the characteristics of three common organisms which grow in soil and water and are often found growing on nutrient agar plates which have been exposed to the air.

Steps in Determination of Identity   It has already been pointed out that the small rodlike cells that cause typhoid

Table 3   RESULTS OF BACTERIAL ACTION ON
SOME COMMON MEDIA

MEDIUM	APPEARANCE	SOURCE MATERIAL	END-PRODUCT
Gelatin	No change, remains solid		
	Becomes liquid	Gelatin	Polypeptides and amino acids which do not form a jelly
Litmus milk	No visible change		
	Coagulated (acid in reaction)	Lactose	Lactic and other organic acids
	Unchanged except reaction becomes alkaline	Lactalbumin	Ammonia
	Appearance of watery solution on top of tube indicating peptonization or digestion (litmus—purple or fading)	Casein	Polypeptides, peptones, amino acids, and ammonia
Glucose broth	No significant change		
	Acid in reaction	Glucose	Lactic, acetic, and other organic acids
	Acid in reaction and gas formed	Glucose	Lactic, acetic, other acids, hydrogen, and carbon dioxide
Other sugars	Same as for glucose		
Blood agar	No change		
	Brownish green zones around colonies	Hemoglobin within red blood cells	
	Hemolytic or clear zones around colonies	Injury to membrane of red cells making it permeable to hemoglobin	

Table 4   CHARACTERISTICS OF THREE COMMON ORGANISMS

CHARACTERISTIC	BACILLUS SUBTILIS	AEROBACTER AEROGENES	SARCINA LUTEA
Colonies	Large, dry, tend to be irregular	Small, moist, sometimes mucoid or sticky	Large, moist, heaped up, granular, circular, yellow
Cells—morphology and staining	Large gram-positive rods with central spores	Small gram-negative rods—no spores	Large gram-positive cocci in packets of 8 or 16
Cells—oxygen requirements	Grows well in air	Grows well with or without oxygen	Grows well with or without oxygen
Cells—motility	Motile	Motile	Nonmotile
Cells—pigment	None	None	Yellow
Cells—enzyme reactions			
Gelatin	Liquefied	Not liquefied	Slowly liquefied
Milk	Peptonized, becoming alkaline	Coagulated, becoming acid	Coagulated, becoming alkaline
Starch	Hydrolyzed	Not hydrolyzed	Not hydrolyzed
Lactose	No acid	Acid and gas	No acid
Glucose	Acid	Acid and gas	No acid

fever resemble harmless organisms growing in the intestines and other harmless organisms growing in water. This is one example demonstrating that the identification of an unknown organism is often a time-consuming process.

The procedure for isolating and identifying unknown bacteria follows a standard pattern although certain details will vary with the type of organism sought. To gain an idea of the steps involved, let us consider a specific example. We will assume that there has been an outbreak of food poisoning (or food infection) and that samples of chicken salad and other foods suspected of causing illness are brought to the laboratory for examination. The first step in isolation of the organism responsible consists in streaking some of the food (mixed with sterile water) over a suitable solid medium in several petri dishes. The dishes are then placed in an incubator to provide a suitable temperature for growth (37° C. in this case). After twenty-four hours, let us assume that the plate shows numerous golden colonies. A small portion of the growth is then transferred to nutrient broth or nutrient agar to obtain a pure culture. Another portion of growth may be used to prepare a stained smear for microscopic examination. As soon as the organism is available in pure culture, it is transferred into tubes of differential media (usually gelatin, litmus milk, and various sugar broths—and, for the organism suspected in this study, blood serum). After a period of growth (usually twenty-four to forty-eight hours) the cultures in differential media are observed for changes. We will assume that by this time the following information has been secured: The organism is spherical and grows in irregular masses and retains the gram stain (gram positive). It produces a golden pigment, liquefies gelatin, coagulates blood serum, and ferments glucose and mannite (forming acid). These then are some of the more important distinguishing characteristics. The next step is to consult "Bergey's Manual of Determinative Bacteriology" or other standard reference book to find out which species of bacteria fits this description. The steps in isolation can be summarized as follows:

STEPS IN THE IDENTIFICATION OF AN "UNKNOWN" BACTERIUM

1st day	Prepare streak plates using suitable solid medium.
2nd day	Pick colonies. Transfer to suitable medium to secure pure culture.
3rd day	Transfer to differential medium such as nutrient gelatin, litmus milk, glucose broth.
2nd or 3rd day	Microscopic examination Gram stain Motility tests
3rd or 4th day	Compare characteristics of the organism with Bergey's manual or other laboratory guide for identification.

Classification   A knowledge of how bacteria are classified is necessary in order to complete the identification of any organism.

When the science of bacteriology was young, each investigator who discovered what he considered to be a new organism gave it a name. As a result, many common organisms discovered by scientists in different places acquired a variety of names. Such chaos could be resolved only by developing an acceptable scheme for classifying and identifying bacteria.

There have been many attempts to place bacteria in related groups. The older systems, which depended chiefly on differences in structure, were soon proved to be inadequate. Today, the structure, or morphology, of the cell gives the first clue to its identity, i.e., it places it in a family or group of families. The complete identification usually depends upon characteristic changes which the organism produces in culture media and growth requirements. In addition antigen-antibody tests and animal inoculation may be necessary to identify bacteria that grow in the animal body.

All systems of classification are arbitrary devices designed to assist the bacteriologist in identifying microorganisms. The general plan of classification presented by "Bergey's Manual of Determinative Bacteriology" is widely accepted in the United States and is similar to that used by botanists and zoologists. It begins with large inclusive units, each of which is, in turn, subdivided into progressively smaller units on the basis of distinguishing characteristics. The largest unit, the *kingdom,* is made up of *subkingdoms,* and they in turn are composed of classes. Each *class* is made up of several orders. The *orders* may be further divided into suborders. Each order comprises a group of related families. A large *family* is made up of *tribes,* which may be divided into subtribes. These *subtribes* may be divided again into genera. Small families are divided immediately into genera. Each *genus* is comprised of a group of several related organisms, such as *Micrococcus pyogenes* (var. *aureus* and *albus*) (commonly known as *Staphylococcus aureus* and *Staphylococcus albus*) and *Micrococcus citreus* (commonly known as *Staphylococcus citreus*). In some cases a genus may include only a single species, but in most cases from several to many species are included. The *species,* therefore, represents one kind of organism (plant or animal) which can be distinguished from all other kinds. Some species are divided into varieties, as for example *Mycobacterium tuberculosis* var. *hominis* and *Mycobacterium tuberculosis* var. *bovis, Micrococcus pyogenes* var. *aureus.*

To illustrate this classification, the distinguishing traits of *Micrococcus pyogenes* (var. *aureus* and *albus*), *Micrococcus citreus,* and *Bacillus subtilis* would place them in the following units:

UNIT	DISTINGUISHING CHARACTERISTICS
Kingdom .... Vegetable	Require soluble food
Subkingdom .... *Thallophyta*	Lack of roots, leaves, or stems
Class .... *Schizomycetes*	Reproduction by fission
Order .... *Eubacteriales*	Simple, unbranched rods, cocci, or spirals
Family .... *Micrococcaceae*	Spherical cells
Genus I .... *Micrococcus*	Spheres in clusters
Species .... *Micrococcus pyogenes* var. *aureus* *Micrococcus pyogenes* var. *albus* *Micrococcus citreus*	
Genus II .... *Gaffkya*	Spheres in fours
Species .. *Gaffkya tetragena*	
Genus III .... *Sarcina*	Spheres in packets of 8, 16, or 32
Species ...... *Sarcina lutea* *Sarcina maxima*	
Family .... *Bacillaceae*	Rod-shaped cells capable of forming spores
Genus I .... *Bacillus*	Aerobic — produce the enzyme catalase
Species .... *Bacillus subtilis*	See page 37

As an example of the use of the classification let us again consider the food-poisoning organism with the golden colonies. Its simple structure would place it among the true bacteria (order—*Eubacteriales*) with spherical cells (family—*Micrococcaceae*) arranged in clusters (genus—*Micrococcus*). Its disease-producing ability and its golden pigment suggest the species *Micrococcus pyogenes* variety *aureus*. The next step would be to compare the data collected with accepted description of the organism. If it shows all or many* of the characteristics

* Bacteria of the same species often show considerable variation with regard to structure and enzyme activities.

listed by Bergey's manual we can be assured that the organism in question is *Micrococcus pyogene* var. *aureus.*

NAMING BACTERIA   Any bacterium has two names. Its first is the *genus* name, usually a Latin noun derived from its structure, form, or the name of a famous scientist. The first letter of the genus name is *always* capitalized. The second or *species* name is a descriptive adjective derived from the color, source, name of the disease, or name of a scientist. The initial letter of the species name is always a small one. The genus name always precedes the species name.

EXAMPLE OF GENUS

NAMES	DESCRIPTION
Bacillus	aerobic spore-forming rod
Clostridium	anaerobic spore-forming rod
Bacterium	a nonsporulating rod
Sarcina	spheres in packets
Micrococcus	spheres in clusters
Hemophilus	blood-loving organisms (rods)
Pasteurella	
Escherichia	
Salmonella	gram-negative rods named for scientists
Shigella	
Brucella	

SOME COMMON SPECIES

NAMES	MEANING
albus	white
aureus	gold
citreus	yellow
vulgaris	common
tetani	tetanus
typhosa	typhoid
coli	colon

Both the official name and classification for some bacteria have been changed many times. Over the years, many species have acquired common names, which are those most frequently used. Thus *Neisseria gonorrhoeae* is known as the gonococcus, the *Escherichia coli* as the colon bacillus and *Salmonella typhosa* as the typhoid bacillus. *Micrococcus pyogenes* var. *aureus* is commonly called by its older name *Staphylococcus aureus*. (See "Bergey's Manual of Determinative Bacteriology" for the system of classification now in common use.)

SUMMARY

1. Bacteria carry on their life processes by means of enzymes.

2. Most bacteria will grow in the laboratory if suitable environmental conditions are provided.

3. Bacteria can be identified on the basis of distinguishing characteristics. Differential media are valuable aids in isolating and identifying bacteria.

4. A system of classification is an artificial device for assisting the bacteriologist to identify bacteria. Although beginning students spend relatively little time identifying bacteria, all use this system of classification when they call the organisms by their genus and species names.

SUPPLEMENTARY READINGS

Breed, R. S., Murray, E. G. D., Hitchens, A. P., and Others: Bergey's Manual of Determinative Bacteriology. 6th ed. Baltimore, Williams & Wilkins Co., 1948.

Burrows, W.: Jordan-Burrows Textbook of Bacteriology. 15th ed. Philadelphia, W. B. Saunders Co., 1949.

Frobisher, M.: Fundamentals of Bacteriology. 5th ed. Philadelphia, W. B. Saunders Co., 1953.

Salle, A. J.: Fundamental Principles of Bacteriology. 3d ed. New York, McGraw-Hill Book Co., 1948.

Werkman, C. H., and Wilson, P. W.: Bacterial Physiology. New York, Academic Press, Inc., 1951.

CHAPTER 4 *Bacteria—Energy Needs*

ALL LIVING cells produce enzymes which enable them to carry on an essential process called *respiration*. At one time the term "respiration" was used to designate an exchange of gases between a cell and its medium. Today it is used to denote any energy-releasing (exothermic) reactions that enable a cell to carry on its work. Cell functions which require energy include (1) synthesis of protoplasm, (2) moving substances across membranes, and (3) motion—in organisms that are motile. The energy for carrying on these and other processes may be derived either from sunlight or from energy-rich chemical substances—either organic or inorganic. Chemical reactions releasing energy are of two types: those that use molecular oxygen (the aerobic) and those which occur without molecular oxygen (the anaerobic). On the basis of their oxygen requirements bacteria (and other microorganisms) can be divided into four groups:

1. *obligate aerobes*—those which require molecular oxygen in order to grow
2. *obligate anaerobes*—those which grow only when molecular oxygen is absent
3. *facultative anaerobes*—those which grow with or without molecular oxygen
4. *microaerophilic*—those which need a small amount of oxygen.

Green plants and bacteria supplied with chlorophyll can use the energy of the sun for the storage of chemical energy by a process called *photosynthesis*. Animals and bacteria without chlorophyll-like pigments get their energy by oxidizing or fermenting energy-rich substances (*chemosynthesis*). Photosynthesis, a process used by relatively few bacteria, will be discussed first.

CHEMICAL ENERGY FROM LIGHT—PHOTOSYNTHESIS

Green plants* secure energy for synthesis from sunlight through the action of chlorophyll, a magnesium compound which enables them to change carbon dioxide and water to carbohydrate and oxygen. Some bacteria also have this power. For example, the green and purple sulfur bacteria (*Chlorobacteriaceae* and *Thiorhodaceae*) contain a chlorophyll-like pigment. Under anaerobic conditions these organisms synthesize compounds from carbon dioxide and hydrogen sulfide:†

$$n\ (2H_2S + CO_2) \xrightarrow[\text{bacteriochlorophyll}]{\text{light}} 2n\ S + (CH_2O)_n\ddagger + n\ H_2O$$

hydrogen sulfide + carbon dioxide → sulfur + water

The sulfur formed in this reaction is deposited as sulfur granules in the cytoplasm within the bacterial cells (purple sulfur bacteria) or in the surrounding medium (green sulfur bacteria). The purple sulfur bacteria can use this sulfur as a reducing agent to synthesize additional carbohydrate:

$$n\ (2S + 5H_2O + 3CO_2) \xrightarrow[\text{bacteriochlorophyll}]{\text{light}} 2n\ (H_2SO_4) + 3(CH_2O)_n$$

Another group, the purple nonsulfur bacteria (*Athiorhodaceae*), uses hydrogen instead of hydrogen sulfide:

$$n\ (CO_2 + 2H_2) \xrightarrow[\text{bacteriochlorophyll}]{\text{light}} n(CH_2O + H_2O)$$

It will be noted that in the examples given that the bacteria used light as a source of energy to build a carbohydrate. These organisms are obviously autotrophs since they use only inorganic compounds. The organisms described above are com-

---

* Algae, diatoms, and certain protozoa also obtain energy by photosynthesis.

† Green plants synthesize carbohydrate using water instead of hydrogen sulfide:

$$n(H_2O + CO_2) = \xrightarrow[\text{chlorophyll}]{\text{light}} n\ O_2 + (CH_2O)_n$$

‡ (CH_2O) represents a reduced form of carbon dioxide—a carbohydrate or intermediate which the organism has synthesized.

monly found in stagnant water, sewage, decaying vegetation, and swamps.

CHEMICAL ENERGY FROM INORGANIC COMPOUNDS

The use of sun as a source of energy by some few bacteria has been described. Most bacteria living on inorganic substances (autotrophs) obtain energy from the oxidation of inorganic substances such as sulfides, ammonia, nitrates, iron compounds, sulfur, and hydrogen gas. Several examples of such reactions will be given although it must be recognized that at present there is disagreement about some of the details. Some of the common soil organisms that oxidize inorganic substances include the sulfur bacteria (those that lack chlorophyll), iron bacteria, and the nitrifying bacteria. For example, one of the sulfur bacteria (*Thiobacillus thiooxidans*) utilizes sulfur and hydrogen sulfide:

$$2H_2S + O_2 \xrightarrow{\text{enzyme}} 2S + 2H_2O + \text{Energy product}$$

$$2S + 3O_2 + 2H_2O \xrightarrow{\text{enzyme}} 2H_2SO_4 + \text{Energy product}$$

Another sulfur bacterium obtains energy by oxidizing reduced sulfur compounds (as, for example, sodium thiosulfate):

$$5Na_2S_2O_3 + H_2O + 4O_2 \xrightarrow{\text{enzyme}} 5Na_2SO_4 + H_2SO_4 + 4S + \text{energy product}$$

These organisms are found in places where free hydrogen sulfide and other sulfur compounds are present: in sulfur hot springs, sewage, mines, peat bogs, and marshes.

Some of the nitrifying bacteria oxidize ammonia to nitrites (*Nitrosomas* and *Nitrococcus*) while others oxidize nitrites to nitrates. The details of these reactions are not fully understood. For simplicity they can be indicated as follows:

$$2NH_4 + 3O_2 \xrightarrow{\text{enzyme}} 2HNO_2 + 2H_2O + H_2 + \text{energy product (75,000 calories)}$$

$$2HNO_2 + O_2 \xrightarrow{\text{enzyme}} 2HNO_3 + \text{energy product (20,000 calories)}$$

The value of these reactions to the organism is, of course, energy for living; the value for man is incalculable because nitrates are the principal food of higher plants. (See page 78.) Nitrifying bacteria are found in the soil.

Numerous kinds of bacteria produce enzymes that enable them to change iron-containing substances. The physiology of these organisms is not fully known but it is thought that the true iron bacteria (*Gallionella ferruginea*) obtain energy by oxidizing inorganic ferrous compounds:

$$4FeCO_3 + O_2 + 6H_2O \xrightarrow{\text{enzyme}} 4Fe(OH)_3 + 4CO_2 + \text{energy product (40 calories)}$$

(Other iron bacteria change organic iron compounds to inorganic iron compounds.) It is thought that iron bacteria have contributed to the deposits of iron ore in the earth. Iron bacteria are found in natural waters which contain iron. They sometimes clog water pipes by precipitating ferrous salts and depositing layer after layer of insoluble iron salts.

In the examples cited the bacteria used atmospheric oxygen as an oxidizing agent. Some bacteria live without air by using nitrates, sulfates, or carbon dioxide as oxidizing agents. For example, some anaerobic sulfate-reducing bacteria (*Pseudomonas liquefaciens*) obtain energy by reducing hydrogen, the oxygen being obtained from hydrogen sulfate:

$$4H_2 + H_2SO_4 \longrightarrow 4H_2O + H_2S + \text{energy product}$$

Methane bacteria (*Clostridium butyricum*) also oxidize hydrogen with oxygen obtained from carbon dioxide:

$$4H_2 + CO_2 \longrightarrow 2H_2O + CH_4 + \text{energy product}$$
$$\text{methane}$$

While the ability to use reactions between inorganic substances is characteristic of the autotrophic bacteria, it is shared by certain organisms that require more complex organic foods (heterotrophs). A considerable number of these so-called heterotrophic bacteria obtain energy by reducing nitrates, sulfates, or carbon dioxide. For example, *Escherichia coli* and *Clostridium perfringens* in the presence of a hydrogen donor such as formic acid (HCOOH) reduce nitrates to nitrites:[*]

[*] There is some disagreement regarding this reaction. Some authorities say that it releases energy, others that it requires energy.

$$\text{HCOOH} + \text{HNO}_3 \xrightarrow{\text{enzymes}} \text{CO}_2 + \text{H}_2\text{O} + \text{HNO}_2 + \text{energy product}$$

Likewise certain bacteria, for example, *Thiobacillus denitrificans* and various clostridia, reduce nitrites to nitrogen gas. These organisms are sometimes called nitrate-reducing bacteria since their actions are the reverse of the nitrifying bacteria described above.

CHEMICAL ENERGY FROM ORGANIC COMPOUNDS

Heterotrophic bacteria, including the disease-producing organisms and many soil organisms that cause decay, obtain energy by oxidizing organic compounds or by fermenting simple sugars. The aerobes and to some extent the facultative anaerobes derive energy by oxidizing energy-rich compounds such as glucose, ethyl alcohol, or lactic acid. The reaction takes place stepwise, each step being catalyzed by one or more enzymes. The oxidation of simple sugars, for example, involves the transfer of hydrogen atoms from the food substance to a series of respiratory enzymes (hexokinases, coenzyme I, flavoprotein, cytochrome, cytochrome oxidase) and at last to the final hydrogen acceptor—molecular oxygen. It is now established that the coenzymes adenosine diphosphate (ADP) and adenosine triphosphate (ATP) and certain vitamins of the B complex group play an important part in the transfer and conversion of energy within the cell. Each step results in the transfer of energy from one carrier to another in a series of oxidations and reductions which result in the formation of *pyruvic acid* and finally complete oxidation with carbon dioxide and water as end products. All the steps in this complex series of reactions probably are not known. For convenience it is possible to represent this complex reaction which takes place in many steps by the simple formula:

$$\text{C}_6\text{H}_{12}\text{O}_6 + 6\text{H}_2\text{O} \longrightarrow 6\text{CO}_2 + 6\text{H}_2\text{O} + \text{energy product}$$

Some bacteria produce all the enzymes required to complete the oxidation of carbohydrate to carbon dioxide and water, but many when grown in pure culture cannot complete the process. For example, most vinegar bacteria oxidize ethyl alcohol to acetic acid. The over-all reaction can be written:

$$2CH_3CH_2OH + O_2 \longrightarrow CH_3CHO + H_2O$$
$$\text{acetaldehyde}$$

$$2CH_3CHO + O_2 \longrightarrow 2CH_3COOH$$
$$\text{acetic acid}$$

Fermentation   Bacteria (heterotrophic) when growing without oxygen usually obtain energy by fermenting simple sugars. Fermentation is an incomplete oxidation of a carbohydrate—usually a simple sugar. As in the complete oxidation process, enzymes liberate energy by the stepwise transfer of hydrogen until pyruvic acid is formed. From this point fermentation differs from complete oxidation in that it ends abruptly with the formation of complex end products.

Some microorganisms produce the enzymes necessary to form a single product such as lactic acid while others form a variety of end products. Some of the common end products of fermentation are lactic acid, acetic acid, succinic acid, formic acid, ethyl alcohol, and the gases hydrogen and carbon dioxide.

Fermentation products formed by the coli-aerogenes group are represented by the following:[*]

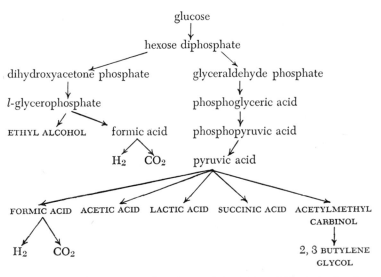

[*] Based on Gale, E. F.: The Chemical Activities of Bacteria. London, University Tutorial Press, 1947, p. 148.

Fermentation is always an anaerobic process, and is relatively inefficient because the energy release is small. Therefore, organisms growing anaerobically require large quantities of carbohydrates. The following formulas show the relative efficiency of fermentation reactions.

Complete oxidation:

$$C_6H_{12}O_6 + 6O_2 \longrightarrow 6CO_2 + 6H_2O + 674 \text{ kilogram calories}$$
glucose + oxygen   carbon dioxide + water

Fermentation:

$$C_6H_{12}O_6 \longrightarrow 2C_2H_5OH + 2CO_2 + 22 \text{ kilogram calories}$$
glucose   alcohol + carbon dioxide

$$C_6H_{12}O_6 \longrightarrow 3CH_3COOH + 15 \text{ kilogram calories}$$
glucose   acetic acid

The many microorganisms which are capable of fermenting carbohydrates are able to grow where the oxygen supply is limited or absent. In this respect they are more versatile than are most forms of life.

End products of fermentation, such as lactic acid, escape from the cell and therefore probably are of no use to the cell that formed them. These products may, however, have commercial value; fermentations by bacteria or other microorganisms are commonly used in the manufacture of many organic chemicals such as ethyl alcohol, lactic acid, butyl alcohol, acetone, and glycerol.

Aerobes and Anaerobes   The fact that some organisms utilize oxygen in respiration while others cannot grow in the presence of oxygen or depend on fermentation for securing energy, reflects a fundamental difference in enzyme structure and physiology. These differences are not completely understood but certain facts seem relevant. Aerobes and facultative anaerobes produce one or more respiratory enzymes of the cytochrome group which enables them to carry on the complex reactions involved in oxidizing carbohydrates such as glucose. (See page 47.) Most aerobic and facultative anaerobic bacteria also produce the enzymes catalase and peroxidase (enzymes which remove hydrogen peroxide from the cell). Catalase, for example, changes hydrogen peroxide to oxygen and water:

$$2H_2O_2 \xrightarrow{\text{catalase}} 2H_2O + O_2$$

It has been suggested that small but toxic amounts of hydrogen peroxide are formed during carbohydrate synthesis.* Anaerobic organisms produce no catalase or peroxidase and thus may be prevented from growing in the presence of oxygen. Peroxidase is an enzyme that catalyzes the oxidation of organic compounds by using hydrogen peroxide as a hydrogen acceptor:

$$\underset{\substack{\text{organic} \\ \text{compound}}}{A\ H_2} + \underset{\substack{\text{hydrogen} \\ \text{peroxide}}}{H_2O_2} \xrightarrow{\text{peroxidase}} \underset{\substack{\text{oxidized} \\ \text{organic} \\ \text{compound}}}{A} + \underset{\text{water}}{2H_2O}$$

Anaerobes are not necessarily killed by the presence of oxygen. In fact many can survive (but not grow) for long periods of time.

Obligate anaerobes are more difficult to cultivate than are the organisms that grow freely in air because free oxygen must be eliminated from the medium. Satisfactory conditions for growing obligate anaerobes can be obtained in one of three ways: by the removal of oxygen, by the replacing of air with inert gases, and by the addition of animal tissues and other reducing agents (liver or brain tissue, glucose, cysteine, sodium thioglycolate). In nature, aerobes and anaerobes often grow in the same medium. By using the available oxygen, the aerobes provide favorable conditions for those organisms that cannot tolerate oxygen. It is thought that aerobic micrococci (staphylococci) which enter wounds with tetanus organisms may act in this way.

SUMMARY

1. All bacteria require energy to enable them to carry on their life processes.

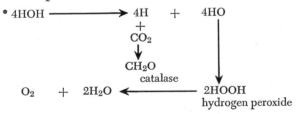

2. Most bacteria obtain energy by oxidizing energy-rich (organic or inorganic) substances. A few bacteria are able to utilize energy from sunlight by means of the chlorophyll-like pigment.

3. Some bacteria (anaerobes) are unable to grow in the presence of oxygen. Others can grow with or without oxygen. Energy for anaerobic growth is commonly obtained by fermenting simple sugars.

4. Obligate anaerobes will grow only in medium that contains no molecular oxygen.

SUPPLEMENTARY READINGS

Frobisher, M.: Fundamentals of Microbiology. 5th ed. Philadelphia, W. B. Saunders Co., 1953.

Fruton, J. S., and Simmonds, S.: General Biochemistry. New York, John Wiley & Sons, Inc., 1953.

Gale, E. F.: The Chemical Activities of Bacteria. 3d ed. New York, Academic Press, Inc., 1951.

Porter, J. R.: Bacterial Chemistry and Physiology. New York, John Wiley & Sons, Inc., 1946.

Smith, D. T., and Conant, N. F.: Zinsser's Textbook of Bacteriology. 10th ed. New York, Appleton-Century-Crofts, Inc., 1952.

Werkman, C. H., and Wilson, P. W.: Bacterial Physiology. New York, Academic Press, Inc., 1951.

CHAPTER 5   *Bacteria—Life Activities and Synthesis*

It will be recalled that bacteria closely resemble other types of living cells in composition and function. This means that in building cells they synthesize all the complex materials found in cells. These include fats, carbohydrates, and proteins as granules of stored materials or as integral parts of the cell or its membranes. The slime layer or capsule is commonly formed of complex carbohydrates or sometimes from proteins in the form of polypeptides. Especially important to the cell is the formation of the various enzymes required to carry on its life processes. Although definite proof is lacking, it seems likely that bacterial enzymes like other enzymes are directed by genes or gene-like bodies which transmit the hereditary traits of the cell. The rapid appearance of new cells in a medium is proof of remarkable synthetic ability on the part of bacteria.

GROWTH MATERIALS

It is obvious that if bacterial cells are to thrive they will need suitable foods to provide for this energy need and for building new cells. For multiplication to take place the following growth materials must be available in suitable form and amount: (1) water, (2) inorganic salts, (3) a source of carbon, and (4) a source of nitrogen. In addition, some bacteria but not all require specific complex organic substances—usually vitamins or amino acids.

Inorganic Salts   All bacteria require many inorganic substances for growth and normal cell activity. To support growth, a medium must supply small amounts of the metals, sodium, potassium, iron, copper, and calcium and traces of other metals as well as appreciable amounts of the ammonium, chloride, sulfate, phosphate, and carbonate ions. Inorganic salts are necessary for the adequate functioning of enzymes and of cell membranes and also for the maintenance and regulation of osmotic pressures. Iron, for example, is essential

52

for the manufacture of certain respiratory enzymes (such as catalase and cytochrome oxidase), and calcium and magnesium are needed because some enzymes function only in the presence of suitable amounts of the salts of these metals. Phosphates too are necessary in many reactions which transfer energy. (See page 47.) In some of the common nutrient media, inorganic salts are provided by yeast or beef extract.

Carbon   Carbon dioxide in small amounts appears to be essential to all bacteria. Some (the autotrophic bacteria) can use carbon dioxide or hydrogen carbonate as their sole source of carbon for synthesizing carbohydrates, fats, and proteins. Most require also an organic compound such as glucose, lactate, or a citrate salt. In addition, some are able to digest complex starches or sugars to obtain, from these, glucose or other suitable carbon compound. Many of the common nutrient media contain glucose although in some the peptone supplies both the carbon and nitrogen needed.

Nitrogen   Since all protoplasm contains proteins, some source of nitrogen is essential to all living cells. Bacteria vary greatly in their ability to utilize nitrogen compounds. Some use inorganic forms such as ammonia or nitrates, while others must be supplied with certain specific amino acids. Another group—the nitrogen-fixing* bacteria—convert free nitrogen gas to cell protein. On the basis of their ability to use different nitrogen-containing substances, bacteria may be divided into three groups: (1) those that are able to build protoplasm from atmospheric nitrogen (nitrogen-fixing bacteria), (2) those that build protoplasm from ammonium or nitrate or nitrite salts, (3) those that require certain specific amino acids, vitamins, or both amino acids and vitamins (these may in addition use ammonium or nitrate salts).

NITROGEN GAS   Most living forms including plants and animals are unable to use nitrogen gas in their life processes. Until recently, few microorganisms were considered capable of fixing nitrogen—that is, using nitrogen gas as the sole source of nitrogen in protein synthesis. It is now known that a number of species of microorganisms (both algae and bacteria) are

* Nitrogen fixation—converting free nitrogen gas to "bound" or fixed nitrogen.

able to transform nitrogen into living cell substance. A variety of species of free-living soil bacteria fix nitrogen. These include a number of photosynthetic bacteria (see page 44) and certain clostridia and azotobacter. Better known are the root nodule bacteria (rhizobia) which live in the nodules of the legumes (peas, beans, clover, alfalfa). These organisms in association with the root cells of the plant can fix atmospheric nitrogen. This is usually considered as symbiosis since neither the bacteria nor the root nodule alone can fix nitrogen.*

AMMONIA   Ammonia or ammonium salts may serve as the sole source of nitrogen for many free-living and for some parasitic bacteria. Many gram-negative bacteria such as the colon bacterium (*Escherichia coli*) grow well in a medium consisting of water, glucose, and ammonium and other inorganic salts. These organisms are capable of building any amino acids, proteins, or growth factors required for cell activities from ammonium salts and other inorganic substances.

Amino Acids   Some bacteria are unable to grow in media lacking one or more specific amino acids. These organisms obviously require amino acids but are unable to synthesize them. When provided with small quantities of the essential amino acids, they are often able to use ammonium salts to meet a part of their nutritional needs. Certain strains of typhoid bacteria (*Salmonella typhosa*) cannot grow in a medium which lacks the amino acid tryptophane. Other strains of typhoid bacteria either are able to synthesize tryptophane or can be "trained" to do so by growing the organisms in serial cultures containing less and less tryptophane. This process is thought to select mutants which carry genes for the formation of the enzymes needed for tryptophane synthesis.

Growth Factors   Growth factors are vitamin-like substances required by some organisms for growth. Usually growth factors are contributed by such materials as beef extract, yeast extract, and blood serum. The following are known to be necessary for the growth of one or more species of bac-

* It has been suggested that the bacteria (rhizobia) transform nitrogen to a compound of nitrogen, hydrogen, and oxygen (possibly hydroxylamine [NH$_2$OH]). This combines with a glucose derivative (from the plant) to form an amino acid. The amino acids in turn combine to form all proteins.

teria: nicotinic acid, co-enzyme I, pantothenic acid, pyridoxine, thiamine, riboflavin, biotin, hematin, and para-aminobenzoic acid. Vitamins and other growth factors form an essential part of the organism's enzyme systems. It will be noted that many of the vitamins required by bacteria are the same as those that function in human cells.

Some bacteria, chiefly parasitic forms, require several specific amino acids and several growth factors. In general, free-living organisms tend to have greater synthetic ability than do the parasitic. Parasitic bacteria, since they live in tissues or fluids containing amino acids and vitamins, have little ability for synthesis—nor do they need such ability.

Many species of bacteria are able to synthesize the vitamins or other growth factors needed. Of interest also is the fact some of the bacteria living in the intestinal tract of men or animals synthesize certain vitamins in large amounts—thus benefiting their host by providing vitamins which his cells need but cannot build.

PRODUCTS OF DECOMPOSITION

In addition to synthesis and energy-releasing reactions, some bacteria, as well as numerous molds, secrete enzymes which digest complex proteins, fats, and carbohydrates. Proteins, fats,* and carbohydrates consist of large complex molecules that are not sufficiently small or simple to pass through bacterial cell membranes. To be available for cell use they must be changed to smaller and simpler forms (amino acids, ammonia, and double or simple sugars). The mechanism is the same as that observed in higher animals, although the compounds split and the intermediate and end products formed by the action of bacterial enzymes are more numerous and varied. Digestion usually involves the chemical process called hydrolysis in which a complex food product is split by water to form two new substances.

Chemical Changes Involving Carbohydrates   Before complex carbohydrate starch can be utilized by bacteria or other living cells, it must be hydrolyzed to maltose, a sugar

---

* The action of bacteria on fats has not been thoroughly investigated. As a rule fats are not used in the ordinary laboratory media.

(disaccharide) capable of diffusing through cell membranes. This reaction, catalyzed by the enzyme amylase (an enzyme secreted into the medium), can be condensed as follows:

$$2(C_6H_{10}O_5)n + nH_2O \xrightarrow{\text{amylase}} nC_{12}H_{22}O_{11}$$
$$\text{starch} \qquad\qquad\qquad\qquad\qquad \text{maltose}$$

After absorption, further hydrolysis by the enzyme maltase transforms the maltose to glucose. This reaction can be suggested by the formula:

$$C_{12}H_{22}O_{11} + H_2O \longrightarrow 2C_6H_{12}O_6$$
$$\text{maltose} \qquad\qquad\qquad\qquad \text{glucose}$$

In like manner cellulose is changed to a disaccharide cellobiose by the exo-enzyme cellulase and to glucose by the endo-enzyme cellobiase. Some bacteria and many molds produce starch-digesting enzymes. Certain bacteria and other microorganisms (protozoa, molds, and actinomycetes) secrete enzymes that digest cellulose. These organisms living in mixed population in the soil carry on the important task of disintegrating the woody structure of dead plants. It is interesting that grass-eating animals do not as a rule secrete cellulose-digesting enzymes, but depend upon the enzymes secreted by microorganisms living in the digestive tract (chiefly bacteria and protozoa) to carry out this function. Some microorganisms change starch by utilizing phosphoric acid instead of water (by phosphorolysis):

$$(C_6H_{10}O_5)n + nH_3PO_4 \longrightarrow C_6H_{11}O_6 \cdot OPO_3H_2$$
$$\text{starch} \quad \text{phosphoric acid} \qquad\qquad \text{glucose phosphate}$$
$$C_{12}H_{22}O_{11} + H_3PO_4 \rightleftarrows C_6H_{11}O_5 \cdot OPO_3H_2 + C_6H_{12}O_6$$
$$\text{sucrose} \quad \text{phosphoric acid} \qquad \text{glucose phosphate} \quad \text{fructose}$$

This reaction is reversible and therefore gives a clue regarding one way in which microorganisms may synthesize carbohydrates.

Chemical Changes Involving Nitrogenous Compounds Although bacteria require nitrogen compounds for growth, proteins are not suitable as food because they will not pass through cell membranes. To enter the cell the complex proteins must be changed to a simpler form, as, for example, peptones, amino acids, or ammonia. Some few bacteria produce the protein-splitting enzymes (proteolytic enzymes) which effect this change. Even proteolytic organisms, however, require some peptones or ammonia to build the enzymes that hydrolyze the proteins.

Many bacteria produce enzymes which change amino acids. One common change, called deamidization, transforms amino acids to ammonia by removing the amino group (NH_2). Other enzymes (carboxylases) split amino acids to carbon dioxide and an amine. Thus bacterial enzymes change complex organic nitrogen compounds to simpler substances. The ammonia so liberated reacts with acids to form salts and becomes available to bacteria for food, or the ammonia may be oxidized to form nitrites and nitrates—compounds which are important foods for green plants. Some bacteria can change (hydrolyze) urea, a nitrogen compound found in urine, to ammonium carbonate:

$$\underset{\text{urea}}{(NH_2)_2CO} + \underset{\text{water}}{2H_2O} \longrightarrow \underset{\text{ammonium carbonate}}{(NH_4)_2CO_3}$$

Mixed populations of bacteria living in the soil will usually produce the enzymes necessary to change proteins, amino acids, and urea to simple inorganic constituents (ammonia, carbon dioxide, and water). Thus bacteria (and other microorganisms), in the process of securing their own food, cause profound changes in the medium which surrounds them.

PRODUCTS OF SYNTHESIS

Cell synthesis is obvious to anyone who has grown a culture of bacteria in the laboratory. Within twenty-four hours after transfer to a suitable medium, the original cells duplicate themselves with great rapidity—until millions of new cells have been formed. Over and over again, genes have directed the pattern for enzyme formation. Enzymes in turn have enabled the cell to obtain energy, to assimilate food, to build cell constituents, and finally to divide.

In addition to cell protoplasm, certain other substances are formed. These include pigments and toxins.

Toxins   Toxins (poisonous substances derived from bacterial cells) are commonly described as exotoxins or endotoxins.

EXOTOXINS   Exotoxins are proteins which are formed within the cell and are excreted into the medium or the tissues in which the bacteria are growing. They are formed by relatively few species of bacteria, such as the *Streptococcus pyogenes, Micrococcus pyogenes* (Staphylococcus), and the organisms causing diphtheria and tetanus. Exotoxin, commonly called toxin, can be obtained by growing the toxin-producing organisms in broth for several days (five to seven) until the toxin is present into the medium. Then the bacteria are removed by filtration, leaving the toxin in the filtrate. These toxins, which in composition resemble those produced by certain snakes and spiders, are so potent that a few drops will kill a guinea pig or mouse. The exotoxins have been extensively studied and are without doubt the most poisonous substances known. The reason for this is not clearly evident. They are protein in nature, in chemical composition resembling harmless proteins such as egg white. It is possible that they injure the susceptible cell by acting as enzymes which attack some essential part of the cell, or they may prevent some essential metabolic process. Some of the exotoxins can be crystallized; all can be changed to harmless substances by treating them with heat or chemicals, such as formaldehyde solution. Most exotoxins are destroyed by the action of (protein-digesting) enzymes and can be rendered harmless by specific protective proteins called *antitoxins.* (See page 241.)

The injection of toxins causes a suitable laboratory animal to develop typical symptoms of disease and predictable injury to certain body tissues. For instance, the injection of tetanus toxin into a guinea pig alters nerve function so that the animal develops characteristic muscular contractions of tetanus (lockjaw). The injection of diphtheria toxin will cause a guinea pig to become ill in twelve to eighteen hours and to die in one to four days. Edema and cell destruction can be observed at the site of injection and in the kidneys, adrenals, and other internal organs. (See page 409.)

To summarize, exotoxins are complex proteins with the capacity to injure animal cells. Some are enzymes; others are thought to be enzyme inhibitors which block some essential metabolic process of the cell. For example, diphtheria toxin prevents animal cells from forming an essential respiratory enzyme (cytochrome) and in that way causes the death of cells. The gas gangrene organism (*Clostridium perfringens*) secretes a proteolytic enzyme (collagenase) which hydrolyzes the collagen material which binds muscle fibers together and also a second enzyme (lecithinase) which acts on an essential constituent of cell walls (lecithin) and thus destroys various cells including red blood cells.

ENDOTOXINS   Endotoxins arc complex compounds of protein, polysaccharides, and fats. They form an integral part of the bacterial cell and are liberated only when the cell is broken or destroyed. In this respect they differ from the exotoxins which escape from the cell. Endotoxins are produced by gram-negative disease-producing bacteria such as the meningococci, gonococci, brucella, pasteurella, and members of the typhoid group. All endotoxins appear to produce similar effects. In laboratory animals they injure capillaries causing widespread congestion, edema, and hemorrhage. It is thought that they produce this effect by interfering with the metabolism of carbon compounds. Injection of endotoxins will commonly cause the death of a laboratory animal in twenty-four hours. Endotoxins differ from exotoxins in that they are not readily changed by heat, chemicals, or proteolytic enzymes. Nor are they rendered harmless by body proteins called antibodies. Both exotoxins and endotoxins are important in disease production.

Pigment   Most bacteria grow without producing color, but the ability to produce pigment is characteristic of some species. Among the bacteria, those living in water are the most common pigment producers. Many form yellow, orange, or red pigments similar to the carotene of carrots and tomatoes. Some common pigment-forming bacteria, their habitat, and colors are listed in Table 5.

Although many free-living and a few parasitic bacteria produce pigment, little is known about the function or process of pigment formation. Some investigators have reasoned that, like the pigment in the human skin, the pigment produced by bacteria serves as protection against the rays of the sun. The theory is interesting, but has not been established by experimental evidence. The fact that pigment production is influenced by environmental factors, such as oxygen, temperature, and food, can easily be demonstrated. For instance, *Serratia marcescens* produces a white growth when deprived of oxygen or grown at body temperature. At room temperature, in the presence of oxygen, the organism produces a deep-red pig-

Table 5   PIGMENT-FORMING BACTERIA

BACTERIA	HABITAT	COLOR PRODUCED
Free-living		
Chromobacterium	Water	Violet
Serratia	Water	Red
Flavobacterium	Water	Orange or yellow
Pseudomonas	Water	Green
Sarcina	Water (air)	Yellow
Parasites		
Micrococcus pyogenes		
(*Staphylococcus aureus*)	Skin, boils, pimples	Orange
Micrococcus citreus	Skin	Yellow
Pseudomonas aeruginosa		
(*Bacillus pyocyaneus*)	Wounds	Green

ment. Also, some organisms form more vivid colors when grown on media enriched by glucose or peptone.

When pigment is formed it offers a definite clue to the identity of the organism and may also account for certain color changes in natural media. Blue milk, for example, is usually due to the presence of a group of bacteria (pseudomonas) that form a soluble blue-green pigment. Likewise, the brilliant colors appearing in the walls of hot springs are due to pigment-forming bacteria.

SUMMARY

1. Microorganisms like other living cells produce enzymes that catalyze chemical changes. These changes include digestion and synthesis.

2. By means of these enzymes, cells build protoplasm and special substances such as toxins and pigments. Bacterial poisons are of two types—exotoxins and endotoxins.

SUPPLEMENTARY READINGS

BOOKS:

Burrows, W.: Jordan-Burrows Textbook of Bacteriology. 15th ed. Philadelphia, W. B. Saunders Co., 1949.

Dubos, R. J.: The Bacterial Cell. Cambridge, Mass., Harvard University Press, 1946.

Frobisher, M.: Fundamentals of Bacteriology. 5th ed. Philadelphia, W. B. Saunders Co., 1953.

Gale, E. F.: The Chemical Activities of Bacteria. 3d ed. New York, Academic Press, Inc., 1951.

Salle, A. J.: Fundamental Principles of Bacteriology. 3d ed. New York, McGraw-Hill Book Co., 1948.

Werkman, C. H., and Wilson, P. W.: Bacterial Physiology. New York, Academic Press, Inc., 1951.

PERIODICAL:

Burrows, W.: Endotoxins. Ann. Rev. Microbiol., 5: 181–196, 1951.

Yeasts and molds are simple fungi that grow best in the dark. They belong to a large group of primitive plants (*Thallophyta*) which produce no chlorophyll, and no true stems, roots, or leaves. They resemble bacteria in their remarkable ability to produce enzymes that change the foods upon which they grow. Their relation to bacteria and to each other is shown in the chart below:

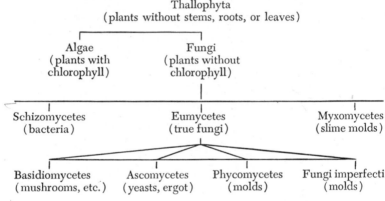

Yeasts and molds can be studied by methods that are similar to those used in observing bacteria. Because they are commonly present in the air, they are often encountered in the bacteriology laboratory as contaminants. These fungi are interesting because, although microscopic, they are large enough to show definite internal structure. In fact, they resemble closely the cells of higher plants and animals.

For detailed information regarding the classification of yeasts and molds the student is referred to textbooks on mycology. A brief general discussion is included here as a basis for distinguishing yeasts and molds from bacteria and protozoa.

YEASTS

Microscopic examination of living yeast in wet preparation

reveals oval or spherical cells which are much larger and more complicated than bacteria. (Yeast cells are commonly 3 to 100μ in length and 3 to 10μ in diameter, in contrast to bacteria which commonly range from 0.2 to 2μ to 0.2 to 10μ.) These cells consist of a definite cell wall and thin cytoplasmic membrane enclosing a mass of transparent cytoplasm. Within the cytoplasm one or more vacuoles (packets of cell sap containing organic acids and salts) may be distinguished in the unstained cells. When appropriately stained, a small round or horseshoe-shaped nucleus is visible. Older cells may contain granules of stored food in the form of nucleic acid, glycogen, and fat. Spore formation in yeast serves as a method of reproduction as well as a means of survival. These spores* enable yeasts to survive unfavorable conditions even though they are less resistant than those of bacteria. In some species, spore formation follows the union of two separate yeast cells.

Most yeasts divide by budding; that is, the mature cell puts out a small projection containing cytoplasm and nuclear material. The bud enlarges and finally separates from the mother cell, and it in turn puts out buds. During active growth, new buds are sometimes formed before this separation takes place. Some yeasts reproduce by fission. It is likely that nuclear division by mitosis precedes budding and spore formation. (See Figure 11.) Sexual reproduction occurs in some yeasts in which two separate cells unite and fuse their nuclear material with consequent rearrangement of the heredity-bearing genes. This process has made possible the development of various hybrid yeasts for experimental and commercial purposes.

Yeasts are widely distributed in nature; in fact, every fruit or berry carries the spores of molds and yeasts on its skin. These spores live through the winter in the soil of the garden or orchard, and are carried to the new fruit by dust or by insects. Yeasts serve as food for some insects such as the fruit flies,

---

* The word spore has several different uses, for example:
  Bacterial spore—a single resistant body formed within a bacillary cell.
  Yeast spore—four to eight moderately resistant bodies formed within the yeast cell.
  Mold spores—numerous reproductive cells, sometimes though not always formed within a sac.
  Protozoan spores—daughter cells that are not particularly resistant.

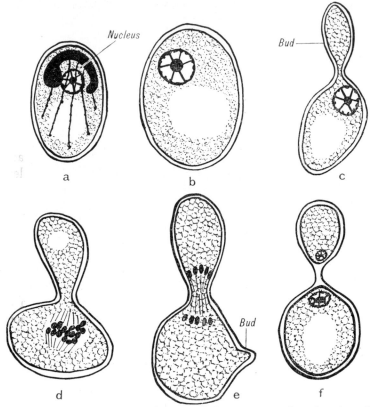

Figure 11   Structure of yeast cell showing: *a*, nucleus; *b*, enlarged cell prior to budding; *c*, early stage in bud formation; *d*, division of nucleus after which nucleus enters the bud; *e*, second bud developing while the original one is in division; and *f*, separation of the bud. (Hentschell: Biology for Medical Students. Longmans, Green & Co.)

and are often found living as harmless parasites in the intestinal tract of various insects. The yeasts grow aerobically when oxygen is present. Under anaerobic conditions, they obtain energy by fermenting sugars. In this process, enzymes formed by the yeast cells rapidly change sugars to alcohol and carbon dioxide. This can be observed by placing a small piece of bakers' yeast and a teaspoonful of molasses or other sugar solution in a flask of warm water. Within a few minutes, a rapid bubbling appears as the newly formed carbon dioxide escapes from the liquid.

Of the many yeasts which may be found, two are of special interest: (1) bakers' or brewers' yeast (*Saccharomyces cerevisiae*), which is used in making bread and beer and as a source of vitamin B, and (2) the "grape" yeast (*Saccharomyces ellipsoideus*), which is found on the skins of that fruit and is the agent that ferments the grape juice to make wine.

Yeasts are important promoters of carbohydrate decomposition both in nature and in industry. A few species grow in the human body and cause disease, but in general they can be considered as free-living forms.

Yeast cells can easily be distinguished from bacteria on the basis of size, shape, the presence of a distinct nucleus, and the formation of buds and multiple spores. They differ also in their fermentation reactions. Many common yeasts characteristically form alcohol and carbon dioxide from the simple sugars.

MOLDS

Structure • Everyone has seen colonies of black, white, green, or yellow threadlike molds on stale foodstuffs. When seen under the microscope, they are far more complicated in structure than are the yeasts and bacteria. A single mold plant is multicellular, i.e., it consists of many cells which vary from one another in size, shape, and function. In some species, clear-cut walls can be seen dividing the fiber into cells containing a single nucleus; these are called *septate* (walled) molds. Others, called *nonseptate* molds, reveal no such partitions. In both types, the cells lie end to end to form the long branching threads. The single fiber is called a *hypha* (pl. *hyphae*), and the network formed by the mass of these threads is called the *mycelium*. This mycelium is often large enough to be visible, and can be observed on the surface of any moldy food.

The usual mold cell is a relatively large cylinder of cytoplasm surrounded by a strong wall. The cytoplasm is often granular, owing to the presence of granules or vacuoles of stored proteins, carbohydrates, and fats. Each cell contains one or more small nuclei. The threads formed by these cells show specialization of function; those that grow into the medium, the *vegetative* fibers, serve as roots to obtain food for the whole plant. Other filaments, called *aerial hyphae,* grow on the surface and develop the fruiting bodies.

Molds reproduce by the formation of enormous number of seedlike bodies called *spores.* These spores may be either sexual or asexual. Sexual spores are formed by the union of two cells (gametes) growing on the same plant or on two different plants of the same species. Asexual spores deriving their inheritance from a single cell may also be formed. Spores are really seeds; one speck of mold may produce hundreds or even thousands of these bodies, each capable of growing to maturity. When introduced into a favorable environment, the spore absorbs water, and begins to develop into a threadlike cell which breaks through the surrounding wall. Continued growth and cell division result in the formation of a typical mold colony. Asexual spores may be developed in several ways: as masses within a closed sac (*sporangium*), as clusters or chains at the end of an aerial fiber (*conidia*), or as segments formed within the threadlike hyphae (*chlamydospores*). In some molds the mycelium breaks into fragments (*arthrospores*) or develops budding yeastlike appendages (*blastospores*). Both the fragments and yeastlike reproductive bodies are capable of initiating growth as a new mold plant.

From this description it is evident that the simple, minute bacterial cells are not likely to be confused with the large, complex cells of the molds. However, it is not always easy to distinguish between yeasts and molds. Certain species of yeasts tend to remain attached, forming threadlike hyphae, and some molds will form typical unicellular yeast cells in one phase of their growth and equally typical woolly mycelia in another phase. This tendency to show alternately the characteristics of yeasts and molds is often seen in parasitic fungi.

Culture and Examination   The growing of molds is not difficult; in fact, if they are not rigorously excluded, they are often very persistent. Since molds grow slowly, they are usually found where conditions are not favorable for bacterial growth. They can thrive at lower temperatures and use foods containing relatively large amounts of sugars or acids. It is not

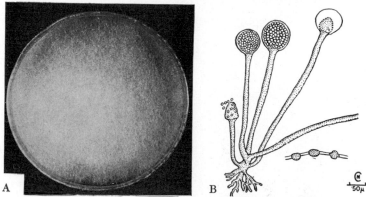

Figure 12   Black mold (*Rhizopus nigricans*). *A*, Mold colony on an agar plate. *B*, Microscopic appearance. (Conant, Martin, Smith, Baker, and Callaway: Manual of Clinical Mycology.)

uncommon to find them growing on fruit jellies or on the surface of a pickling vat. A piece of moist bread, cake, or cheese, or a slice of lemon or orange, if permitted to stand in the dark for a few days, will become a thriving mold culture. Since molds require atmospheric oxygen, they will always be found on the surface of the medium.

For microscopic examination, mold fibers can be transferred to a glass slide and mounted with water and a coverslip. This method is not entirely satisfactory because it results in breaking the mold plants. A better method is provided by the slide culture that enables one to see the mold intact. It is made by inoculating a thin section of nutrient agar, placed on a glass slide, with mold spores. This is overlaid with a coverslip and placed on a moist filter paper in a petri dish. After incubation, the slide can be examined under the microscope without disturbing the mold. (See Figure 14.) Fungi grown in petri dishes can be examined by placing the lower plate on the stage of the microscope and examining it with the low-power lens. Furthermore, placing a drop of water and a coverslip over a young colony will enable one to use the high-power lens to observe the developing mold.

Importance   Many varieties of molds are widely distributed in nature. Like the yeasts and bacteria, they form

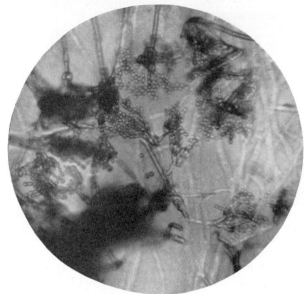

Figure 13   Blue mold (*Penicillium notatum*) (× 600). (E. R. Squibb & Sons.)

complex metabolic products and are active agents of decay. The soil fungi are thus important in maintaining soil fertility by decomposing starch, cellulose, chitin, and proteins of dead plants and animals. In the tropics, where temperature and moisture favor molds, they constitute a definite problem since they may grow on leather, books, paper, and clothing as well as on food. Some species of molds are very useful in the preparation of certain cheeses such as Roquefort and Camembert. A few are capable of producing disease; for example, ringworm or athlete's foot is caused by fungi.

Characteristics of Common Varieties   Although it is neither possible nor profitable to make an extensive study of molds at this time, one may learn something of the characteristic structure of molds by observing three common varieties: bread mold, blue mold, and pigmented mold.

Black mold (*Rhizopus nigricans*), the common bread mold, is frequently seen on old bread. Since commercial bakeries often add chemicals which inhibit the growth of molds, a

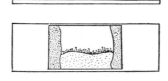

Figure 14   Pigmented mold (*Aspergillus*) growing in slide culture. (Henrici, A. T.: Molds, Yeasts, and Actinomycetes. John Wiley & Sons.)

moistened cracker or piece of homemade cake may be a better source. Examination with a hand lens will reveal threads growing on and below the surface of the mass. Other white fibers rise above the surface and support a minute black body. This is the *sporangium* or spore sac which upon maturity scatters the enclosed spores (see Figure 12).

Blue mold (Penicillium notatum) is a common fungus with characteristic blue-green color. Members of this genus are often seen growing on oranges, lemons, and other fruits. Two species, *Penicillium roqueforti* and *Penicillium camemberti,* are used in cheesemaking. *Penicillium notatum* is used in the production of *penicillin,* a powerful antibacterial substance used in treating infections. The vegetative fibers penetrate the food first; this is followed by the development of the reproductive threads with spores (*conidia*) which appear to the naked eye as blue-green powder. Under the microscope this powder mass appears as branched septate stalks supporting brushlike chains of spores (see Figure 13).

Pigmented mold (Aspergillus) is another common mold often observed growing on decaying vegetables, fruit, or bread.

It appears as a powdery growth, green, yellow, orange, black, or brown in color. Magnification reveals a branched septate mycelium and large sexual fruiting bodies containing eight spores within sacs. In addition, chains of asexual spores arise from the rounded heads of the aerial threads. (See Figure 14.)

SUMMARY

1. Most yeasts are relatively large, single, oval or round cells of complex structure which reproduce by budding and spore-formation. The yeasts which ferment sugars, forming alcohol and carbon dioxide, are useful in making wine, beer, and bread.

2. Molds are complex multicellular fungi which grow luxuriantly on many foods. Their many and varied metabolic processes promote decay. Certain species of molds are used in cheesemaking, and others in the manufacture of antibiotics.

SUPPLEMENTARY READINGS

BOOKS:

Alexopoulous, C. J.: Introductory Mycology. New York, John Wiley & Sons, 1952.

Burrows, W.: Jordan-Burrows Textbook of Bacteriology. 15th ed. Philadelphia, W. B. Saunders Co., 1949.

Frobisher, M.: Fundamentals of Bacteriology. 5th ed. Philadelphia, W. B. Saunders Co., 1953.

Henrici, A. T.: Molds, Yeasts and Actinomycetes. 2d ed. New York, John Wiley & Sons, 1947.

Salle, A. J.: Fundamental Principles of Bacteriology. 3d ed. New York, McGraw-Hill Book Co., 1948.

Tanner, F. W.: Bacteriology; a Textbook of Microorganisms. 4th ed. New York, John Wiley & Sons, 1948.

PERIODICAL:

Emerson, R.: Molds and Men. Scient. Am., *186:* 28–32, 1952.

CHAPTER 7   *Protozoa*

PROTOZOA are single-celled animals that are more complex in structure than the fungi. Though they vary greatly in size and appearance, most are relatively large, well-differentiated cells with clearly defined internal structures. The cytoplasm of the cell is usually composed of an external layer, the ectoplasm, that is concentrated and viscid, and an internal layer, the fluid entoplasm, enclosing a well-defined nucleus, granuoles, and vacuoles. The contractile vacuoles, which appear as clear areas constantly changing their size, are thought to serve as respiratory and excretory organs. Most protozoa possess organs of motion, and may have special structures such as an oral groove, a gullet, or an anal pore. Function also is differentiated, in that the external layer (ectoplasm) is chiefly concerned with protection, motion, securing food, excretion, and respiration. The innermost part of the cell (entoplasm) functions in nutrition and reproduction.

Most protozoa differ from fungi in that they are able to catch and ingest solid food consisting of plant cells, bacteria, or other protozoa. It is possible to cultivate some protozoa in the laboratory by supplying them with suitable animal or plant cells as food. Unlike the bacteria, yeasts, and molds, they will not grow on simple media such as nutrient broth.

The protozoa are widely distributed in nature; some live in stagnant water and in moist, decaying matter, while others live as parasites within the digestive tract or tissues of larger animals. Most protozoa survive unfavorable conditions by forming a *cyst,* a resistant body that is comparable to the spore formed by some bacterial cells. When food and water supplies fail, the cell forms a round ball and secretes a hard protective covering. In this state, the cell becomes inactive and very resistant to physical and chemical agents. When the environment again becomes favorable, the animal leaves the cyst and resumes its life activities. Protozoa also vary in their mode of reproduction. Some multiply by longitudinal fission, and some by the formation of a mass of daughter cells; in other species, reproduction is sexual, involving the union of two cells. Protozoa are large enough to demonstrate indirect cell division, or *mitosis*, a process by which the nuclear material is distributed equally to the daughter cells.

On the basis of locomotion, protozoa can be divided into four distinct classes: (1) the *amebas*, that move by means of false feet or pseudopods; (2) the *flagellates*, that are propelled by long whiplike projections called flagella; (3) the *ciliates*, that move by means of hairlike projections of the ectoplasm; and (4) the *sporozoa*, that have little motility.

AMEBAS

The ameba is a protozoan cell found wherever decaying materials and moisture are abundant. The cell is relatively large and contains one or more nuclei and contractile vacuoles as well as food particles. The ameba is constantly changing its shape; it moves by projecting a mass of protoplasm which is then followed by the rest of the cell. It feeds by wrapping itself around the food particle, and later eliminates undigestible material by reversing the process. Any part of the cytoplasm appears to be able to carry on any of the life processes. Though lacking visible organs, the ameba distinguishes between food and other particles, and moves away from harmful substances. When injured, it rolls up in a tight ball and remains motionless. Its method of reproduction is simple; the mother cell enlarges and then divides, forming two identical daughter cells. (See Figure 15.) Some amebas live as parasites in the intestinal tract of man or animals, but most of the species are free-living. The organism that causes amebic dysentery in man is an example of this class of organisms. (See Figure 15.)

FLAGELLATES

The flagellates are elongated cells, supporting flagella on the anterior end. The cytoplasm contains a nucleus in anterior position, and also one or more vacuoles. Many species are characterized by a waving or undulating membrane. Some species live in pond water and sewage, while others live in the intestinal tract or the blood stream of man or animals. The

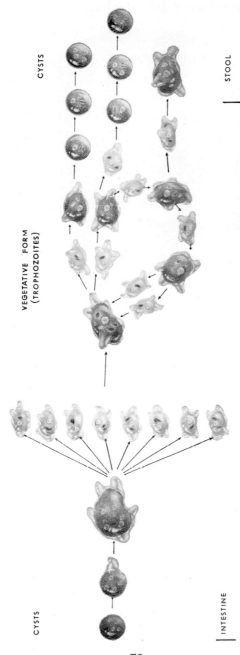

CYSTS

VEGETATIVE FORM
(TROPHOZOITES)

CYSTS

INTESTINE

STOOL

Figure 15 Life cycle, *Endamoeba histolytica.* Infection caused by ingestion of cysts from feces, fingers, food, fluid, and flies. Cysts do not invade tissue but vegetative forms do. (Courtesy of Harold W. Brown, Sharp & Dohme Seminar.)

73

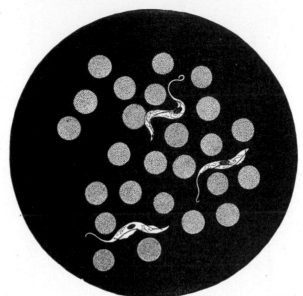

Figure 16   Flagellates (*Trypanosoma gambiense*) with red blood
cells.

trypanosome, the blood parasite causing African sleeping sickness, is an example of a flagellate (see Figure 16).

CILIATES

The ciliates are the most highly developed of the protozoa;
they show a definite entoplasm containing two nuclei—a macro-
nucleus and a micronucleus—and contractile vacuoles with
acid or alkaline digestive secretions. The ectoplasm contains
numerous granules which support hairlike organs of locomotion called *cilia.* Virtually all ciliates are free-living forms. One
exception of interest, the *Balantidium coli,* lives in the intestine
of hogs and monkeys and is occasionally found in man.

SPOROZOA

The sporozoa, a group of protozoa with no organs of locomotion, are all parasitic. They are called sporozoa because in
one phase of development the parasite divides into a mass of
daughter cells called *spores.* These cells are simple in structure
and have no special organs for taking food. As a rule, they

have a very complex life history and are transferred from bird to bird or from mammal to mammal by blood-sucking anthropods. Some of these organisms are harmless, while others cause serious disease; the malaria parasite is an example of this type of organism. Its life history is discussed on page 503.

IMPORTANCE OF PROTOZOA

The free-living protozoa are important because they form a part of the food chain; i.e., they feed upon small microscopic animals and plants and in turn serve as food for small aquatic animals. Like free-living bacteria, they are active in maintaining the fertility of the soil and in the purification of sewage. Other species are important because they cause disease in man and animals.

SUMMARY

1. Protozoa are relatively large microorganisms that are varied and complex in their structure. Structural and cultural characteristics distinguish them from each other and from the fungi.

2. The common protozoa include amebas, flagellates, ciliates, and sporozoa.

3. These organisms, like the fungi, change their environment and are important in maintaining the fertility of the soil and in the purification of sewage.

4. Protozoa include many free-living species as well as others that live as parasites in the bodies of other animals.

SUPPLEMENTARY READINGS

Belding, D. L.: Clinical Parasitology. 2nd ed. New York, Appleton-Century-Crofts, Inc., 1952.

Buchsbaum, R. M.: Animals without Backbones. 2d ed. Chicago, The University of Chicago Press, 1948.

Burrows, W.: Jordan-Burrows Textbook of Bacteriology. 15th ed. Philadelphia, W. B. Saunders Co., 1949.

Craig, C. F., and Faust, E. C.: Clinical Parasitology. 5th ed. Philadelphia, Lea & Febiger, 1951.

Hall, R. P.: Protozoology. New York, Prentice-Hall, 1953.

Kudo, R. R.: Protozoology. 3d ed. Springfield, Ill., Charles C Thomas, 1945.

Lwoff, A.: Biochemistry and Physiology of Protozoa. New York, Academic Press, Inc., 1951.

CHAPTER 8

Ecology—The Interdepend-
ence of Living Organisms

THE STUDY of the complex relations of a given species to its living and nonliving environment is called *ecology*. Whether or not a particular organism (microbe, plant, or animal) will thrive depends upon many factors including the presence of other living organisms. In nature, various species of microorganisms are found in close proximity. As would be expected, contact between active living agents leads to some type of relationship—neutral, antagonistic, or supporting. Antagonism between species may result either from competition for food or from the secretion of harmful products. For example, lactic acid formed by bacteria in sauerkraut prevents the growth of many forms of organisms by rendering the medium very acid. The mold *Penicillium* forms penicillin, a secretion which prevents the growth of various organisms by interfering with metabolism of the susceptible cells. (See page 274.) The rapid death of disease-producing organisms when introduced into the soil is probably due in large part to the antagonism of the hardy soil organisms. Supporting relationships are also common among microbes in nature; since different species vary in their nutritional requirements the products of excretion or digestion of one group serve as food for others. For example, fungi which digest proteins, wood, and other complex substances make simpler foods available in usable form for many other organisms. Not only do microorganisms support or antagonize one another but they may exert similar effects on higher plants and animals. The undesirable effects of organisms that cause plant and animal diseases are well known and can easily be overemphasized. Far more important are the many organisms which maintain the fertility of the soil. Bacteria, yeasts, molds, algae, diatoms, protozoa, insects, and worms are all very numerous in cultivated soils. Here they carry on their life processes, sometimes independently but more often cooperatively. Many, perhaps all, form a part of an endless food chain. Bacteria serve as food for protozoa while protozoa in turn serve as food for larger animals. All synthesize *protoplasm* and contribute this material to the soil as do larger animals and plants. Many microorganisms by their chemical activities transform complex compounds to inorganic substances. Proteins, for example, are changed to amino acids and ammonia. Ammonia in turn is changed to nitrites and nitrates which serve as food for the higher plants. As a result plants and animals are so dependent on microorganisms that without them all plant and animal life would cease.

GREEN PLANTS BUILD FOOD

Since green plants are an obvious and essential part of the food chain, their contribution will be considered first. Plants like all other living forms are composed of cells. Within the cells of the green leaves is a pigment compound called *chlorophyll*. Chlorophyll resembles hemoglobin but differs in that it contains magnesium instead of iron. Plants having chlorophyll within their cells can use carbon dioxide and water to make carbohydrate for their own cell structure and oxygen which is returned to the air. The chlorophyll enables the cells to use the radiant energy of the sun to supply the chemical energy essential for building these substances. By this process, known as photosynthesis, they make energy-rich plant carbohydrates. This very complex process can be indicated by the following formula:

$$6CO_2 + 12H_2O + 677.2 \text{ large calories}^* \xrightarrow[\text{chlorophyll}]{\text{light}} C_6H_{12}O_6 +$$
$$6O_2 + 6H_2O + 677.2 \text{ calories (found in carbohydrate)}$$

It will be noted that photosynthesis is the reverse of the oxidation of carbohydrates:

$$(C_6H_{12}O_6 + 677.2 \text{ Kg. calories}) + 6O_2 \longrightarrow 6CO_2 + 6H_2O +$$
$$677.2 \text{ Kg. calories}$$

Only green plants and a few species of bacteria and protozoa

---

* One mole of glucose when oxidized yields:

$$\frac{\text{Kg. calories}}{\text{Molecular wt. of glucose}} \frac{677.2}{180} = 3.75 \text{ or (4) small calories per gram}$$
$$\text{of glucose}$$

can use the energy of the sun to build substances from non-living materials. All other forms of life depend on cells or substances produced in other living cells for nutrients.

ANIMALS DEPEND ON PLANTS

Animals and plants without chlorophyll require foods provided directly or indirectly by green plants. Animals and fungi destroy ready-made cells in order to obtain building materials and chemical energy to build their own cell structures (see page 55). For example, molds growing on bread secrete digestive fluids which aid in the digestion of proteins and starches of the bread. The cellular structure of the mold increases until all the available food is used. In a similar manner the digestive secretions of the cow change foods of plant origin to amino acids, simple sugars, fatty acids, and glycerol. Then these units are rebuilt to form beef protein, glycogen, and fat. When man eats beefsteak, a similar process occurs. Life is thus interdependent; animals depend on chlorophyll-bearing plants, while green plants, in turn, depend on microorganisms.

MICROORGANISMS REDISTRIBUTE BUILDING MATERIALS

As every gardener knows, plants require nitrates from the soil together with inorganic salts, water and carbon dioxide from the air, to build the proteins of their tissues. As plants grow they remove nitrates from the earth, transforming them into plant structures. Were this process to continue the soil would be so depleted that it could no longer support plant life. This in turn would mean starvation for man and animals.

This does not occur because, sooner or later, plant and animal substance is returned to the soil where it serves as food for yeasts, molds, bacteria, protozoa, and various worms. Microorganisms return essential material to the soil by disintegrating wastes and dead bodies. These lifeless proteins, fats, and carbohydrates are changed, step by step, to simpler compounds, which serve as plant food. In short, microorganisms keep essential materials in circulation. The progress of chemical elements through many chemical reactions is often expressed in terms of cycles, as "the nitrogen cycle," "the carbon cycle." (See Figures 17 and 18.) These cycles consist of two

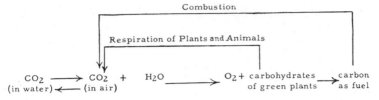

Figure 17   The carbon cycle in nature. (Modified from Fruton.)

phases: the building of simple materials into complex substances by living cells, and the disintegration of these materials by other living organisms. Both building and decomposition involve a series of chemical reactions. The beginning and the end of these processes are known with certainty, but not all the intermediate steps have been recognized. These reactions are in reality more complex than the following statements would indicate. The term "carbon cycle" is used to describe the successive changes of carbon in nature. Green plants store energy in the process of synthesis of carbohydrates, proteins, and fats. Respiration by living organisms changes complex carbon compounds to carbon dioxide which is again available to plants for synthesis. The chemical changes associated with the breakdown of carbon compounds have already been described. (See page 55.)

Nitrogen Cycle   The nitrogen cycle involves two phases: (1) the building of complex proteins from organic or inorganic substances, and (2) the changing of proteins and amino acids to inorganic substances. Green plants build their protein from plant carbohydrates, water, and minerals—including nitrates and phosphates. Animals and many fungi build their proteins from animal and plant cells or substances derived from them. In utilizing nitrogenous material, microorganisms produce numerous and varied changes which are important to other forms of life. The bacteria that act on nitrogenous material can be divided into five main groups: (1) the putrefactive bacteria, (2) the nitrifying bacteria, (3) the denitrifying bacteria, (4) nitrate-reducing bacteria, and (5) the nitrogen-fixing bacteria.

PUTREFACTIVE BACTERIA   Many bacteria as well as molds and protozoa are able to decompose plant and animal proteins.

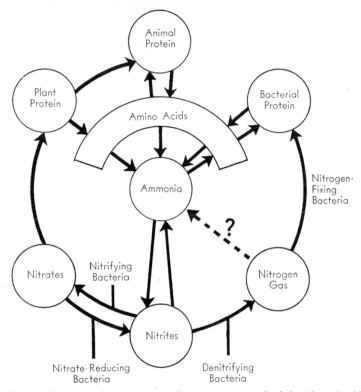

Figure 18   The nitrogen cycle. Beginning at the left: Plants build their protoplasm from soil nitrates, carbon dioxide, and water. Plant proteins in turn serve as food for animals. Both plant and animal proteins are changed to amino acids and ammonia by enzymes secreted by bacteria and other organisms. Nitrifying bacteria oxidize ammonia to nitrites and nitrates. Other bacteria reduce nitrates to nitrites and nitrogen gas. Various nitrogen-fixing bacteria transform nitrogen gas into bacterial protoplasm thus completing the cycle.

This process when it occurs in the presence of oxygen is called decay, and in the absence of oxygen, *putrefaction*. In both processes the complex proteins are eventually changed to amino acids and ammonia. Decay and putrefaction of animal and plant bodies constitute an important step in maintaining the fertility of the soil.

NITRIFYING BACTERIA   The nitrifying bacteria (*Nitrosomas* and *Nitrobacter*) are an important group of soil organisms which grow best in warm, moist, alkaline earth with an adequate oxygen supply. They utilize only inorganic salts in their metabolism. They oxidize ammonia or nitrous acid to nitric acid which reacts with alkalies to form nitrate salts. This process enriches the soil by changing ammonium and nitrite compounds into utilizable plant food in the form of nitrates. This group of organisms will not grow on nutrient broth or agar made from peptones because organic compounds are poisonous to them and inhibit their growth.

NITRATE-REDUCING BACTERIA   Many bacteria when deprived of molecular oxygen secure oxygen by reducing nitrates to nitrites, while others are capable of reducing nitrites to ammonia.* This reduction of nitrates constitutes a definite loss of available plant food which would be serious were it not reversed by the nitrogen-fixing bacteria. Nitrate reduction is common in wet soils, and in part accounts for the lack of fertility of swamplands.

DENITRIFYING BACTERIA   A few bacteria (certain species of *Serratia* and *Pseudomonas*) give off nitrogen gas when grown on media containing nitrates or nitrites as the only available source of nitrogen. The chemistry of this process is not understood. It is clear, however, that these organisms complete the cycle by returning the element nitrogen to the air.

NITROGEN-FIXING BACTERIA   Until recently few organisms were considered capable of fixing nitrogen—that is, building protoplasm from nitrogen gas. It is now known that a considerable number of different organisms—algae and bacteria—are able to transform inert nitrogen gas into living cell substance. The nitrogen-fixing bacteria include a variety of free-living organisms—certain *Clostridia* and *Azotobacter* and many photosynthetic bacteria. Better known are the root nodule bacteria (*Rhizobium*) which inhabit the root hairs of the legumes (peas, beans, alfalfa, clover). The invaded root nodule reacts by forming nodules which surround a colony of these useful bacteria. The organisms growing in the root nodules use carbon compounds from the plant and nitrogen from the air to build cell protein and complex nitrogen compounds which are excreted into the soil. As the plants and bacteria die, their cell

* There is not complete agreement on this point.

protoplasm in turn is changed to ammonia, nitrites, and nitrates, thus enriching the soil. (See page 80.) To insure an adequate supply of these bacteria, farmers often pour cultures of nitrogen-fixing bacteria over the seeds of the legumes before they are planted.

CONCERTED ACTION OF BACTERIA IN NITROGEN TRANSFORMATION   Thus, different groups of bacteria effect many transformations of nitrogen. Some species transform gas into protoplasm, although most require nitrogen compounds for this purpose. Some bacteria also are able to use simple or complex nitrogen compounds in reactions which release energy. (See Figure 18 and Table 6.)

Many groups of bacteria are active in nitrogen transformation. Like other living forms all synthesize protein from some simpler nitrogen source. In addition, the five groups listed above produce other important changes. A mixed population of organisms living in soil or sewage may contain all the bacteria and enzymes needed to carry on all the chemical reactions of the nitrogen cycle. All of these organisms will not be active at the same time, since the conditions which encourage one group may temporarily prevent the growth of another group. For example, the presence of organic matter favors the growth of putrefactive bacteria but inhibits certain autotrophic bacteria. Later, when the organic matter has been changed to ammonia or nitrites, the putrefactive bacteria will subside and the autotrophic become active. Likewise the presence of oxygen will inhibit the growth of anaerobes and encourage the growth and activity of aerobes. These activities and conditions needed for growth are summarized in Table 6.

Redistribution of Sulfur, Iron, Manganese, and Phosphorus   Animal and plant proteins always contain small but essential amounts of the elements sulfur, manganese, iron, and phosphorus in organic combination. When putrefactive bacteria destroy proteins, these materials are left in the soil as organic or inorganic compounds. Certain microorganisms use these compounds in their metabolism and change them into forms suitable for plant use. For example, hydrogen sulfide, a product of decaying plant and animal protein, is changed to sulfur and sulfuric acid by red and purple sulfur bacteria.

Table 6   CHANGES EFFECTED BY VARIOUS BACTERIA
ACTING ON NITROGENOUS COMPOUNDS

CHEMICAL CHANGE	TYPE OF BACTERIA	CONDITIONS FAVORING ACTIVITY
Atmospheric nitrogen to organic compounds (protein synthesis)	Nitrogen-fixing bacteria	Absence of organic nitrogen
Organic nitrogen to ammonia	Putrefactive bacteria	Excess of organic nitrogen
Ammonia to organic nitrogen (protein synthesis)	Many heterotrophic bacteria	Excess of ammonia and a suitable source of carbon compounds
Ammonia to nitrites or nitrates	Nitrifying bacteria	Absence of organic matter and presence of oxygen
Nitrates to nitrites to ammonia	Various heterotrophic bacteria: facultative and obligate anaerobes	Presence of organic matter or hydrogen and the absence of oxygen
Nitrate or nitrite to nitrogen	Dentrifying bacteria	Nitrate or nitrite as the only available source of nitrogen

(See page 44.) Other sulfur bacteria obtain their energy by oxidizing sulfur and sulfur compounds to sulfuric acid, which in turn reacts with alkalies to form sulfate salts. These sulfates are utilized by plants in building their protein, and thus are available to the animals which use plants as food. Various species of sulfur bacteria are found in hot springs, in sulfur mines, in water, and especially in wet soils where there is active decomposition of organic matter. Likewise, organic iron compounds are changed to ferric hydroxide by certain "iron bacteria." Soil organisms are also responsible for converting insoluble calcium phosphate to the soluble forms required by plant life.

ECONOMIC IMPORTANCE

It can be seen that the organisms of the soil play an indispensable role in transforming complex building materials into forms that can be used again. Under natural conditions the bodies of plants and animals are returned to the soil which nourished them, thus maintaining a constant supply of building materials. Man often disturbs this natural relationship. He may raise plants and animals and ship them across the country or use poor agricultural methods that encourage the loss of the "living" top soil by the action of wind and rain. Furthermore, by congregating herds of cattle or acres of corn in close proximity, he sets up conditions which favor the transmission of disease-producing organisms that may destroy the cattle or the corn. These activities are examples of disturbing the balance of nature in which microorganisms, plants, and animals each make their contribution to maintaining life.

Soils will readily lose their fertility unless efforts are made to conserve top soil and to replace building materials. Both plants and animals which are raised for food are prone to disease unless special precautions are taken. It is obvious that microorganisms play a vital role in the world economy.

SUMMARY

1. The relationships of one species of living organisms to other species are complex and varied.

2. In general there is a large degree of interdependence. Animals are directly or indirectly dependent on plants for food. Plants in turn are dependent on soil organisms to change organic compounds to the inorganic forms that may be used as plant food.

3. Competitive and antagonistic relationships manifest themselves when disease-producing organisms kill large numbers of a given species. This in turn may have adverse effects on other living forms by destroying their source of food or shelter.

4. Man may disturb the balance of nature by careless use of natural resources.

SUPPLEMENTARY READINGS

Frobisher, M.: Fundamentals of Microbiology. 5th ed. Philadelphia, W. B. Saunders Co., 1953.

Fruton, J. S., and Simmons, S.: General Biochemistry. New York, John Wiley & Sons, Inc., 1953.

Galdston, I. (Ed.): The Epidemiology of Health. New York, Health Education Council, 1953.

Porter, J. R.: Bacterial Chemistry and Physiology. New York, John Wiley & Sons, Inc., 1946.

Werkman, C. H., and Wilson, P. W.: Bacterial Physiology. New York, Academic Press, Inc., 1951.

Winslow, C. E. A.: Man and Epidemics. Princeton, New Jersey, Princeton University Press, 1952.

Suggested Laboratory Experience for Unit I

PART I. INTRODUCTION

Problem Solving by the Expert   In all scientific fields research workers are busy discovering new facts. Many of these facts are discovered by laboratory studies. The word *laboratory* (L. *laborare*—to work) literally means a place for work. As commonly used, it means the place or room where scientific experiments are conducted. Such experiments include carefully planned observations made to establish or to learn new facts. The statements found in scientific text and reference books usually represent a summary of the available evidence together with the best interpretation by experts. Because many such statements are based on incomplete evidence, they may need to be revised from time to time. For example, it was generally accepted for years that bacteria had no (visible) cell wall, but in 1940 the new electron microscope (magnification × 10,000) revealed a definite cell wall. "Facts," then, are the statement of truth that the experts can give on the basis of the evidence at hand. Such experimental evidence is the result of scientific investigation. Sound scientific investigation of a single problem, or even of one unknown aspect of that problem, involves the use of a special, carefully planned technique commonly called the "scientific method" of investigation. As a rule, this method involves the following sequence of procedures: (1) selecting the problem, (2) limiting the problem, (3) selecting the method of study, (4) making observations and collecting data, (5) analyzing the data, and (6) drawing conclusions. A fact is established not upon evidence of a single experiment but by making a series of carefully controlled experiments.

SELECTING THE PROBLEM   Suppose that a bacteriologist in studying a newly discovered microorganism (Bacterium X) desires to determine the lowest temperature that will kill the organism in ten minutes. This, then, is the problem.

LIMITING THE PROBLEM   Since only one aspect of the

86

problem can be pursued at one time, the investigator decides to restrict the investigation to determining the resistance of the test organism to heat. For another experiment he might set other limitations. The method is designed to control the conditions of the experiment so that there is only one variable —the temperature. To this end, all cultures are grown for twenty-four hours in a carefully standardized broth. The temperatures to be used may be limited to five, instead of using fifty or a hundred different degrees of heat.

SELECTING THE METHOD OF STUDY   The method of investigation must be carefully planned in order that it will be both suitable and practical. In this experiment, the following method was chosen: Measured quantities of culture were added to measured quantities of nutrient broth and then held at the selected temperatures for ten minutes. After heating, they were cooled and incubated at 37° C. (98.6° F.) for twenty-four hours. Certain tubes, the controls, were left unheated.

MAKING OBSERVATIONS AND COLLECTING DATA   The investigator's task is to observe and to record accurately—not to prove or disprove some preconceived idea or theory. Careful and complete records of all observations must be kept. As a rule, charts are prepared for making permanent records of observations. For example: in the experiment described above, the investigator would observe the tubes of broth (previously inoculated, heated, and incubated) for evidence of bacterial growth. His observations could be recorded as follows:

Date *May 9, 1948*   Investigator *John Smith*

Results of heating Bacterium X at 60° C. for 10 minutes:

Tube	1	Growth
"	2	Growth
"	3	No growth
"	4	Growth
"	5	Growth
"	6	No growth
"	7	Growth
"	8	Growth
"	9	No growth
"	10	No growth
Control		Growth

ANALYZING DATA   When all experiments had been completed, the data from each separate experiment could be classified and summarized on a master chart that would serve as the basis for making conclusions. In the experiment described, the data might be summarized as follows:

THE EFFECT OF VARIOUS TEMPERATURES ON BACTERIUM X

TEMPERATURE	NUMBER OF TESTS	NOT KILLED IN 10 MINUTES	KILLED IN 10 MINUTES
50° C.	20	20	0
60° C.	20	12	8
70° C.	20	0	20
80° C.	20	0	20
90° C.	20	0	20
Control (not heated)	10	10	0

Observe that the data show that the control suspensions and those heated at 50° C. (122° F.) survived while those heated at 70°, 80°, and 90° C. (158°, 176°, and 194° F.) were killed.

DRAWING CONCLUSIONS   To draw valid conclusions, the conditions of the experiment must be carefully controlled so that there is only one variable, e.g., temperature. Furthermore, a large number of observations must be made to rule out chance errors. In the experiment cited, the following conclusion would be warranted: Under the conditions of the test, 70° C. (158° F.) can be expected to kill this particular organism in ten minutes. If the test conditions are changed, however, the results may also change.

Generalizations on the basis of a small number of observations are dangerous. Consider the following: Two men who had pneumonia and were treated with sulfonamides died while one man, who had the same illness and who received no sulfonamides, lived. No valid conclusions can be drawn on these data because the observations did not rule out other variables such as age, nutrition, and occupation. The danger of basing conclusions on a small number of observations can be illustrated by the following problem: Suppose that an investigator wishes to determine the average height of the men in a certain American regiment. If he measured the height of the first five men he met, the data might show that the average height was

5 feet, 2 inches or perhaps 6 feet, 2 inches. Neither would be the true average because the figures were obtained by measuring a few short or a few tall men of the group. Measurements of 1000 men, selected at random, would show that a few were over 6 feet, 2 inches; a few under 5 feet, 2 inches; and that the true average lay between those figures—perhaps 5 feet, 7 inches. In addition to care in selection, the more complicated data will usually require statistical analysis in order to determine whether the observed differences could occur by chance alone. After considering the effects of such chance occurrences, the investigator can evaluate the experimental evidence and determine to what extent the observed differences are truly significant.

Problem Solving by Professional Workers in the Health Field Nurses and other health workers are constantly confronted with the problem of dealing with microorganisms. The steps to be taken in solving these problems will be similar to those discussed in the preceding paragraphs, although the methods may vary somewhat. Consider the common problem of disinfecting thermometers. Methods now in use vary greatly in regard to solutions used, time of exposure, and handling of the instrument. Carefully controlled laboratory experiments have proved that many techniques now in current use are unsafe since they do not assure the killing of all pathogenic bacteria that are on the thermometers. Assume that a group of nurses wish to evaluate the safety of the technique now used by their organization. This is essentially a problem in applied microbiology. Many of the facts related to this problem are already known to bacteriologists and are available in reference books and journals. The problem may be stated as: *Will the method now in use kill any and all disease-producing bacteria which may be found on mouth thermometers?* The next step is to ask the questions which must be answered before one can draw conclusions regarding the safety of the procedure in question. These might include the following: *What relatively resistant organisms may be found in the mouth? How long can these organisms survive exposure to the disinfectant used? Does our procedure provide optimum contact between organisms and disinfectant? Does it provide an* *adequate margin of safety?* To answer these questions one needs to know where authentic sources of information may be found and must possess the ability to interpret the data secured from these sources. Often the data can be obtained from current reference books and periodicals devoted to scientific investigation. (It is seldom practical for nurses to carry out the technical aspects of laboratory studies although they may well initiate requests for such studies and cooperate with the investigators.) The answers to the first three questions can be used as guides in judging the efficiency of the method under study. Finally comes the decision: Shall we retain the method in present use or develop a new one? The new technique in turn must also be judged by the available facts.

Other suggested problems for investigation might include:

1. Care of specimens for bacterial culture.
2. Handling of needles and syringes.
3. Sterilization of various kinds of equipment including needles and syringes.
4. Preparation of formulas for feeding infants.

The ability to evaluate all aspects of his practice is needed by every professional worker. It is well to remember that ways of working have often developed empirically and are supported by tradition rather than facts. Practice regarding thermometer disinfection is a case in point. To mention another example, before 1945 in many clinics it was customary to place multiple doses of vaccine or medication into a syringe and merely by changing needles to inject the medication into a number of individuals in succession. This method is now in disrepute because it may result in transmission of the virus of infectious hepatitis (page 371). At one time it was standard practice, but well established facts now prove it to be unsafe. It is probable that many other aspects of current practice may need revision when critical examination of them is made.

Problem Solving by the Student   Obviously, the careful collecting and weighing of data require skill and judgment which the inexperienced student does not possess. For the beginner, the laboratory is a place for learning. It provides the conditions which enable the student to discover for himself facts already well known to scientists. He may, for instance, see bacteria, grow bacteria, and observe the chemical changes which they produce. Because of limits of time, materials, and skill, the student usually makes a small number of observations on any one phase. The results of his observation must be regarded as one sample; it may or may not be a typical sample. For this reason, his experimental results must be interpreted in the light of reports by experts. For instance, if an agar plate touched by the student's fingers shows no growth after incubation, the evidence would be insufficient to prove that there were no bacteria on his fingers. A better conclusion would be that this one contact did not result in the transfer of bacteria which can grow on the medium provided.

The laboratory exercise should make the student aware of microorganisms by providing some personal experience with bacteria as living entities. Large problems such as those listed on page 92 are useful because they stimulate thinking, reading, and questioning on the part of the students. Before a plan can be developed, there must be clear recognition of the purpose to be accomplished and of additional information required and techniques to be learned. Thus the problem provides a reason for laboratory activity, reading, and discussion. The suggested laboratory techniques and exercises should be used only if they contribute to solution of the students' problems. Class discussions should emphasize the fundamental principles which underlie the observations made in the laboratory. Furthermore, the laboratory experience should provide an opportunity to learn the nature of scientific evidence and should encourage a critical attitude that asks: What is the evidence? How was it established? Are the observations valid? Were precautions taken to rule out errors? Has it been confirmed by other scientists? If it is true, of what significance is it in everyday living? This learning experience is not designed to develop in the student a mastery of laboratory skills such as are required of the technician—though of course it is necessary to develop some degree of skill. On the other hand, it is intended primarily to give the student an understanding of microorganisms as an essential part of the environment, a part that cannot safely be ignored. Laboratory experience should develop the skill to listen and read more intelligently so that the student can use the facts learned in daily living. To accomplish this purpose, it is essential that the student regard the laboratory experience as a method of learning. He needs to be aware of the contribution that each laboratory exercise can make to his understanding of the subject.

PART II. SUGGESTED LABORATORY PROBLEMS

1. Design an environment for growing common bacteria, yeasts, and molds. Test your plan by culturing organisms from the environment.
2. Design a series of experiments to test the effects of environmental factors which are likely to be more or less unfavorable.
3. Make a plan for isolating a pure culture of bacteria from a mixed culture obtained from some natural source.
4. Make a plan to demonstrate enzyme activity by various kinds of bacterial cells.
5. Other problems suggested by students or teacher.

PART III. LABORATORY TECHNIQUES AND EXPERIMENTS WHICH MAY BE USEFUL IN SOLVING PROBLEMS

A. *Culture Methods*

1. PREPARATION OF NUTRIENT MEDIA

A *medium* is any substance, liquid or solid, that can be used for growing microorganisms. Any material containing the necessary food elements can be used. The early bacteriologists used potato, carrot, milk, blood serum, and urine. Today most media are made from meat extract or meat infusion broth, or a very satisfactory medium can be prepared from *Difco-dehydrated nutrient broth.* Nutrient broth and nutrient agar are excellent media for growing common bacteria and yeasts. When enriched with sterile blood, they will usually support the growth of more fastidious bacteria. Bacteria which are unable to grow in the presence of oxygen require special media with active reducing substances. (See pages 49 and 94.) Sabouraud's medium is suitable for growing molds.

NUTRIENT BROTH: RECIPE I

Materials: Difco-dehydrated nutrient broth .... 8 gm.
Meat extract .... 3 gm.
Peptone .... 5 gm.
Distilled water .... 1 liter
Sodium chloride (optional) .... 8 gm.

Method: Dissolve nutrient broth powder in distilled water. (This requires no filtration and no modification of reaction since the medium is adjusted to *p*H 6.8.) Place in tubes and sterilize at 121° C. (249.8° F.) for 15 minutes (in the autoclave).

NUTRIENT BROTH: RECIPE II

Materials: Meat extract .... 3 gm.
Peptone .... 5 gm.
Sodium chloride (optional) .... 8 gm.
Water ...:.............................. 1 liter

Method: Dissolve ingredients in water. Filter. Adjust reaction to approximately *p*H 7. Place in tubes and sterilize at 121° C. (249.8° F.) for 15 minutes (in the autoclave).

This medium supplies vitamins, muscle sugar, and minerals (from meat extract), peptones, and amino acids (peptone). It is suitable food for many bacteria. It can be used plain or modified by adding agar, gelatin, starch, or blood serum.

NUTRIENT AGAR: RECIPE I

Materials: Difco-dehydrated nutrient agar .... 31 gm.
Beef extract .... 3 gm.
Peptone .... 5 gm.
Sodium chloride .... 8 gm.
Agar .... 15 gm.
Distilled water .... 1 liter

Method: Mix powder with cold distilled water; boil to dissolve. Tube and sterilize in autoclave at 121° C. (249.8° F.) for 15 minutes. The final *p*H is 7.3.

NUTRIENT AGAR: RECIPE II

Materials: Meat extract .... 3 gm.
Peptone .... 5 gm.
Sodium chloride .... 8 gm. (optional)
Agar .... 15 gm.
Water .... 1 liter

Method: Dissolve ingredients by boiling. Replace water lost by evaporation. Adjust reaction to approximately pH 7.3. Filter through hot, moist (but not wet) absorbent-cotton filter. Tube and sterilize in autoclave at 121° C. (249.8° F.) for 15 minutes.

SABOURAUD'S MEDIUM FOR GROWING MOLDS

Materials: Maltose .... 40 gm.
         Peptone .... 10 gm.
         Agar .... 20 gm.
         Water .... 1 liter

Method: Dissolve the agar in water by boiling. Add peptone and stir until dissolved. Add maltose and stir until dissolved. Place in tubes and sterilize at 121° C. (249.8° F.) for 15 minutes (in autoclave). (Brown sugar may be used instead of maltose.) No adjustment of reaction is required: the final reaction is pH 5.2 to 5.4.

ANAEROBIC AGAR

Materials: Anaerobic agar* .... 58 gm.
         Polypeptone 2.0%
         Sodium chloride 0.5%
         Dextrose 1.0%
         Agar 2.0%
         Sodium thioglycolate 0.2%
         Sodium formaldehyde sulfoxylate . 0.1%
         Methylene blue 0.0002%
         Distilled water .... 1 liter

Method: Suspend 58 gm. of the powder in 1000 cc. of distilled water. Allow to soak from 5 to 10 minutes. Heat gently until mixture boils and the powder is dissolved. Tube and autoclave 20 minutes at 15 lbs. pressure (121° C.).

FLUID THIOGLYCOLATE MEDIUM FOR GROWING ANAEROBES

Materials: Difco-fluid thioglycolate medium .... 29.5 gm.
         Bacto-casitone .... 15 gm.
         Bacto-yeast extract .... 5 gm.
         Bacto-dextrose .... 5 gm.
         Sodium chloride .... 2.5 gm.
         l-cystine, Difco .... 0.75 gm.
         Thioglycolic acid .... 0.3 cc.
         Bacto-agar .... 0.75 gm.
         Resazurin, certified .... 0.001 gm.
         Distilled water, cold .... 1 liter

Method: Suspend 29.5 gm. fluid thioglycolate medium in 1000 cc. cold distilled water and heat to boiling to dissolve the medium com-

---

* Baltimore Biological Laboratories.

pletely. Tube and sterilize in the autoclave at from 15 to 17 pounds pressure (121° C. to 123° C.) for 18 to 20 minutes. Cool to 25° C. (77° F.) and store in the dark at room temperature.

From this observation, the student should become acquainted with the appearance and the actual food content of the media to be used in the laboratory. Indirectly, this ought to throw some light upon the demands which microorganisms make upon their environment. This experience should serve also as a basis for discussion and reading on media and the conditions that encourage the growth of bacteria.

2. STERILIZATION OF MEDIA

As microorganisms are found virtually everywhere, it is reasonable to assume that the broth just made may contain some bacteria unless it has been sterilized. These organisms find themselves in very favorable conditions with plenty of water, plenty of food, the proper reaction, and a moderate temperature. Under these circumstances, microorganisms start to grow and multiply rapidly. Such growth within the medium may be expected to change the appearance of the broth. The presence of numerous particles (bacteria) in the broth cause it to appear cloudy. If the organisms are uniformly distributed, the broth will be cloudy throughout; otherwise a white film or pellicle may form on the surface, or a white powdery mass appear in the bottom of the tube. The assumption that microorganisms will grow in the broth may be tested by carrying out the following simple experiment.

EXPERIMENT

Materials: 2 or 4 tubes of fresh, unsterilized nutrient broth.

Method: Treat the tubes as directed:

a.
   Tube 1—Sterilize immediately (in autoclave at 121° C. [249.8° F.] for 15 minutes). Return to room temperature.

   Tube 2—Leave at room temperature.

b. (optional)
   Tube 3—Place in icebox for twelve hours; then sterilize in autoclave. Return to room temperature.

   Tube 4—Place in icebox for twelve hours; then return to room temperature.

Observe the tubes after forty-eight hours. Observe the stained smears made from the broth in tubes 2 and 4 under the demonstration microscope. Compare these tubes with each other and with a tube of sterile broth from the stock supply. Explain what is visible. How valid are the observed results? What do they mean in terms of practice?

Cultures   Microscopic examination shows the presence of microorganisms in the cloudy broth. This tube of medium, which contains many living bacteria, is a *culture*. Since it contains more than one kind, it is a *mixed culture* of bacteria. If only one type were present (not likely in this instance) it would be a *pure culture*.

From this experience, the student ought to learn to recognize evidence of bacterial growth in broth. He should become aware of the fact that bacteria are common in the environment and that they can be expected to thrive whenever chance provides the necessary conditions. The meaning of the terms *sterile* and *unsterile*, or *contaminated*, may be clarified by a thoughtful review of this experiment. Likewise, the phrases *pure culture* and *mixed culture* should acquire real meaning.

3. Inoculation

Bacteria can be maintained in the laboratory by growing them in liquid or solid media; as a rule, it is desirable to grow and to keep them in pure culture. A bacterial culture growing in a test tube is like a besieged city in that its supply of food is constantly decreasing and at the same time waste products in the media increase with the age of the culture; that is to say, the character of the medium becomes less and less suitable for bacterial growth. It is necessary, therefore, to transfer a few cells to a new culture medium, in order to obtain a culture of young, active cells.

Techniques may vary slightly, but any method is satisfactory which serves to keep the culture pure by avoiding contamination from without, and to keep the bacteria handled within the safe confines of the culture tubes. (See Figure 8, page 29.) Observe that the tubes are held parallel to the fingers, with the bases resting in the palm of the left hand and that the cotton stoppers are held between the third and fourth and fourth and fifth fingers of the right hand. The inoculating needle is handled as if it were a pencil. Though this process may seem difficult at first, a little careful practice will develop the necessary dexterity.

EXPERIMENT

Materials: Agar slants
Bunsen burner
Inoculating needle (loop)
China marking pencil
Broth cultures—24 hours old
    (1) *Escherichia coli*
    (2) *Serratia marcescens*
    (3) *Sarcina lutea*
    (4) *Micrococcus pyogenes* (*Staphylococcus aureus*)
    (5) *Micrococcus pyogenes* (*Staphylococcus albus*)
    (6) *Micrococcus citreus* (*Staphylococcus citreus*)
    (7) *Bacillus subtilis*

Method:
1. Practice the technique, using empty tubes or tubes containing about 10 cc. of water.
2. Transfer two of the broth cultures provided to agar slants, label, and incubate at room temperature.
3. Transfer the same cultures to broth, label, and incubate as in 2.

Inoculation procedure:
  a. Label culture tube; loosen the stoppers by a twisting movement.
  b. Flame the inoculating needle.
  c. Remove the cotton plugs from tubes (hold in right hand).
  d. Flame lips of tubes.
  e. Transfer a small amount of material from the culture tube (the near tube) to the fresh medium (far tube). Streak gently to avoid breaking the surface of the agar.
  f. Flame lips of tubes and replace plugs.
  g. Flame needle.

An understanding of the precautions used in this technique should provide the key to understanding all *aseptic* methods. Aseptic technique aims to keep a working area (culture medium, surgical instruments, wounds) free from external contaminants. The success of such methods depends upon the recognition of the possible sources from which bacteria may enter, and upon the protecting of sterile or clean areas from these sources.

4. Study of Cultures

The agar slant provides a large surface for bacterial growth. After a twenty-four-hour incubation period, the bacterial population becomes so large that it forms visible masses on the surface of the medium. These often present distinct characteristics which are useful in recognizing the organism. Broth cultures are less varied in their appearance.

EXPERIMENT

Materials: The broth and agar cultures inoculated in experiment No. 3.

Method: Observe cultures; did growth occur? Describe the cultures. If the words suggested do not fit, supply your own. Try to form a clear mental picture of bacterial cultures. Do they present distinct characteristics? Does the appearance suggest that they are pure or mixed?

Items to notice when observing cultures on agar slants:

1. The relative amount of growth—none, scant, moderate, abundant (based on the observation of several cultures).
2. Form—if any.
3. Elevation—raised or effuse (close to the surface).
4. Surface—smooth, rough, granular; dry, moist, glistening.
5. Odor.
6. Pigment—(white, gray, and brown are not considered pigments).

Items to notice when observing broth cultures:

1. Turbidity or cloudiness—absent, present—slight, moderate. Character: uniform, granular, flocculent.
2. Deposit—absent, present—amount. Character: powdery, granular, flocculent. Does it disappear on shaking?
3. Surface growth—absent, present: amount. Character: ring, pellicle. Does it disappear on shaking?
4. Odor.

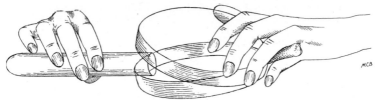

Figure 19   Pouring an agar plate. Observe that the cover protects
                   the petri dish while the agar is poured.

This experience should help the student to see that bacterial
species are distinct entities. It should also provide mental pictures which will enable the student to read descriptions of
cultures without confusion.

5. Separating Mixed Cultures

A. ***By Streak and Dilution Plates***   Materials which
come to the laboratory for examination usually contain more
than one type of microorganism. The first step in the study
of such materials is to secure pure cultures of the important
organisms present. One of the common methods of separating
mixed cultures is by the use of agar plates.

EXPERIMENT—THE STREAK PLATE

Materials: Sterile petri dishes
            Tubes of melted agar
            Broth cultures of: *Serratia*
                              Escherichia coli
                              Sarcina lutea
                              Micrococcus pyogenes
(Agar plates may be prepared before class; cultures should be
grown separately and mixed by the instructor before use.)

Method:
  a. Preparation of an agar plate:
      1. Cool melted agar to approximately 45° C. (113° F.).
      2. Loosen stopper by a twisting movement.
      3. Remove stopper (hold); flame mouth of the tube.
      4. Lift the cover of the petri dish just enough to permit the
          mouth of the tube to enter (see Figure 19).
      5. Pour the medium and cover the dish. (Avoid dropping
          agar on desk.)
      6. Replace stopper.
      7. Rotate petri dish *gently* to spread medium.

8. Allow to stand on a level surface until the agar is solid.

b. Inoculation

Materials: Agar plates—cool and solid
      Inoculating needle
      Mixed cultures: (1)
             (2)
             (3)

Method:

1. Label petri dish; invert for Method A and leave right side up for Method B.
2. Loosen stopper; flame needle.
3. Remove cotton stopper (hold).
4. Flame mouth of tube; remove loopful of culture.
5. Flame tube and replace stopper.
6. Place culture tube in rack.
7. Streak by method A or method B:

Method A:

1. With agar plate upside down pick up the agar plate in the left hand (see Figure 20).
2. Touch the edge of the agar with the transfer needle to remove most of the culture. Then make many parallel strokes to distribute the culture material to all parts of the plate. Return plate to cover.
3. Without returning to the culture, streak a second plate in the same way.

Method B:

1. Place agar plate right side up on the desk.
2. Lift the cover enough to allow the transfer needle to enter.
3. Touch the agar with the needle to remove excess culture. Then make many parallel strokes on the surface.
4. Without returning to the culture, streak a second plate in the same way.

EXPERIMENT—THE DILUTION PLATE

Materials: 3 sterile petri dishes
      3 tubes of melted agar
      Broth cultures of: (1) *Serratia*
              (2) *Escherichia coli*
              (3) *Sarcina lutea*
              (4) *Micrococcus pyogenes*

(Grown separately—mixed by the instructor before use.)

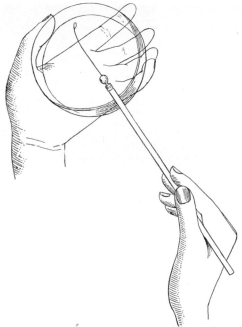

Figure 20   Streaking an agar plate.

Method:
  a. Making the dilution plates:
     1. Melt agar by placing tubes in a pan of boiling water. Cool to approximately 45° C. (113° F.).
     2. Label tubes and petri dishes I, II, III.
     3. Transfer a loopful of culture to tube I; mix by rotating the tube.
     4. Transfer a loopful of medium in tube I to tube II; Mix.
     5. Pour agar from tube I to plate I. Rotate gently.
     6. Transfer a loopful of medium from tube II to tube III.
     7. Mix and pour into plates II and III respectively.

Incubate the plates just inoculated for 48 hours at room temperature. Examine plates to determine which method secures the better separation of colonies. Transfer one colony of each type to agar slants or to broth.

Both of the methods just described depend upon mechanical separation of the cells on the plate so that a single organism will give rise to a colony. Since the colony masses are usually

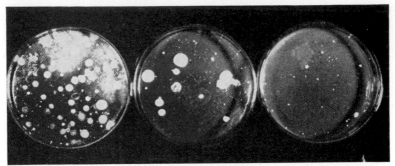

Figure 21   Dilution plates inoculated with 1/1000, 1/10,000, and 1/100,000 grams of soil. (Rahn, O.: Microbes of Merit. The Ronald Press Co.)

characteristic, one may recognize the presence of two or more types of organisms. (See Figure 21.) A pure culture can be obtained by transferring from an isolated colony to a sterile medium.

B. *By Heating the Culture*   Bacteria differ in their ability to stand heat; the spore forms are much more resistant than others. When subjected to moderate heat, the more hardy species will outlive the less resistant.

EXPERIMENT

Materials: Two agar plates
    Broth culture of *Micrococcus pyogenes*
    Broth culture of *Bacillus subtilis*—72 hours
Method:
1. Transfer a loopful of *Bacillus subtilis* to the tube containing the *Micrococcus pyogenes*.
2. Streak an agar plate with the mixed culture just prepared. Label plate I—"before heating."
3. Heat broth in a water bath (80° C. [176° F.] for 10 minutes).
4. Streak second agar plate. Label plate II—"after heating."
5. Invert and incubate both plates for 24 hours.
6. Observe and explain results.

C. *By Means of a Differential Medium*   Differential media are of value because they are designed to show by means of chemical changes when there are two groups of organisms present. They are especially useful when dealing with bacteria which produce similar colonies on agar. Lactose agar with an indicator enables one to distinguish between lactose-fermenting organisms and those that do not use lactose. This simple test makes it possible to separate the harmless lactose fermenter *Escherichia coli* from the intestinal organisms which produce disease. Lactose fermentation results in acid formation, which in turn changes the color of the medium according to the indicator used. Bile salt agar (MacConkey) and eosin-methylene blue agar are both satisfactory for separating lactose from nonlactose-fermenting organisms. Their composition is indicated below.

BILE SALT AGAR

Materials: MacConkey's agar (Difco) .... 50 gm.
Bacto-peptone .... 17 gm.
Proteose-peptone (Difco) .... 3 gm.
Bacto-lactose .... 10 gm.
Bacto-bile salts #3 .... 1.5 gm.
Sodium chloride .... 5 gm.
Bacto-agar .... 13.5 gm.
Bacto-neutral red .... 0.03 gm.
Bacto-crystal violet .... 0.001 gm.
Distilled water, cold .... 1 liter

Method: Suspend 50 gm. of MacConkey's agar in 1000 cc. of cold distilled water and heat to boiling to dissolve the medium. Sterilize at 15 lbs. pressure (121° C. [249.8° F.]) for 20 minutes.

EOSIN-METHYLENE BLUE AGAR

Materials: Eosin-methylene blue agar (Difco) .... 36 gm.
Bacto-peptone .... 10 gm.
Bacto-lactose .... 5 gm.
Bacto-saccharose .... 5 gm.
Dipotassium phosphate ...... 2 gm.
Bacto-eosin Y .... 0.4 gm.
Bacto-agar .... 13.5 gm.
Bacto-methylene blue .... 0.065 gm.
Distilled water, cold .... 1 liter

Method: Suspend 36 gm. eosin-methylene blue agar in 1000 cc. cold distilled water and heat to boiling to dissolve the medium completely. Sterilize in the autoclave at 15 pounds pressure (121° C. [249.8° F.]) for 20 minutes.

Materials: Lactose agar plate containing indicator:
Bile salt, or eosin-methylene blue or

Nutrient agar with lactose 1 per cent and acid fuchsin
(Andrade's*) indicator 1 per cent

Method: Streak one half of plate with *Escherichia coli* and the
other with *Alcaligenes faecalis* or *Proteus vulgaris.*

Invert plate and incubate for 24 hours at 37° C. (98.6° F.).

Observe and explain changes which occur in the medium.

D. *By the Use of an Inhibiting Agent*   Dyes or antibiotics often exhibit a selective action on bacteria because the
same dilution may prevent the growth of one organism while
allowing another kind of organism to grow freely. An example
of this action is seen by the use of a gentian violet plate.

EXPERIMENT

Materials: Tube of melted agar

Aqueous gentian violet 1 per cent

Cultures: *Micrococcus pyogenes* or *Bacillus subtilis*
(gram-positive)

Escherichia coli or *Proteus vulgaris* (gram-
negative)

Method: Add one or two loopfuls of gentian violet solution to a
tube of melted agar and pour into a petri dish. When the solution is
solid, inoculate one half with one of the gram-positive organisms
and the other half with one of the gram-negative. Incubate at 37° C.
(98.6° F.) for 24 hours.

This method is very useful when the hardy organisms are so
numerous that they may outgrow the more delicate varieties.
When stools are cultured for the typhoid organisms, brilliant
green dye is sometimes used in the medium to prevent the
growth of the ever-present *Escherichia coli.* Antibiotics may be
used to inhibit the growth of certain organisms. For example,
penicillin is often added to a medium used for isolating the
whooping cough organism (*Hemophilus pertussis*) from throat
secretions which normally carry many gram-positive organisms.

* Acid fuchsin (Andrade's) indicator—a solution of acid fuchsin, 0.5
gm. in 100 cc. of water which is decolorized to a yellow color by a
sodium hydroxide solution.

B. Bacteria—Life Activities

Microorganisms as a group are very versatile in their ability to use the materials in their environment. An almost endless variety of substances can be produced by the action of bacterial enzymes. Not all bacteria produce the same enzymes and will, therefore, differ in the foods used and the products formed. Some of these differences can be detected by the use of suitable media. In general, these changes will fall into two groups: (1) synthesis, the building of something new (anabolism) or (2) destroying some more or less complex substance (catabolism).

The following are examples of bacterial enzymes building something new:

1. All synthesize bacterial protoplasm—this increase is easily observed in cultures.
2. Some bacteria produce carbohydrate capsules which can be observed by microscopic study of the cells.
3. Some bacteria produce pigment.

6. Pigment Production

EXPERIMENT

Materials: Dextrose agar slants

Cultures of: (1) *Serratia*
(2) *Sarcina*
(3) *Micrococcus pyogenes* (*Staphylococcus aureus*)
(4) *Micrococcus pyogenes* (*Staphylococcus albus*)
(5) *Micrococcus citreus*
(6) *Escherichia coli*

Method: Inoculate slants and incubate at room temperature for 48 hours.

Observe cultures for the color produced. What conclusions may be drawn concerning pigment formation on the basis of this limited observation?

7. Digestion of Foods by Bacterial Enzymes

Many of the food substances in natural or artificial media are too complex for the use of the cell. Many, but not all, bacteria possess enzymes which enable them to digest one or more of these complex substances. The results of such digestion can easily be observed in media containing gelatin, starch, or milk.

The Liquefaction of Gelatin   Gelatin is a complex protein which can be split to form polypeptides and amino acids. The gelatin medium, which is a firm jelly, can therefore be changed to a permanent liquid form by the gelatin-digesting enzyme—*gelatinase.*

Nutrient gelatin is solid at room temperature and liquid at higher temperatures. Therefore, all gelatin cultures in a very warm room or in the body-temperature incubator become liquid. One can determine which have been liquefied by heat by placing them in a dish of ice water. The tubes that still contain the unchanged gelatin will become solid, while those containing the simpler proteins will remain liquid.

EXPERIMENT

Materials: Tubes of nutrient gelatin medium (15 per cent gelatin in
    nutrient broth)
    Cultures of *Bacillus subtilis*
        Escherichia coli
        Proteus vulgaris
        Serratia marcescens

Method: Using a straight needle, inoculate the gelatin by stabbing to the bottom of the tube. Incubate at room temperature for 48 hours. Observe the cultures and determine which of these organisms use the gelatin.

Record results. What conclusions may be drawn? What does this observation mean?

The Hydrolysis of Starch   Starch is a polysaccharide which can be hydrolyzed by acids or enzymes to form dextrin and maltose. Starch is easily identified by the fact that it combines with iodine to form a blue compound.

EXPERIMENT

Materials: Dilute iodine solution
    3 starch agar slants (nutrient agar with 1 per cent starch)
    Cultures of *Bacillus subtilis*
        Escherichia coli

Method: Inoculate tube 1 with *Bacillus subtilis*, tube 2 with *Escherichia coli*, and keep the third as a control. Incubate at room temperature for 48 hours. Add a few drops of iodine to each tube. Observe and explain. Why was the control tube used? What conclusions may be drawn?

The Decomposition of Milk Milk is a satisfactory food for many bacteria. Litmus milk is prepared by adding litmus, an acid-base indicator, to skim milk.

The chief changes occurring when bacteria grow in milk are: (1) the appearance of acid and coagulation resulting from the fermentation of lactose; (2) the change of the soluble lactalbumin to amino acids and to ammonia resulting in a basic reaction in the medium; (3) the digestion of the protein solid, casein, as indicated by the change to a watery fluid with a basic reaction; (4) the decomposition of the litmus— reduction of litmus. (See page 36.)

EXPERIMENT

Materials: Tubes of sterile litmus milk
Cultures of: (1) *Alcaligenes faecalis*
(2) *Escherichia coli*
(3) *Proteus vulgaris*
(4) *Bacillus subtilis*

Method: Inoculate media and incubate at room temperature for 48 hours. Observe and explain the changes which have occurred. Explain the spontaneous souring of milk which occurs outside of the laboratory. Conclusions?

8. RESPIRATION BY BACTERIAL ENZYMES

It is common knowledge that living things breathe; i.e., secure the energy for living by decomposing some fuel substance such as glucose. To promote this change, they take oxygen from the air and return carbon dioxide and water. Many microorganisms use the oxygen from the air when it is available. That a limited amount of this gas is dissolved in laboratory media can be shown by adding a drop of methylene blue to the medium.

Methylene blue may be used as an indicator of oxygen since this dye is blue or green in the presence of oxygen and colorless when oxygen is absent. Petrolatum may be used as a seal to keep additional oxygen from diffusing into the medium during the course of the experiment.

The Use of Oxygen

Materials: 3 tubes of warm sterile broth
Methylene blue stain (see page 113)
Sterile petrolatum or mineral oil
8-hour or 12-hour cultures of (1) *Escherichia coli*
(2) *Bacillus subtilis*

Method:
1. To each tube of broth add 1 loopful of methylene blue stain (enough to make the medium pale blue or green).
2. Add 1 cc. of *Escherichia coli* to tube 1, 1 cc. of *Bacillus subtilis* to tube 2, and keep tube 3 as a control.
3. Add a small amount of liquid petrolatum or mineral oil to each tube to exclude the air.
4. Incubate at 37° C. (98.6° F.) for a few hours.
5. Observe from time to time. Compare the color of the cultures with that of the control tube.
6. When the color has faded, shake the tube vigorously (or if possible bubble oxygen gas into the fluid). Does the color return? Why? Do these microorganisms use the oxygen from the air which is dissolved in the medium?

The Use of Oxygen from Chemical Compounds

Many bacteria live where atmospheric oxygen is not readily available, some of them obtaining energy by a chemical reaction, which reduces one compound and oxidizes another. Nutrient media contain some compounds that can be reduced and others that can be oxidized. These changes are not always easy to detect. The change of a nitrate salt to nitrite is an example of reduction. Many bacteria produce enzymes to bring about this change.

Materials: 3 tubes of nitrate broth
(0.1 per cent potassium nitrate in peptone water)
Cultures of: (1) *Escherichia coli*
(2) *Bacillus subtilis*
Test solution   I: sulfanilic acid
(8 gm. in 1000 cc. 5 N acetic acid)
Test solution II: a naphthylamine
(5 gm. in 1000 cc. 5 N acetic acid)

Method:

1. Inoculate tubes of nitrate broth with cultures provided; save one as a control.
2. Incubate for 48 to 96 hours.
3. Observe and test for the presence of nitrites. Add 2 cc. of solution I and 2 cc. of solution II to each tube. A pink color indicates the presence of nitrites.
4. Conclusion? Of what significance is the reduction of nitrates?

If the control is negative, the presence of nitrites in the cultures indicates that the organisms have reduced the nitrate salt. This ability to reduce compounds is common to many bacteria and in part accounts for their ability to live where little or no atmospheric oxygen is available.

Fermentation   Fermentation is a common process. It is always catalyzed by enzyme action and always proceeds without the use of oxygen. Bacterial enzymes cause a partial release of stored energy by changing compounds like glucose to organic acids or to alcohol.

A. LACTIC ACID FERMENTATION   a. IN LIQUID MEDIUM

EXPERIMENT

Materials: Sterile sugar broths containing sugar 1 per cent, acid fuchsin (Andrade's) indicator, 1 per cent, and inverted vial.

Cultures of: (1) *Escherichia coli*
                (2) *Alcaligenes faecalis*
                (3) *Proteus vulgaris*

Method:

1. Inoculate the sugar broths with the cultures provided.
2. Observe and record results after 24 or 48 hours.
3. Conclusions? Of what significance is fermentation in determining where bacteria can live? Of what significance is fermentation in industry?

b. ON SOLID MEDIUM

EXPERIMENT

Materials: Lactose agar slants or plates (lactose agar with acid fuchsin [see p. 104] [Andrade's] indicator or eosin-methylene blue agar or bile salt agar [MacConkey]) can be used.

Cultures: same as for a.

Method:

1. Inoculate lactose agar slants or sections of a lactose agar plate with the cultures provided. Invert the petri dish and incubate at 37° C. (98.6° F.) for 24 hours.
2. Observe and record results. Can the differences observed be put to any practical use?

B. ALCOHOLIC FERMENTATION   Some bacteria have enzymes which produce small amounts of alcohol as well as organic acids. Other fungi, called yeasts, rapidly change carbohydrates to alcohol and carbon dioxide.

EXPERIMENT

Materials: Molasses solution (1 teaspoonful to a pint of warm water) ¼ cake of compressed yeast
Filtered calcium hydroxide (lime water)

Method:

1. Mix yeast with sugar solutions; fill a large tube or bottle (1 inch from the top). Cap with a tight stopper fitted with an "L" tube. Place the long arm of the "L" tube into a tube of filtered lime water. Incubate for a few minutes at 37° C. (98.6° F.) (in water bath or incubator).
2. Watch for evidence of fermentation. What gas is formed? Note the odor of the solution after a few hours.
3. Conclusions? How does fermentation by bacteria differ from that catalyzed by yeasts?

C. Bacteria—Cell Structure

9. THE HANGING DROP

The hanging drop is a device for observing living organisms. It enables one to see the size, shape, and arrangement of the cells, and also to determine whether or not the organisms are motile. (See Figure 6, page 19.) Motile bacteria have long appendages called flagella. These flagella are never visible in the hanging drop or ordinary stained preparations. They become visible only when special staining methods are used.

Brownian Movement   All minute bodies including motile and nonmotile bacteria are subject to vibratory or quivering motion (Brownian movement). This slight movement must be distinguished from true motility or progression from place to place.

Materials: Hanging-drop (concave) slides
    Coverglasses
    Petrolatum
    18-hour broth cultures of: (1) *Bacillus subtilis*
             (2) *Escherichia coli*
             (3) *Proteus vulgaris*
             (4) *Sarcina lutea*
             (5) *Micrococcus pyogenes*

Method:

A. *Preparation of the Hanging Drop*
 1. Apply a layer of petrolatum around the depression of a clean concave slide.
 2. Place a loopful of the culture on the flamed coverglass. *Do not spread the drop.*
 3. Invert the slide over the coverglass so that the drop is in the center of the concave area.
 4. Press gently to seal the slide and cover; turn the slide right side up. *The drop must hang from the coverglass.*

B. *Examination of the Hanging Drop*
 1. Mount the slide on the stage of the microscope; adjust the light.
 2. Find the edge of the drop with the low-power (16-mm.) objective. Lower the substage condenser when using the low-power lens.
 3. Raise the substage condenser. Place the high-power (4-mm.) lens so that it almost touches the slide. Decrease the light by partially closing the diaphragm.
 4. Focus upward slowly using the coarse adjustment screw until the organisms are seen, *then use the fine adjustment* screw to improve the focus.
 5. Observe size, shape, and arrangement of cells and note whether they are motile or nonmotile. Record. Conclusions?

C. *Disposal of Hanging-Drop Slides*
 1. Break the petrolatum seal by displacing the coverglass with the inoculating needle; flame the needle.
 2. Place slide and coverglass in pan of water.
 3. Boil for 10 minutes.
 4. Wash with soap and water.

10. Observation of Stained Preparations

It is often convenient to use stained preparations for the study of bacterial structure. With few exceptions, these prepared slides of bacteria are always examined with the oil-immersion lens (1.8 mm.) which magnifies approximately 1000 times. As the names of bacteria are often derived from structural details, it is desirable to learn to recognize the common shapes and the arrangements of the cells.

EXPERIMENT

Materials: Prepared slides of
  a. *Bacterial cells*
      1. The spheres—*diplococcus* (pl. *diplococci*)
                        micrococcus (pl. *micrococci*)
                        streptococcus (pl. *streptococci*)
                        sarcina (pl. *sarcinae*)
      2. The rod forms—*bacterium** (pl. *bacteria*)
                        bacillus (pl. *bacilli*)
                        clostridium (pl. *clostridia*)
      3. The spiral forms—*vibrio* (pl. *vibriones*)
                        spirillum (pl. *spirilla*)
                        spirochete (pl. *spirochetes*)
  b. *Bacteria cells showing special structures*
      1. Spores
      2. Capsules
      3. Flagella (special flagella stain)

This experience should help the student acquire a mental picture of common bacterial forms and special structures. It may well serve as a basis for developing a vocabulary and as a stimulus for reading.

11. SIMPLE STAINS

Stains are useful in making bacteria clearly visible for microscopic examination. Basic aniline dyes, which combine with the bacterial protoplasm, are commonly used for this purpose. This method is called *positive* staining. Some stains form a film over the slide but leave the cells colorless; this is called *negative* staining.

---

* The word *bacteria,* commonly used to denote fungi other than yeasts and molds, is sometimes used to refer to gram-negative rods. The term *bacillus* means an aerobic spore-forming rod, but may also be used to refer to any rod. The word *clostridium* always means an anaerobic spore-forming rod.

The Methylene Blue Stain

EXPERIMENT

Materials: Loeffler's methylene blue stain.*
Slides
Cultures: (1)
(2)
(3)

Method:
1. Prepare thin smears from cultures.
   a. Place a loopful of water on a clean slide. (This step is not necessary if a broth culture is used.)
   b. Flame the inoculating needle.
   c. Transfer a minute amount of the culture to the slide.
   d. Spread over an area the size of a dime. (The film should be faintly gray but not white.)
   e. Flame the needle.
2. Allow smear to dry in the air. Then fix it by passing the slide through the flame three times.
3. Cover the smear with methylene blue stain for 1 minute.
4. Wash. Dry. Label. Examine with the oil-immersion lens.

This process will stain the cells blue. The same procedure can be used with other aniline dyes such as safranin, dilute carbol-fuchsin, or dilute gentian violet.

The India Ink Method—Negative Staining

EXPERIMENT

Materials: India ink
Slides
Cultures or tartar from the teeth

Method:
1. Place a drop of the culture on one end of the slide.
2. Beside it place a drop or two of India ink.
3. Touch the drops with a second slide held obliquely.
4. When the fluid has spread, make a thin smear over the entire slide by carrying the edge of the second slide over the surface of the first.
5. Examine under the oil-immersion objective. Compare with the methylene blue stain.

---

* Loeffler's methylene blue
  Solution A: Methylene blue 0.3 gm.
  Ethyl alcohol (95%) 30 cc.
  Solution B: Potassium hydroxide (0.01 per cent) 100 cc.
  Mix solutions A and B. Filter before use.

Negative staining is of value for organisms that do not stain easily with aniline dyes, but it is used less frequently than the positive staining methods.

12. Gram's Stain

Gram's stain is a differential stain which divides bacteria into two classes: (1) those which retain the purple color of the gentian violet (gram-positive organisms), and (2) those which are decolorized by the solvent and take the counterstain (gram-negative organisms). So useful is this characteristic that the gram reaction is practically always reported in the description of bacteria. When properly stained, gram-negative organisms are always gram negative; but gram-positive organisms in old cultures may fail to retain the stain. For that reason it is desirable to use young cultures. (See page 19.)

EXPERIMENT

Materials: Cultures of: (1) *Escherichia coli*
(2) *Proteus vulgaris*
(3) *Bacillus subtilis*
(4) *Micrococcus pyogenes*

Stains: Aqueous gentian or crystal violet
(1 gm. in 100 cc. distilled water)
Sodium bicarbonate
(5 gm. in 100 cc. distilled water)

Mordant: Iodine (2 gm. of iodine in 10 cc. of normal sodium hydroxide and distilled water to make 100 cc.)

Decolorizing agent: Alcohol 95 per cent or acetone

Counterstain: Safranin (2.5 per cent safranin in 95 per cent alcohol)—use 10 cc. in 100 cc. of distilled water or 0.1 gm. of basic fuchsin in 100 cc. of distilled water

Method:

1. Place a thin smear of the culture on a clean slide.
2. Dry in air; fix by passing through the flame three times.
3. Place equal amounts of gentian violet and sodium bicarbonate on the smear. Leave for 20 seconds; tilt slide to allow stain to run off. Wash with water.
4. Cover smear with iodine solution for 20 seconds; tilt slide to remove solution.
5. Decolorize with 95 per cent alcohol or with acetone; wash well with water.

6. Counterstain with safranin for 30 seconds. Wash with water. Dry.
7. Examine with the oil-immersion objective. Determine which organisms are gram positive and which are gram negative. Discuss briefly.

13. THE ACID-FAST STAIN
(ZIEHL-NEELSEN METHOD)

EXPERIMENT

Materials: Smears of tuberculous sputum which have been dried and fixed. Stains*—carbol-fuchsin
methylene blue
Decolorizing acid alcohol

Method:
1. Cover smear with carbol-fuchsin and steam for 5 minutes. Add more stain as needed.
2. Wash with water.
3. Decolorize with acid alcohol.
4. Wash with water.
5. Stain with methylene blue from 10 to 30 seconds.
6. Wash and dry. Examine under the oil-immersion lens.
7. Observe red (acid-fast) rods on a blue field consisting of cells, strings of mucus, and other bacteria.

D. Yeasts and Molds
14. YEASTS

Yeasts are relatively large, oval cells which are usually easy to distinguish from bacteria on the basis of the differences in size, shape, method of reproduction, and type of nucleus. The multiplication of yeast cells by forming buds (budding) can be observed in growing cultures. A bud consists of an enlarging mass of protoplasm projecting from any surface of the yeast cell. Also a large cavity of fluid called the *water reservoir* or *vacuole* is visible within the yeast cell. Stained preparations of old cultures sometimes show multiple spores within the cells. A horseshoe-shaped nucleus is sometimes visible in stained

---

* Solution A: Basic Fuchsin (sat. alcoholic solution)—10 cc.
      5 per cent aqueous phenol solution—90 cc.
  Solution B: Decolorizing acid alcohol:
          Hydrochloric acid (conc.)—3 cc.
          95 per cent alcohol—97 cc.

preparations when examined with the oil-immersion lens. The nucleus is often invisible in both stained and unstained preparations, but can be demonstrated by special staining technique.

EXPERIMENT

Materials: Yeast in broth culture (if made from commercial yeast it will contain some bacteria)

Slides, coverglasses

Methylene blue stain

Dilute iodine solution (0.2 per cent)

Method:

1. Examine prepared slides; observe cells showing nuclei and spores.
2. Examine living yeast cells; observe water reservoir and buds; also size and shape.

   Method:

   a. Place a drop of yeast culture on a clean glass slide; and a drop of dilute iodine solution.

   b. Place coverglass and examine with the high dry objective.

3. Stain yeast cells with methylene blue.

   a. Place a thin smear of yeast culture on a clean slide; dry in air.

   b. Cover with methylene blue for 1 minute.

   c. Wash and dry; place a drop of water and coverglass on smear.

   d. Examine under high dry objective. Compare with unstained cells.

   e. Remove coverglass and dry slide. Add drop of immersion oil.

   f. Examine under oil-immersion objective. Observe and draw cells.

15. THE MOLDS

Molds present a much more complicated structure than either yeasts or bacteria. They are characteristically multicellular. Molds are so common in the environment that anything exposed to the air is likely to collect mold spores. They are commonly present on foods such as stale bread and fruits.

Mold fibers may consist of long, slender cylinders placed end to end or they may appear without cell structure. The fine threads, the *hyphae,* increase in number until they form a dense network called the *mycelium*. The filaments that grow into the food are called the *vegetative hyphae;* those that grow upward, the *aerial* or *reproductive hyphae*. These external fibers bear the reproductive bodies or spores of the molds. Some mold fibers show microscopic walls dividing them into typical cells; other species show no such walls.

EXPERIMENT

Materials: Small pieces of lemon, orange, cheese, moist bread
Petri dishes or other glass containers
Sabouraud's agar (page 94).
Filter paper

Method:

1. Line several petri dishes with filter paper.
2. Moisten the paper.
3. Place portions of fruit in the petri dishes and incubate at room temperature in a dark place.
4. Expose the sugar agar plate to the air for 15 minutes. Incubate at room temperature.
5. Examine all materials for evidence of molds in 48 or 72 hours using a hand lens.
6. Remove the cover of the petri dish to be examined. Place the lower part of the dish on the stage of the microscope. Examine the edge of the mold colony with the low-power objective. Look (1) for threadlike hyphae, (2) for mycelium, and (3) for fruiting bodies on the aerial fibers.

How do molds differ from bacteria? from yeasts? In what ways are they similar?

16. Growing Molds from Pure Cultures

EXPERIMENT

Materials: Cultures of molds
Sterile petri dishes
Sterile crackers
Sterile pipettes
Sterile water
Forceps

Method:

1. Flame forceps; transfer a few mold spores to a sterile, moistened cracker.
2. Incubate at room temperature.
3. Observe growing mold under the low-power objective.
4. Transfer a small piece of mold to a drop of water on a glass slide. Mount with a coverglass.

5. Examine under the low and high dry objectives.

How do molds differ from bacteria? from yeasts? In what way are they similar?

E. Protozoa

17. COMMON PROTOZOA

Protozoa are unicellular animal forms. Usually they are larger than the fungi and they often present more complex structure. The living forms ingest solid food and eliminate undigested particles. Different parts of the cell often show some degree of specialization; for example, an oral groove, a gullet, or an anal pore. Like the fungi, the protozoa include many species, some free-living and some parasitic.

EXPERIMENT

Materials: Living cells—
water from a pond or aquarium or other living cultures
slides and coverglasses
Killed cells—
prepared slides of various protozoa

Method:
1. Mount a drop of culture on a slide with a coverglass. Examine under low and high power objectives. Note size, shape, and motility of organisms.
2. Examine prepared slides.

These observations of various fungi and protozoa should give the student a mental picture of the common forms of microorganisms and should orient him to the scope of the field of microbiology.

SUPPLEMENTARY READINGS

American Public Health Association: Diagnostic Procedures and Reagents. 2d ed. New York, American Public Health Association, 1945.

Frobisher, M.: Fundamentals of Bacteriology. 5th ed. Philadelphia, W. B. Saunders Co., 1953.

Salle, A. J.: Laboratory Manual on Fundamental Principles of Bacteriology. 3d ed. New York, McGraw-Hill Book Co., 1948.

Simmons, J. S., and Gentzkow, C. J.: Laboratory Methods of the United States Army. 5th ed. Philadelphia, Lea & Febiger, 1944.

Smith, D. T., and Conant, N. F.: Zinsser's Textbook of Bacteriology. 10th ed. New York, Appleton-Century-Crofts, Inc., 1952.

Unit II   BACTERIA AND ENVIRONMENT

CHAPTER 9   *Favorable Environment*

CONDITIONS NEEDED FOR GROWTH

MICROORGANISMS are widely distributed in nature. They are present in air, soil, water, and in body wastes. Even in such unlikely places as cold-storage plants and hot springs, a few bacteria will be found. These organisms vary in character and require different living conditions. The organisms living in the sea will not grow in fresh water, and vice versa. Likewise, the bacteria that grow in the soil are usually wholly unsuited to life within the animal body.

In other words, conditions that are favorable for one species may be unfavorable for others. Nevertheless, regardless of differences, every organism demands from its environment: (1) food and water, (2) a suitable acid-base balance in the medium, and (3) a temperature that encourages growth. In addition to these four essentials, the presence or absence of oxygen is important for some organisms, though most bacteria will grow with or without oxygen if the other growth-promoting conditions are present.

119

The presence of other organisms or their products may either encourage or discourage the growth of a particular species of bacteria. In nature, various species of microorganisms are found in close proximity. As would be expected, contact between living agents leads to some type of relationship—neutral, antagonistic, or supporting. (See page 76.)

Food and Water   Bacteria vary greatly in their synthetic abilities. Some can utilize simple inorganic compounds as sources of food and energy. Another group requires a combination of organic and inorganic foods, while still others need amino acids and carbohydrates. Bacteria may, therefore, be placed along a scale, with parasites possessing limited synthetic ability at one end and the nitrogen-fixing and sulfur bacteria at the other. (See page 53.) It is obvious that an artificial or natural medium which meets the needs of one group will be of little or no use to others.

The nutritional requirements of most bacteria are not completely known, although many details have been determined by the use of synthetic media of known composition. By changing the composition of such media, it is possible to determine which of the constituents are essential for bacterial growth. It has been shown, for example, that certain organisms require specific amino acids (tryptophane or glutamine), while others will grow in a medium deficient in these substances, since they are able to synthesize them from other nutrients in the medium; still other organisms may develop the ability to form the needed amino acids by growing them in successive cultures in media containing gradually decreasing amounts of the needed substance. Similar observations have been made with regard to the need of microorganisms for the presence of minute quantities of certain vitamin-like substances or "growth factors" of known or unknown composition. Some bacteria fail to grow in media deficient in the growth factor, while others grow well and actually produce the essential substance. Thiamine chloride, biotin, riboflavin, nicotinic acid, nicotinamide, pyridoxine, p-aminobenzoic acid, pimelic acid, β-alanine, glutamic acid, glutamine, folic acid, glutathione, and various purines and pyrimidines are some of the growth factors required by certain bacteria. (See Figure 22.) The fact that bac-

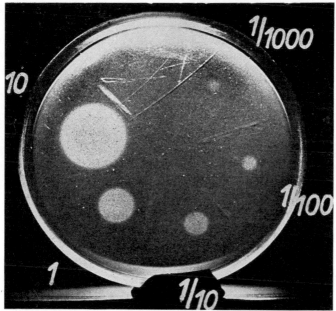

Figure 22   The response of yeast (Rhodotorula sp.) to different concentrations of thiamine. The plate was made by placing a drop of the vitamin solution (containing 0.001 to 10 micrograms per milliliter) on the seeded plate. (Mayer, J., and Aschner, M.: J. Bact., 53.)

teria grow well in nature and in the complex laboratory media indicates that these media do meet the intricate nutritional requirements of the organisms.

Water is essential to the life of the cell, since it makes up the cell fluid in which the other constituents of protoplasm are dissolved or suspended. It is also important as a surrounding medium which transports food substances to the cell and carries away waste products. Without water absorption, secretion and excretion cannot take place. The outer membrane of the bacterial cell appears to be able to limit the passage of water through it, thus making the organism relatively resistant to changes in the salt content of the surrounding medium. Certain micrococci (staphylococci), for example, are so tolerant of sodium chloride that they will grow in a nutrient medium which contains from 2 to 10 per cent of the salt.

Nature supplies food for microorganisms in a variety of

forms and places. Pond water, earth, and decaying animal and vegetable matter provide foods suitable for many microorganisms. As would be expected, these dead materials support huge populations of microorganisms which are called *saprophytes.* Such organisms may be expected to grow rapidly except when the materials are very cold or very dry; and even during periods that are unfavorable for growth, the hardy organisms remain dormant until the conditions that permit growth are present.

Table 7   STRENGTHS OF SOLUTIONS OF HCL AND NAOH AND THEIR APPROXIMATE PH VALUES

ACID OR BASE	STRENGTH OF SOLUTION	GRAMS HYDROGEN PER LITER	EXPRESSED IN LOGA-RITHMS	pH
Acid	N/1 HCl	1.0	10^{-0}	0.0
Acid	N/10 HCl	0.1	10^{-1}	1.0
Acid	N/100 HCl	0.01	10^{-2}	2.0
Acid	N/1000 HCl	0.001	10^{-3}	3.0
Acid	N/10,000 HCl	0.000,1	10^{-4}	4.0
Acid	N/100,000 HCl	0.000,01	10^{-5}	5.0
Acid	N/1,000,000 HCl	0.000,001	10^{-6}	6.0
Neutral	*Pure Water*	0.000,000,1	10^{-7}	7.0
Basic	N/1,000,000 NaOH	0.000,000,01	10^{-8}	8.0
Basic	N/100,000 NaOH	0.000,000,001	10^{-9}	9.0
Basic	N/10,000 NaOH	0.000,000,000,1	10^{-10}	10.0
Basic	N/1,000 NaOH	0.000,000,000,01	10^{-11}	11.0
Basic	N/100 NaOH	0.000,000,000,001	10^{-12}	12.0
Basic	N/10 NaOH	0.000,000,000,000,1	10^{-13}	13.0
Basic	N/1 NaOH	0.000,000,000,000,01	10^{-14}	14.0

(From Salle, A. J.: Fundamental Principles of Bacteriology. New York, McGraw-Hill Book Co., 1948, p. 262.)

In the laboratory, when nutrient broth is allowed to stand without sterilization, the student may observe that the liquid becomes cloudy and that a white scum forms on the surface. Microscopic examination of this broth will reveal the presence of millions of bacteria. It is evident that the broth supplies the conditions necessary for growth; i.e., food, water, a neutral reaction, and a moderate temperature.

Acid Content   All living cells are sensitive to the

acidity or alkalinity of their medium because an excess of acid or of base disturbs the normal functions of the cell. The acid content of a fluid is expressed in *p*H which is literally the *power of the hydrogen ion.* Table 7 shows the relation of *p*H values to the hydrochloric acid or sodium hydroxide content of the fluid. Most bacteria grow well in a nutritive fluid that is approximately neutral (*p*H 7), but many body organisms grow best in a medium which has approximately the same reaction as the blood, one that is slightly alkaline (*p*H 7.4 to 7.6). Organisms differ in their ability to tolerate acid; molds, for example, often grow on lemons and other acid foods which would inhibit bacterial growth. Some microorganisms which form acids in carbohydrate media must of necessity be able to live in the presence of the acids which they form, but even this tolerance has its limits. As fermentation continues, and the acid increases to the point where it inhibits growth, the cells that produced it eventually die.

   Temperature   Bacteria respond to the temperature of their surroundings. In general, moderate temperatures favor growth of microorganisms, while the extremes of heat and cold inhibit or destroy living cells. Different species of organisms vary in their temperature requirements. Some will grow only at body temperature, 37° C. (98.6° F.), while others will grow only at temperatures below 30° C. (86° F.). Some of the saprophytes are so adjustable that they grow at a wide temperature range of 15° to 44° C. (59° to 111.2° F.) but as a rule their growth at 15° and 44° C. will be less luxuriant than at 20° C. (68° F.) or 30° C. A few bacteria require temperatures above 44° C. or below 15° C. For each species, three temperatures can be determined:

   1. The *minimum*—the lowest temperature which permits growth
   2. The *maximum*—the highest temperature which permits growth
   3. The *optimum*—the temperature at which the organism grows best.

It is possible to have several optimum temperatures for the same organism, depending upon the objective of the scientist. One temperature may be optimum for mere growth, while

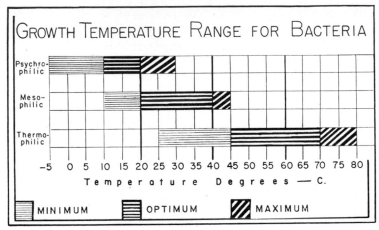

Figure 23   Most bacteria grow well at moderate temperatures while some thrive at temperatures above 45° C. and others require temperatures below 30° C.

another is better for the formation of pigment or capsules. Most saprophytic bacteria grow well at the temperatures that range between 20° and 37° C.

Bacteria may be classified according to the temperatures at which they grow: (1) the cold-loving (psychrophilic), which grow at temperatures ranging from —5° to 30° C. (26.6° to 86° F.); (2) the moderate (mesophilic), which grow from 10° to 45° C. (50° to 113° F.); and (3) the heat-loving (thermophilic), which thrive at temperatures ranging from 25° to 80° C. (77° to 176° F.). (See Figure 23.)

REPRODUCTION

The fact that bacteria utilize food substances to build the various complex constituents of cell protoplasm has already been discussed. When conditions are favorable, this process commonly occurs with astonishing rapidity. If one streaks a loopful of a broth culture of *Micrococcus pyogenes* (*Staphylococcus aureus*) over the surface of a sterile agar slant, no evidence of bacteria will be seen. The same tube after a twenty-four-hour incubation at body temperature will show a heavy, moist, glistening, orange layer of new growth. In this short time, the bacterial population has increased a billionfold.

Bacteria commonly reproduce by simple fission—a process which takes place in three steps. First there is division of nuclear material; then a cytoplasmic membrane forms near the middle of the cell. This in turn is followed by splitting and the formation of a central cell wall by each of the daughter cells. The two new cells may remain attached or may separate completely. These new cells grow and mature rapidly; sometimes after twenty or thirty minutes they are ready to divide again. When bacteria are transferred from an old culture into a cold medium, reproduction takes place slowly for the first hour or two and then proceeds more rapidly. The rate of growth during the early hours of incubation can be markedly accelerated by transferring a culture that is growing rapidly to a warm medium. The results of the prolific increase thus brought about are rather astounding as may be seen from the following calculations: Suppose that 100 bacterial cells are placed in a tube of broth in a completely favorable environment and that each cell divides twice per hour. The population would increase thus: 100; 200; 400; 800; 1600; 3200; 6400; 12,800; 25,600.

If growth could continue at this rate, one culture would soon produce enough bacteria to fill the culture tube and extend into the laboratory. This does not occur, for, as with human populations, there are deaths as well as births even during the period of rapid growth. A maximum population is often reached in eighteen or twenty-four hours. After that, reproduction takes place more slowly and the number of living cells in the culture gradually decreases. (See Figure 24.) The exhaustion of essential food supplies and the accumulation of waste products by the huge population are two factors which put on the brakes.

Some scientists have reported reproduction of bacteria by (1) budding, (2) cell segmentation, (3) the formation of large bodies which fragment to form minute particles (sometimes called pleuropneumonia bodies) or even filtrable forms. From time to time someone reports evidence of conjugation or sexual reproduction. It is evident that there is no agreement about the way or ways in which bacteria multiply. The fact remains that they do reproduce with astonishing rapidity and that

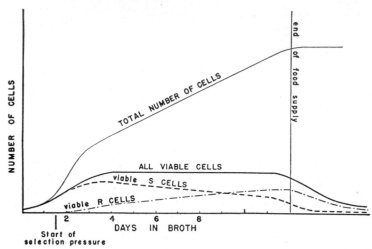

Figure 24   A graphic representation of the total number of cells and viable cells during growth of bacterial populations in a closed system and after the cessation of growth due to exhaustion of food supply. During the early stages of growth, most of the cells produced are of the *smooth* or S type (that is, they produce smooth colonies on solid medium). With the passage of time more and more *rough* or R type cells (those that produce rough colonies on solid medium) are formed. Note that in ten days (dissociation index) the R type cells exceed the S type. (Braun: Bacterial Genetics.)

hereditary (genetic) characteristics are transmitted from mother cell to daughter cells generation after generation. Mutations do occur and are of considerable interest. (See page 130.)

A Bacterial Count   The rise and fall of a bacterial population can be followed by planting bacteria in a flask of broth. Measured quantities in appropriate dilutions can be removed at intervals and mixed with melted agar and poured into petri dishes in order to grow the bacteria in isolated colonies. After incubation, the colonies on the plates can be counted and the total population estimated. These counts give a fair picture of population trends, which can be shown graphically by plotting the numbers of organisms against the time of incubation. Note that the curve in Figure 24 shows five distinct periods:

1. Period of slow growth
2. Period of rapid growth

3. Period of stationary population
4. Period of decreasing growth rate
5. Period of decline; deaths exceed replacements.

Organisms grow slowly for the first hour or two while they are adapting themselves to a new medium then rapidly while food supplies are abundant. The rate of growth declines as essential food diminish.

ENVIRONMENTAL CONTROL

The growing of bacteria may seem to be the work of the bacteriologist. This is true only in a limited sense, for microorganisms cultivate themselves in nature whenever food, water, and suitable temperature are present. The scientist who desires to grow bacteria in the laboratory strives to duplicate the natural growing conditions for the particular type of organism in which he is interested. Body organisms which refuse to grow on nutrient agar will often grow well when blood is added to the medium, and molds which cause the spoilage of bread thrive when transferred to moistened cracker or dextrose agar.

The spoiling of food is a good example of bacteria cultivating themselves. When moist foods are left at room temperature, bacteria develop within the food and change its chemical composition. In the icebox, the growth of microorganisms goes on at a very low rate, delaying the spoiling process for days or weeks. (See Figure 25.) All methods of preserving foods depend upon producing conditions that will deprive the bacteria present of one or more of the conditions essential for their growth. Following are some of the common ways of preserving foods:

METHOD	ACTION

1. Salting
   Drying
   Preserving in heavy syrup
	Removal of water

2. Pickling	Addition of excessive amounts of acid
3. Freezing	Introduction of an unfavorable temperature
4. Canning	Killing and excluding of organisms

It is common knowledge that these foods will again be subject to bacterial action and spoilage as soon as the inhibiting factor is removed.

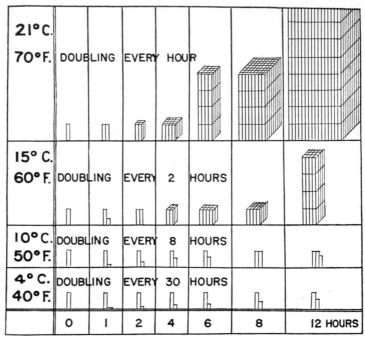

Figure 25   Multiplication of bacteria in milk. Each unit represents
100 bacteria. (Rahn, O.: Microbes of Merit. The Ronald Press Co.)

SUMMARY

1. Microorganisms will grow whenever and wherever they find water, suitable food, a medium which is neither too acid nor too alkaline, and a favorable temperature.

2. Different varieties of microorganisms require different conditions for growth in nature and in the laboratory.

3. Bacteria and other microorganisms can be encouraged in nature and in the laboratory by supplying the conditions that enable them to grow. This may be done quite unintentionally, as when food is left outside of the refrigerator.

4. It is possible to limit or inhibit bacterial growth by producing conditions that either slow the process or make it impossible. Foods can be preserved by changing their character so that they no longer supply all the growth requirements for microorganisms.

SUPPLEMENTARY READINGS

Burrows, W.: Jordan-Burrows Textbook of Bacteriology. 15th ed. Philadelphia, W. B. Saunders Co., 1949.
Dubos, R. J. (Ed.): Bacterial and Mycotic Infections of Man. 2d ed. Philadelphia, J. B. Lippincott Co., 1952.
Frobisher, M.: Fundamentals of Bacteriology. 5th ed. Philadelphia, W. B. Saunders Co., 1953.
Smith, D. T., and Conant, N. F.: Zinsser's Textbook of Bacteriology. 10th ed. New York, Appleton-Century-Crofts, Inc., 1952.
Werkman, C. H., and Wilson, P. W.: Bacterial Physiology. New York, Academic Press, Inc., 1951.

CHAPTER 10

Unfavorable Environment
            —Physical Agents

BACTERIAL RESPONSES

ALL LIVING THINGS, including bacteria, respond to their environment. The common bacterial responses that can be observed are: (1) increased growth, (2) variation, and (3) inhibition or death. The increase in cell activity has already been discussed in the preceding chapter.

Variation or Mutation   In pure cultures of bacteria, from time to time progeny will appear that differ from the parent strain. Since these changed characteristics are hereditary the process of variation is considered to be true mutation resulting from changes in the genes or genelike structures of the bacterial cell. Variants differ from the parent type in form or function, or both. The structural changes most frequently noticed are a difference in the size or the shape of the cells, or the loss of the ability to form pigment, capsules, or flagella. Likewise, the appearance of colonies may change. One of the common variations is the change from a smooth colony form to a rough one. *Smooth* (S-type) colonies are usually circular and glistening with even contours. In contrast, *rough* (R-type) colonies are characterized by a dull appearance and a folded or uneven surface. The change from the S-type to the R-type is usually accompanied by other changes such as decreased ability to produce disease. Biochemical variations appear in (1) the loss of the ability to produce toxins, or (2) the loss of the ability to form specific enzymes, vitamins, or antibiotic substances. Sometimes new enzymes appear to be synthesized as certain bacteria adjust themselves to a new environment. Increased resistance to destructive agents may also be observed. These changed organisms have sometimes been considered atypical or abnormal. Of course they do not fit into any artificial scheme of classification, but they may be quite normal for all that. Variation is evidence of the fact that bacteria are highly adjustable living things, differing from one

130

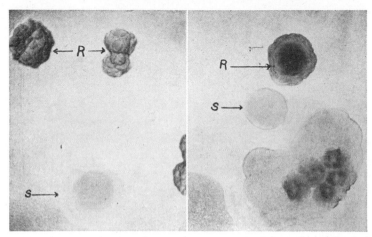

Figure 26   Photographs showing *smooth* (S) and *rough* (R) colonies of *Neisseria intracellularis* (× 10). (Evans, F.: J. Bact., 54.)

another as members of any other species differ from one another. It is likely that any bacterial culture contains a few variants which will usually go unnoticed. An environment sufficiently unfavorable to inhibit the typical organism may, however, give the variant a chance to grow freely, thus developing a new strain. (See Figures 26 and 27.)

Variation or mutation becomes apparent when the laboratory provides conditions which favor a particular variant at the expense of the typical cells. Unfavorable conditions probably do not cause mutation but rather select those mutants which are able to grow under conditions provided. For example, a susceptible strain of micrococcus (staphylococcus) can be made penicillin-resistant by growing it in a medium to which increasing amounts of the drug have been added. By adjusting the penicillin to the amount which will permit growth, one inhibits the susceptible cells and encourages any organisms capable of multiplying. By repeating the process over and over again, a highly resistant variant can be obtained. Bacteria living in the body often become resistant to an antibiotic, especially if inadequate doses of the drug are given. In the same way, new strains of organisms may arise which

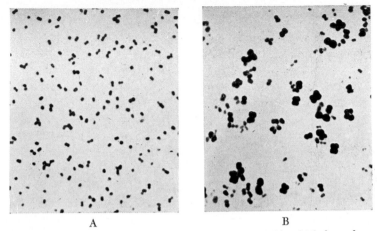

A   B

Figure 27   Meningococci (strain 274, Type 1) which have been grown in medium containing A, no penicillin, and B, penicillin in concentrations which permit growth. Antibiotics often encourage variants which differ from the parent strain in appearance and function. Note that cells grown in penicillin are larger than the parent strain. (Miller and Bohnhoff: J. Infect. Dis., *81.*)

are more or less resistant to heat and chemicals than the parent strain. Laboratory cultures often show evidence of variation by the loss of certain enzymes. For example, pneumococci after long culture on an artificial medium fail to produce capsules, and *Proteus vulgaris,* which in nature uses complex protein, may lose its ability to hydrolyze proteins. Likewise, long cultivation of disease-producing organisms on artificial medium is often associated with decreased ability to invade or injure body tissues. The loss of the ability to produce disease may be of importance both to the organism and to man, since the bacterium that can live on a host without producing disease has a better chance of surviving than the parasite that kills its host. A variant, then, is an organism that has lost or changed certain distinctive characteristics. Slight variation occurs whenever bacteria are growing, but it becomes more evident when conditions are moderately unfavorable.

Inhibition and Death   Death comes to bacterial cells, as it must to all living things. The rate of dying in a bacterial population is low in the growth phase and higher in unfavorable environments. Sterilization procedures merely increase the rate of dying to the point where the whole population dies within a short time. It is sometimes difficult to determine just when bacteria die. For practical purposes, a culture is considered killed if it no longer shows the ability to reproduce, but even this is a variable factor, for cells which have been injured by heat may fail to grow in ordinary broth but may grow well in blood broth. A similar "killed" culture which shows no evidence of growth in forty-eight hours may grow if incubation is continued for one week. This suggests that adverse conditions may cause either temporary or permanent injury to the cells. Damage to a cell probably results in the destruction of enzymes and other active proteins and may occur with or without coagulation of cell proteins. Cell membranes and genes may be altered also. The survival of the cell, then, depends upon its ability to repair and maintain normal structure and function. With this in mind, it is well to have a large margin of safety in planning sterilization procedures. In other words, any process designed to kill bacteria must be continued to the point where injured organisms cannot recover. In fact, it is well to remember that time is important in all disinfection and sterilization procedures.

PHYSICAL AGENTS

The physical agents which may injure or kill bacteria include:

1. Temperature: heat, cold (dry and moist)
2. Drying
3. Sunlight and ultraviolet light
4. Supersonic waves
5. Agitation.

Temperature   COLD   Cold is a useful agent in limiting the growth of bacteria and thereby preventing the results of bacterial activity. A low temperature, like the action of a cold spring on the growth of a garden, slows the life processes and thereby actually prolongs the life of the bacterial culture. For that reason, stock cultures of hardy bacteria are often refrigerated to preserve them. However, the total number of bacterial cells in a culture decreases slowly when exposed to

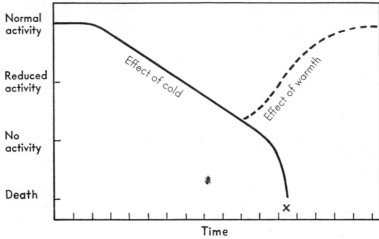

Figure 28   The effects of chilling on the vital activities of a bacterial cell. (Redrawn from Price, P.: The Meaning of Bacteriostasis.)

cold. (See Figure 28.) This is well illustrated by an experiment in which ice-cream custard was inoculated with typhoid organisms (*Salmonella typhosa*) then frozen and stored. Cultures made at intervals showed that living organisms were still present after a period of two years although the numbers had decreased from 51,000,000 to 6300 per cc. (See Figure 29.)

Observe that the bacterial count was higher after freezing. Apparently the bacteria inoculated into a good medium (ice cream) at a favorable temperature had time to multiply before the mixture was chilled sufficiently to prevent further growth, but as time went on, the number of living organisms decreased. This experiment well illustrates the importance of time in the killing of microorganisms, and shows that freezing kills too slowly to be of practical use in destroying hardy organisms. The fact that quick-frozen foods spoil rapidly after thawing presents further evidence that bacteria can survive cold for long periods of time. According to Hartsell,[2] pathogenic bacteria (*Micrococcus pyogenes* var. *aureus, Salmonella oranienburg, Salmonella typhosa,* and *Shigella dysenteriae*) survived for many months on experimentally contaminated frozen beef. The freezing process apparently changes the nutritional re-

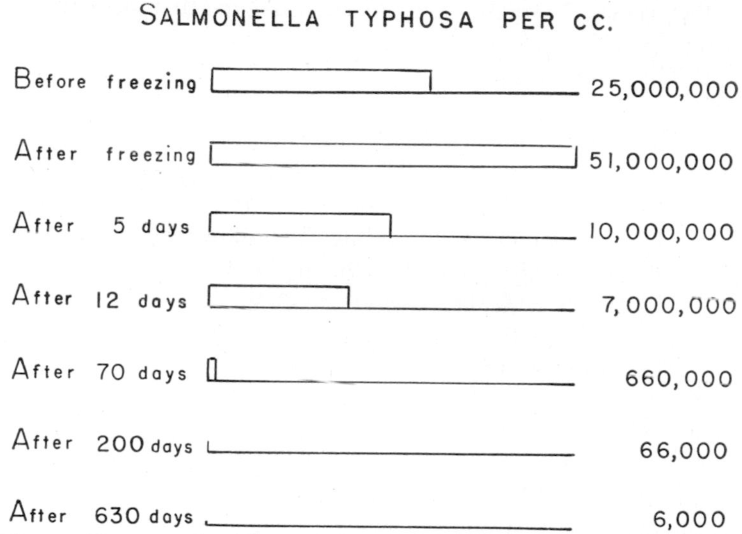

SALMONELLA TYPHOSA PER CC.

Before freezing ⟦bar⟧ — 25,000,000

After freezing ⟦bar⟧ 51,000,000

After 5 days ⟦bar⟧ — 10,000,000

After 12 days ⟦bar⟧ — 7,000,000

After 70 days ⟦bar⟧ — 660,000

After 200 days ⟦bar⟧ — 66,000

After 630 days ⟦bar⟧ — 6,000

Figure 29   The effect of freezing and storage upon *Salmonella typhosa*. (Based on McCulloch.[1])

quirements of the organisms. Its effect upon their ability to produce disease is not known.

Thermal Death Time   High temperatures are definitely more destructive than cold, but time is again an important factor in the killing process. The time and temperature combination required to kill a particular bacterial population under laboratory conditions is called the *thermal death time*. Usually the lower the temperature used the longer the time required, and vice versa. It is possible, therefore, to state several thermal death times for a single organism. For example, the typhoid bacillus (*Salmonella typhosa*) can be killed[3] by heating at

$$47° \text{ C. for } 120 \text{ minutes}$$
$$51° \text{ C. for } 18 \text{ minutes}$$
$$53° \text{ C. for } 7 \text{ minutes}$$
$$55° \text{ C. for } 2\tfrac{1}{2} \text{ minutes}$$

The destruction of microorganisms is a complex process which is influenced by a number of variables. The more important ones will be discussed here.

VARIABLES   In practice, the thermal death time will depend upon:

1. The type of organism to be killed
    (*a*) varies with species
    (*b*) varies with ability to form endospores
    (*c*) varies with the number of organisms present
    (*d*) varies with the age of the culture
2. The environment surrounding the organisms
    (*a*) varies with the *p*H of the medium
    (*b*) varies with the moisture content
    (*c*) varies with the presence of proteins
3. The nature and the intensity of the killing agent.

SPECIES   As would be expected, microorganisms differ in their ability to withstand hardship. Following is a group of common organisms arranged in the relative order of resistance by placing those with least resistance to heat at the beginning of the list and then adding those showing greater degrees of resistance.

Treponema pallidum (syphilis)
Neisseria gonorrhoeae (gonorrhea)
Diplococcus pneumoniae (pneumonia)
Corynebacterium diphtheriae (diphtheria)
Streptococcus pyogenes (miscellaneous infections)
Micrococcus pyogenes var. *aureus* (boils)
Vaccine virus (cowpox)
Escherichia coli (some strains)
Brucella abortus (undulant fever)
Spores of molds and yeasts (saprophytes)
Coxiella burnetii (Q fever)

} Readily killed by boiling

Virus of infectious hepatitis
Bacillus anthracis spores (anthrax)
Bacillus subtilis (saprophyte)
Clostridium botulinus spores (botulism)
Clostridium perfringens spores (gas gangrene)
Clostridium tetani spores (tetanus)

} Relatively resistant to heat and chemicals

Observe that the spore-forming bacteria are among the most resistant of the organisms listed. The presence of spores is an important factor in the ability of these organisms to survive unfavorable conditions. Therefore, more drastic measures will be required to kill spore-forming organisms. The virus of infectious hepatitis also may survive common disinfection procedures. Syringes, needles, and other objects that have been contaminated by human blood should be sterilized by steam under pressure. (See page 371.)

NUMBERS   The sequence of events leading to the death of bacteria is not understood. Regardless of the agent responsible, the process is undoubtedly in part chemical. Experimental evidence, however, has brought to light two important facts: (1) it takes time to kill bacteria and (2) not all bacteria die at the same time. Therefore, the more bacteria that are present at any one time, the longer will be the time required to kill them.

Suppose that one subjects a culture of bacteria to unfavorable conditions which kill 90 per cent of the surviving organisms each minute. If culture A contains 1,000,000 cells per cc., the living organisms would be reduced to 100,000 then to 10,000, then to 100, and so on in successive minutes. Then at the end of eight minutes, the living organisms would be reduced to 0.01 per cc. However, if culture B contained only 10,000 organisms per cc., the same reduction will occur in six minutes. (See Figure 30.)

This means that a test tube of broth containing culture A will be sterile at the end of eight minutes, whereas a quart or gallon of culture will still contain some living bacteria. Of course, in an actual situation, the per cent of the total number of organisms killed might be 10, 60, or 87 per cent instead of 90 per cent. Likewise, the periods of time might be seconds or hours depending upon the many factors determining the rate at which bacteria are killed. Culture B would be free from bacteria in less time than culture A. This shows that the time required for complete sterilization varies with the number of organisms present. In practice, the number of organisms and the rate of killing are seldom known; therefore, any sterilization procedure must be continued long enough to kill all the organisms present, regardless of the size of the population.

OTHER FACTORS   As bacteria are susceptible to the presence of acids, the combined action of acid and heat is more injurious than the action of either alone. This may be due in part to the fact that the acid medium inhibits the growth of bacteria so that there are fewer bacteria to be killed. Evidence

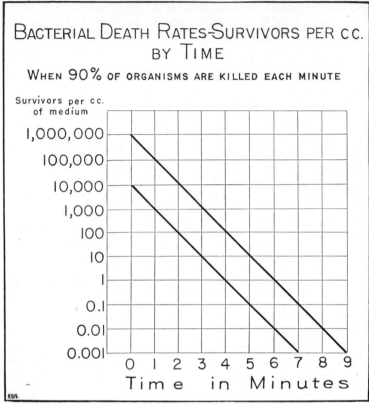

BACTERIAL DEATH RATES-SURVIVORS PER C.C.
BY TIME

WHEN 90% OF ORGANISMS ARE KILLED EACH MINUTE

Figure 30　　　The time required to kill bacteria varies with the
number of organisms present.

of this is seen in the fact that the housewife finds it easier to
can acid fruits successfully than the slightly alkaline vegetables, such as peas, beans, and corn. In spite of the many
variables that influence the rate of sterilization, heat remains
a most effective way of killing microorganisms and is the agent
most commonly employed.

Both moist and dry heat destroy the protoplasm of cells.
As a killing agent, however, moist heat is the more effective.
This was well demonstrated by the early bacteriologist Robert
Koch in 1881. In his experiment, packages of garden soil were
wrapped with twenty, forty, or one hundred layers of cloth.

Thermometers were placed so that the temperatures inside of the packages could be determined. Then the packages were subjected to hot air or to steam. The packages subjected to steam were heated to 101° C. (213.8° F.) and were sterile in three hours. In contrast, the packages heated in the hot air oven still contained living organisms at the end of four hours because the temperatures within the packages remained below 86° C. (186.8° F.). The results are indicated in Table 8.

Table 8   RESULTS OF HEAT ON LIVING ORGANISMS

AGENT	TEMPER-ATURE	TIME IN HOURS	THICKNESSES OF LINEN TEMPERATURES REACHED WITHIN			STERIL-IZATION
			TWENTY THICK-NESSES	FORTY THICK-NESSES	ONE HUN-DRED THICK-NESSES	
Hot air	130–140° C.	4	86° C.	72° C.	below 70° C.	incomplete
Steam	90–105.3° C.	3	101° C.	101° C.	101.5° C.	complete

As the steam condensed on the surface of the packages, it transferred heat to the linen, to the soil, and to the bacteria within the soil. This prolonged contact with the bacterial cells resulted in the killing of all those present. Hot air failed to sterilize the packages, although it was continued for a longer period and at a higher temperature. The point to be observed is that steam, a good conductor of heat, is more effective in killing microorganisms than is hot air.

METHODS   Heat for killing bacteria may be supplied by: (1) an open flame, (2) an oven, (3) a boiler, or (4) a pressure sterilizer.

OPEN FLAME   The student has used the method of fire to sterilize the needle used in transferring cultures. This effective method can be applied to articles of little value which have been contaminated with disease-producing organisms. Paper handkerchiefs, tongue blades, swabs, cotton pledgets, magazines, and toys may well be disposed of in this way.

OVEN   Dry heat is usually applied by some type of oven.

In the laboratory it can be used for dry objects, such as petri dishes and test tubes. It is also an effective means of sterilizing powders, fats, oils,* and waxes because it penetrates these substances better than moist heat. In the home, dry heat is sometimes used for sterilizing feeding bottles and linen. A temperature of 160° C. (320° F.) must be applied for one hour or more to kill spore forms.

BOILER   The boiler may consist of a covered pan of water over an open flame or it may be the instrument-sterilizer type, which consists of a chamber of water heated by live steam. Exposure to boiling water is an effective means of destroying vegetative forms but this method may fail to kill spores unless it is continued for many hours. The time required will vary with the species, the number of cells, and the *p*H of the medium. To provide an adequate margin of safety, this method is usually applied for five, ten, or twenty minutes. To be certain that the organisms have actually been subjected to 100° C. (212° F.), the articles being disinfected must be *entirely* submerged in the boiling water.

The *Arnold sterilizer* is a device for providing a steam chamber in which articles can be placed. Essentially it consists of a lower chamber of boiling water and an upper chamber which collects the steam as it vaporizes. A covered wash boiler equipped with a wood or metal rack can be used. Arnold or *fractional sterilization* is sometimes used for sterilizing carbohydrate media which may be hydrolyzed by the high temperature of the autoclave. The medium is steamed for thirty to sixty minutes on three or four successive days. Between the heating periods, the material is left at room temperature. The first heating kills the vegetative forms present. Then an incubation period at room temperature provides opportunity for the spores to develop into vegetative forms. These may be killed during the next heating period. This method is suitable only for those materials that will support growth of the spore-

* In a recent letter, Beckett[4] states that petroleum jelly can be sterilized in the autoclave provided small quantities are placed in small jars, set in a pan of water, and heated for sixty to ninety minutes at 121° C.

forming bacteria present. It is unsatisfactory for surgical supplies because the spores would continue in the spore form. In practice, this method is used only when there is no other satisfactory method available.

PRESSURE STERILIZER   The autoclave, or pressure sterilizer, is an essential part of the equipment of the modern hospital, clinic, and bacteriology laboratory. Some space will be devoted to the structure and operation of the autoclave because an understanding of its mechanism is necessary to insure adequate sterilization procedures.

The autoclave is a machine for holding steam under pressure. It is really a large pressure cooker consisting of a chamber with a double jacket and a self-locking door. Four types of valves may be found on most models:

1. *Steam inlets,* which permit the entry of steam to the outer jacket alone or to both the jacket and the chamber.
2. *Steam outlets,* which permit the escape of the heavier air as it is displaced by the lighter steam.
3. *The emergency,* a safety device which permits the escape of steam when the pressure becomes excessive.
4. *The vacuum,* a device for connecting the chamber with a low-pressure area, allowing steam to escape from packages leaving them dry.

The operation of the autoclave is not difficult if one understands the purpose of each step, and since each model differs with respect to the placement of valves, it is important to study and to follow the charts and directions issued by the manufacturers. The operation of the autoclave is summarized on the next page.

As the steam enters after the door and outlet valve are closed, the pressure rises. The water-saturated vapor condenses on the surface of the materials and gives its latent heat to the objects. The pressure makes it possible for the hot steam to penetrate the inside of the bundles. The pressure in itself is not important because bacteria can withstand great pressures (two or three atmospheres) without injury. It is merely a device for raising the temperature and increasing the penetration of steam. Steam without pressure has a temperature of

THE OPERATION OF THE AUTOCLAVE

THE PURPOSE	THE OPERATION
1. To load the chamber	1. Place articles so that there are many spaces between them to permit the free circulation of steam. Place large (flat) bundles on their sides, and enamel trays, basins, and jars on their sides (never upright).
2. To heat the jacket	2. Open the steam inlet valve which connects the jacket with the steam supply.
3. To fill chamber with steam and to exclude air	3. Close the door. Open the (chamber) steam inlet valve. Open the outlet valve.
4. To raise the temperature within the chamber to 121° C. (250° F.) (15 lbs. pressure) and to hold for an appropriate period: 15–20 minutes for small articles; 30–45 minutes for packages or drums	4. Close the outlet valve when a steady stream of steam begins to escape. Watch temperature and pressure gauges; begin to time process when the temperature reaches 121° C.
5. To dry linen. (This step is unnecessary when sterilizing media or liquids)	5. Close steam inlet valve. When pressure drops to zero, open the vacuum.
6. To open the autoclave	6. Close the vacuum. Open the outlet valve *slowly*. Release the locking device on the door.

100° C. (212° F.), while saturated steam at ten and fifteen pounds pressure reaches temperatures of 115° and 121° C. (239° and 249.8° F.) respectively. (See Figure 32.)

Since air is a poor conductor of heat, its presence in the chamber will prevent the steam from reaching temperatures above 120° C. (248° F.). It has been demonstrated that when air is not removed from the autoclave, steam under fifteen pounds pressure attains a temperature of only 100° C. (212° F.), whereas when all air is removed the temperature under the same pressure is 121° C. (249.8° F.). (See Figure 33.)

Sterilization by steam depends upon the ability of steam to penetrate the materials, and to heat them for a period that exceeds the *thermal death time* of spore-forming bacteria. Anything that makes possible the free circulation of the steam

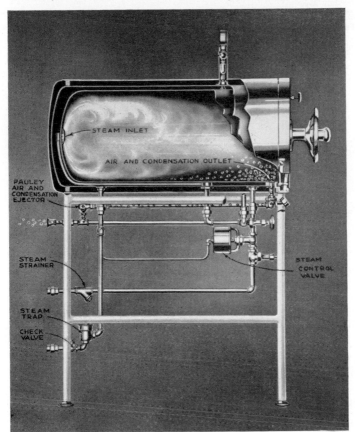

Figure 31　　　Phantom view of an autoclave showing steam jacket, sterilizing chamber, and steam flow through the sterilizer. (Ohio Chemical and Manufacturing Co., Madison, Wis.)

furthers this process; anything that interferes with the circulation of steam, such as covered jars, tightly wrapped bundles, or overloading, may prevent sterilization. Basins and trays should be placed on their sides to permit the escape of the air; if they are in an upright position, the lighter steam settles over the air of the containers and imprisons it in the bottom of the containers thereby decreasing the temperature in that area. Such articles as rubber tubing and gloves are difficult to sterilize because steam does not penetrate rubber. The equipment,

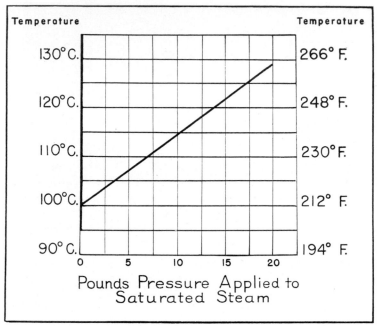

Figure 32   The relation of pressure to temperature of steam in the
autoclave—all air excluded.

therefore, must be placed in such a manner that the steam can
readily reach both the inside and outside of the glove or tube.
This can be accomplished by coiling the tubing around a
cardboard to keep the lumen open and by using gauze inserts
to hold the gloves open and to separate the cuff from the body
of the glove.

In order to secure adequate sterilization by the use of the
autoclave, it is important to observe the following suggestions:

1. Study the directions issued by the manufacturer of the
sterilizer and follow them.

2. Wrap linen in loose, flat bundles and place on their sides
to permit the penetration of steam.

3. Leave plenty of free spaces between packages in the
chamber. Raise temperature slowly after packing the chamber
to insure adequate heating of all packages.

4. Allow a longer time for the sterilization of large bundles
than for the small ones.

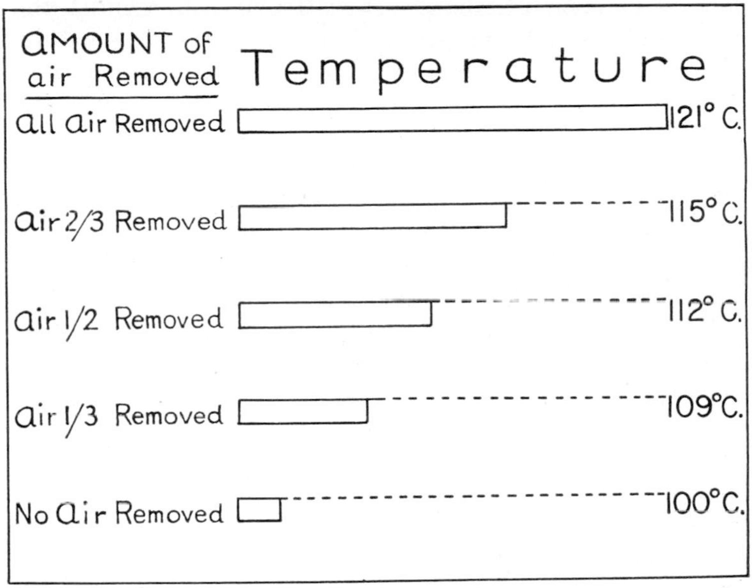

AMOUNT of
air Removed T e m p e r a t u r e

All air Removed ⊏━━━━━━━━━━━━━━━━━━━⊐121° C.

Air 2/3 Removed ⊏━━━━━━━━━━━⊐- - - - - - - ⌐115° C.

Air 1/2 Removed ⊏━━━━━━━⌐- - - - - - - - - ⌐112° C.

Air 1/3 Removed ⊏━━━⌐- - - - - - - - - - - - - - ⌐109°C.

No Air Removed ⊏━⌐- - - - - - - - - - - - - - - - - ⌐100°C.

Figure 33   The influence of air on the temperature of steam in the autoclave under 15 pounds pressure.

5. Do not allow anything to touch the door, which is cooler than other parts of the chamber; the lower temperature may interfere with sterilization, and the water of condensation which collects on it will soak dressings or linens.

6. Remove tight covers from jars to permit steam to enter; place jars on their sides so that air can escape.

7. Decrease the pressure very slowly when the chamber contains solutions in flasks or tubes. A rapid change in pressure will cause the stoppers and the liquid to leave the containers.

8. Avoid excessive sterilization periods; heat has a destructive action on linen and rubber.

9. Watch the temperature gauge as well as the pressure indicator. Microorganisms are killed by heat, not by pressure.

Drying   Drying is a valuable inhibiting agent because bacteria require water to carry on their life activities. In nature, few things are completely free from water. Hardy organisms, therefore, often survive and sometimes grow moderately in materials that appear dry. The destructive action of drying depends on many variables, such as the kind of organism, the number of cells, the thickness of the layer, the temperature, and the presence or absence of oxygen. Delicate parasites, such as the gonococcus, are killed by drying within a few hours, while tubercle bacilli may resist drying for weeks or months. Spore-forming bacteria can withstand drying almost indefinitely. McCulloch[5] reports spores of anthrax alive and capable of producing disease after being stored in a glass bottle exposed to diffuse light for forty years.

Under some conditions, drying does not kill bacteria. Bacterial cultures which have been frozen quickly and completely dried in a vacuum at low temperature will remain alive for years. Under natural conditions, however, drying provides one of the means by which the death of vegetative forms is hastened. For obvious reasons, this method is not usually suitable for active disinfection or sterilization. It is very useful as a method of preserving food supplies, such as milk, eggs, fruits, or cereals. It is important to remember that dried foods contain living bacteria. Usually these organisms are harmless but sometimes they may be capable of causing disease. For example, dried eggs may be contaminated with salmonella organisms.

Light   Direct sunlight has a definite destructive action on living cells. Everyone has seen and perhaps experienced the stimulating, irritating, and destructive action of the sun in the form of sunburn. The action is probably the same for bacterial cells. Visible light inhibits bacteria, while the ultraviolet rays actually destroy microorganisms. Neither visible light nor ultraviolet light rays have much power of penetration, so that their action is limited to the organisms on or near the surface of the medium. Diffuse light is even less effective. As the destructive action of light is inversely proportional to the distance from the source, sunlight kills slowly. In the laboratory, it usually requires an exposure of two to six hours to demonstrate the injurious effect of direct light on bacteria. Sunlight, together with drying, is a useful agent in freeing the air and exposed objects from pathogenic organisms, but because its action is slow, it is best reserved as an adjunct to other methods or used when other methods are not available. It may be used successfully for disinfecting mattresses, pillows, and blankets, provided they are placed so that all surfaces receive the direct rays of the sun for several hours. Since the ultraviolet rays of sunlight do not pass through windows, the sunning of rooms depends upon the mild action of diffuse light. Because of its limitations, this measure is best used in conjunction with other measures, such as ventilation and thorough washing of walls, floor, and furniture with soap and water.

Ultraviolet light generated by special lamps is very injurious to surface bacteria, but like sunlight, it has little or no ability to penetrate beneath the surface of objects. Such ultraviolet lamps must be properly screened to prevent injury to the eyes and skin of human beings. They markedly decrease the number of bacteria in the air and have been successfully used in hospital operating rooms, in nurseries, and in communicable disease wards. They have also proved of value in bakeries and other establishments where foods are processed. Some restaurants have installed ultraviolet lamps as a means of sanitizing dishes and glassware. For this purpose, ultraviolet light will be effective only if the dishes are mechanically clean and free from dirt, since the light does not penetrate either dirt or glass. The same principle applies to the use of ultraviolet light for sterilizing toilet seats; namely, it will be effective only when applied to clean surfaces.

Sound Waves and Agitation   Sound waves with a frequency of 32,000 to 2,250,000 vibrations per second are injurious to both bacteria and viruses. Some cells appear to be torn to pieces by the action of the sound waves, while others appear normal but are unable to multiply. Mechanical agitation of bacterial cells in machines where they are whirled with abrasives will also cause the disruption of the cells. Today, these processes are used primarily in research. It is possible that some day sound waves may prove useful in processing of food and vaccines.

Ionizing Radiations   At the present time concerted experimentation is being directed toward using ionizing radiations for cold sterilization of various products. It is known that ionizing radiations will kill microorganisms. Bacteria vary in their susceptibility to radiation. Spore-forming bacteria are more resistant than nonspore-formers and bacterial spores are more resistant than mold spores. If methods can be perfected it is expected that by ionizing radiation sterilization can be used for many purposes such as (1) pasteurization of milk, (2) sterilization of blood, drugs, and biologicals, (3) sterilization of food, and (4) destruction of insects and trichina. Before these processes can be put into use, extensive tests will need to be made to make certain that foods so treated are safe for use.

SUMMARY

1. Microorganisms respond to their environment by (1) increased growth, (2) variation, or (3) inhibition and death.

2. Microorganisms can be inhibited or destroyed by cold, heat, drying, light, sound waves, mechanical agitation, and ionizing radiation.

3. Cold prevents the growth of bacteria, but is not particularly destructive to most bacteria. Therefore, bacteria subjected to cold may survive for long periods of time.

4. Moist heat is more effective in destroying bacteria than dry heat. Moist heat can be obtained (1) by boiling in water, (2) by steam without pressure, and (3) by steam under pressure. The autoclave, which provides steam under pressure at a temperature of 121° C. (249.8° F.), is the most satisfactory way to sterilize linens, instruments, syringes, and needles. Powders, oils, waxes, and ointments which are not penetrated by steam should be sterilized by hot air.

5. Drying increases the death rate of bacteria, especially when oxygen is present. Different microorganisms vary greatly in their ability to withstand drying.

6. Visible and ultraviolet light are injurious to bacterial protoplasm. Both agents act only on organisms present on the surface of objects and media. Neither ray can penetrate materials.

7. The rate at which bacteria are killed depends upon many variables. Time is an important factor in any sterilization procedure.

REFERENCES

1. McCulloch, E. C.: Disinfection and Sterilization. 2d ed. Philadelphia, Lea & Febiger, 1945, p. 155.
2. Hartsell, S. E.: The Longevity and Behavior of Pathogenic Bacteria

in Frozen Food: The Influence of Plating Media. Am. J. Pub. Health, *41:* 1072–1081, 1951.
3. McCulloch, E. C.: Disinfection and Sterilization. 2d ed. Philadelphia, Lea & Febiger, 1945, p. 70.
4. Beckett, J. S.: Sterilizing Vaseline. Am. J. Nursing, *53:* 135, 136, 1953.
5. McCulloch, E. C.: Disinfection and Sterilization. 2d ed. Philadelphia, Lea & Febiger, 1945, p. 162.

SUPPLEMENTARY READINGS

BOOKS:

Braun, W.: Bacterial Genetics. Philadelphia, W. B. Saunders Co., 1953.
Burrows, W.: Jordan-Burrows Textbook of Bacteriology. 15th ed. Philadelphia, W. B. Saunders Co., 1949.
Frobisher, M.: Fundamentals of Bacteriology. 5th ed. Philadelphia, W. B. Saunders Co., 1953.
Lederberg, J.: Inheritance, Variation, and Adaptation. In Werkman, C. H., and Wilson, P. W.: Bacterial Physiology. New York, Academic Press, Inc., 1951, pp. 68–100.
Mitchell, P.: Physical Factors Affecting Growth and Death. In Werkman, C. H., and Wilson, P. W.: Bacterial Physiology. New York, Academic Press, Inc., 1951, Chapter V.
Smith, D. T., and Conant, N. F.: Zinsser's Textbook of Bacteriology. New York, Appleton-Century-Crofts, Inc., 1952.
Walter, C. W.: Aseptic Treatment of Wounds. New York, The Macmillan Co., 1948.
Wyss, O.: Chemical Factors Affecting Growth and Death. In Werkman, C. H., and Wilson, P. W.: Bacterial Physiology. New York, Academic Press, Inc., 1951, Chapter VI.

PERIODICALS:

Berman, P., and Beckett, J. S.: Sterilizing Surgical Supplies. Am. J. Nursing, *52:* 1212–1214, 1952.
Nickerson, J. T., and others: Public Health Aspects of Electronic Food Sterilization. Am. J. Pub. Health, *43:* 554–560, 1953.
Vera, H. D.: Sterility Testing: The Control of Efficiency of Sterilization Techniques. Applied Microbiology, *1:* 117–119, 1953.

CHAPTER 11   *Unfavorable Environment (Continued)*

CHEMICAL DISINFECTION

THE NATURE and composition of the surrounding medium is an important factor for all forms of life. Animals cannot live in an atmosphere where oxygen is limited or where injurious substances such as carbon monoxide or hydrocyanic acid are present. Microorganisms likewise are sensitive to stress. Severe stresses injure or kill bacterial cells by changing or disorganizing their active proteins, genes, or cell membranes. It is often desirable to create an unfavorable environment by making certain that it is deficient in growth essentials or that it contains cell poisons. For instance, distilled water will not support bacterial growth, although hardy organisms may be able to survive in it for hours or days and bacterial spores may remain alive for weeks. Distilled water containing traces of salts or acids, contributed by the still or bottles, may cause more rapid destruction of bacteria.

Poisons have been used for centuries to destroy competing forms of life, such as animals and insects. It is not surprising, therefore, to find that they can be effectively used against microorganisms. Special names have been applied to chemical agents used to destroy bacterial life. Those that prevent the growth of bacteria are called *antiseptic* or *bacteriostatic* substances. The terms *disinfectants, germicides,* and *bactericides* denote substances that kill bacteria. The word "disinfect" is sometimes used to indicate the killing of all harmful bacteria in contrast to the word "sterilize," which means to free from all forms of microorganisms. Actually, there is no clear-cut difference between antiseptics and disinfectants because prolonged contact with an antiseptic will cause irreversible changes in cells. The same concentration of a drug acting for a given period of time may kill pneumococci, prevent the growth of micrococci, and show no injurious effects on the spores of *Bacillus subtilis*. If the time or the temperature were

150

increased sufficiently, the same solution may kill the cells of the micrococci, and a weaker solution may inhibit the pneumococci instead of killing them. Obviously, then, the terms are inaccurate, since the same reagent may act either as an antiseptic or as a disinfectant.

Disinfectants and antiseptics are likely to harm both human and bacterial cells. In contrast, certain *antibiotics* and chemotherapeutic agents are very effective against certain bacteria and yet are relatively harmless for animal cells. (See Chapter 18, page 272.)

Inhibiting Action TESTING OF DISINFECTANTS How can the injurious effects of a chemical agent be determined? By what methods is it possible to ascertain the length of time and the concentration of the drug required to destroy certain microorganisms? There is no completely satisfactory way of testing disinfectants. There are, however, several methods of gaining useful information concerning their ability to kill or injure certain bacteria. One common method is as follows: A measured quantity of test organisms is added to tubes containing different concentrations of the drug. At intervals (one, two and one-half, five, ten, fifteen minutes), samples are transferred to sterile broth and incubated at 37° C. (98.6° F.). After twenty-four hours and again, a week later, the tubes are examined for evidence of growth.

To enable one investigator to compare his results with those of another, these tests are rigidly standardized with regard to equipment, media, and methods. Such standardization creates artificial conditions which are quite different from those encountered by bacteria outside of the laboratory. Therefore, the conclusions drawn apply only to the experiment but not necessarily to conditions found outside of the laboratory.

THE PHENOL COEFFICIENT TEST* The purpose of the phenol coefficient test is to compare the efficiency of a new drug with that of phenol in inhibiting a test organism such as *Micrococcus pyogenes* or *Salmonella typhosa*. The materials used are (1) different concentrations of phenol, (2) different concentrations of the new drug, (3) standard suspensions of the test organism, (4) standard broth medium, and (5)

---

* This test is commonly called the official F.D.A. phenol coefficient test since the Food and Drug Administration of the United States Department of Agriculture sets the standards for this procedure.

equipment for maintaining a constant temperature. Measured quantities of bacterial suspension are added to each dilution of the new drug and of phenol. After contacts of one minute, five minutes, ten minutes, and fifteen minutes, samples are transferred to tubes of nutrient broth which are then labeled and incubated at 37° C. After forty-eight hours the results are observed and tabulated. On the basis of these results and a mathematical formula, a number is derived which indicates the relative value of the disinfectant that is compared with phenol. For instance, the tabulated results might be as follows:

DISINFECTANT	DILUTION	FIVE MINUTES	TEN MINUTES	FIFTEEN MINUTES
"X"	1:400	0	0	0
	1:450	+	0	0
	1:500	+	+	0
Phenol	1:80	0	0	0
	1:90	+	0	0
	1:100	+	+	0

+ = growth in broth   0 = no growth in broth

The results of exposing a twenty-four-hour culture of *Micrococcus pyogenes* (*Staphylococcus aureus*) to various dilutions of disinfectant X and phenol for five, ten, and fifteen minutes provide the necessary data.

The phenol coefficient is determined by using the following formula:

$$\text{The phenol coefficient} = \frac{\text{the lowest concentration of phenol which prevents growth in 10 minutes}}{\text{the lowest concentration of drug which prevents growth in 10 minutes}}$$

$$= \frac{1/90}{1/450} = \frac{450}{90} = 5 \text{ the phenol coefficient of X when } \textit{Micrococcus pyogenes} \text{ var. } \textit{aureus} \text{ is used.}$$

In theory, a phenol coefficient of 5 means that the new disinfectant is five times as effective as phenol in preventing the growth of test organisms under rigid laboratory conditions. One weakness of this test is the fact that it compares the effectiveness of germicides under laboratory conditions—conditions in no way resembling the actual situations in which the disinfectants are used. This means that one cannot accept the verdict of a phenol coefficient test as a completely valid measure of the value of a disinfectant. In fact, it is at times very misleading. For example, the test does not distinguish between bacteriocidal and bacteriostatic action since in a culture tube certain organisms may fail to grow because sufficient antiseptic has been transferred into the medium to prevent growth of living bacteria.

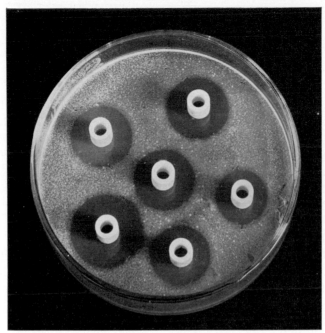

Figure 34　　Cylinder plate showing the effects of penicillin. The medium has been heavily seeded with *Micrococcus pyogenes* or *B. subtilis*. A measured quantity of penicillin was placed in each cylinder. Following incubation, zones of inhibition are visible (dark circles around the cylinder). Measurement of these zones and comparison with those produced by standard solutions permits standardization of penicillin in Oxford units. (Therapeutic Notes, March, 1944. Parke, Davis & Co.)

AGAR PLATE METHOD   Another way of demonstrating inhibition is to seed an agar plate with the test organism and then place a cylinder or filter paper moistened with the drug on the center of the plate. (See Figure 34.) A clear area surrounding the filter paper shows the ability of the drug to inhibit the growth of the organisms in nutrient agar.

Toxic Action   There is a variety of methods which will demonstrate the ability of a drug to injure animal cells. The following are some of the harmful effects which may occur when toxic antiseptics are placed in contact with specific cells or tissues:

CELLS OR TISSUES TESTED	TOXIC EFFECTS
Red blood cells	Destruction of red blood cells (*hemolysis*)
White blood cells mixed with bacterial cells	Destruction of white blood cells or decrease in ability to engulf bacteria
Eye of a rabbit	Inflammation (redness, swelling, etc.)
Wounds	Inflammation
Chick embryo	Death of embryo
Subcutaneous tissues—injection into	Inflammation, with or without death of tissue
Blood stream—injection into	Illness or death of the animal with or without demonstrable injury to liver, kidneys, etc.

At the present time, there is no standard test for determining the toxicity of any drug. However, a number of these methods may be used to good advantage.

VARIABLES THAT INFLUENCE GERMICIDAL ACTION

The thousands of experiments on disinfection that have been reported have not always been in complete agreement, but out of the mass of data the following facts may be accepted:

1. Certain chemical substances are injurious to bacterial cells. The damage appears to be gradual and in the early stages is reversible. Although the mechanism by which injury takes place is not completely known, there is considerable evidence to suggest that the chemical agent combines with and destroys enzymes or other proteins that are essential to the life of the cell. In some instances genes may be injured or cell membranes altered so that they become more permeable. Certain chemicals appear to prevent reproduction by interfering with the nutrition of the cell. To be effective, a disinfectant must reach and combine with the individual bacterial cell.

2. The process of disinfection is complex and its success or failure is influenced by many factors. The following are important variables:

    (a) The kind of microorganism—species, age, number

of cells, presence of capsules or spores, and Gram staining reaction.

(b) The kind of disinfectant—concentration, solubility in water, or cell fluids.

(c) The kind of environment:

    (1) Temperature

    (2) Hydrogen ion concentration, usually referred to as pH (see page 122)

    (3) Organic materials, such as food, proteins, salts, soaps, etc.

(d) The time of action.

Despite the fact that chemical disinfection is thus complicated, it still remains one of the important ways of controlling bacteria.

The Organism   Some organisms are distinctly hardy, while others are easily killed. For example, pneumococci and gonococci are easily killed; *Micrococcus pyogenes* and *Escherichia coli* are moderately resistant. In contrast, some viruses (those causing vaccinia and infectious hepatitis) are very resistant to chemical disinfection. Likewise the cysts of certain protozoa are relatively resistant. The spore-forming rods are especially difficult to kill. This is probably due to the inactive condition of the spore state when the cell is relatively impermeable. Nothing enters the cell and the spore escapes injury. Bacteria that do not form spores also differ in their resistance to harmful agents. Many disinfectants are selective in their action, since they inhibit gram-positive organisms in concentrations which would produce no effects on gram-negative organisms. In general, the gram-positive organisms are more susceptible to injury by chemical agents than are the gram-negative. It will be seen that the kind of organisms present must be considered when selecting a disinfectant. Age too is important since young active cells are more susceptible to chemical injury than are old resting cells.

The number of bacterial cells is a factor to consider in determining the amount of time required to kill all the bacteria present. Not all bacteria die at one and the same time. Laboratory investigations indicate that any single bacterial culture contains different groups of organisms: some sensitive and some more resistant. The sensitive cells die promptly while the more resistant cells survive longer contacts with a disinfectant solution. The concentration of drug and of water are important and should be determined on the basis of laboratory tests. For each drug there is an optimum strength for effective disinfection. Increasing the concentration of a drug will always add to the expense of the process, and may not improve its efficiency. In the case of ethyl alcohol, increasing the amount of alcohol to 95 per cent actually lessens the efficiency by decreasing the water content. Water being the natural exchange medium of the cell, anything that penetrates the cell enters in a watery solution or emulsion. Without water, this cannot take place. The results of experiments in which cultures of *Micrococcus pyogenes* (*Staphylococcus aureus*) were exposed to different concentrations of iodine and isopropyl and ethyl alcohol are shown in Table 9. Alcohol in concentrations below 50 per cent is relatively ineffective because it contains too little alcohol. Concentrations above 80 per cent contain too little water to be effective with the usual bacterium. Ethyl and isopropyl alcohol are commonly used in concentrations of 50 or 70 per cent by volume or weight. The greater effectiveness 50 and 70 per cent alcohol is well demonstrated when the tuberculosis organism (*Mycobacterium tuberculosis*) is treated with different concentrations of alcohol.[1] (See Figure 35. The ineffectiveness of alcohol against spore-forming organisms such as *Bacillus anthracis* is shown in the lower part of the figure.) The importance of water is well illustrated by phenol. One per cent phenol in water is a good disinfectant, while 1 per cent phenol in alcohol or petrolatum is practically inert.

Time and Temperature   Disinfection is not magic. It is an orderly process which requires time and intimate contact between the chemical and the cells to be killed. Time is the one factor that can be increased without fear of lessening the efficiency of the procedure. Of course, if the drug is injurious to equipment, prolonged contact is undesirable.

Disinfection is essentially a chemical process, and, like all chemical reactions, it proceeds more rapidly as the temperature

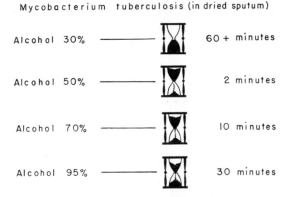

Mycobacterium tuberculosis (in dried sputum)

Alcohol 30% ——————— 60 + minutes

Alcohol 50% ——————— 2 minutes

Alcohol 70% ——————— 10 minutes

Alcohol 95% ——————— 30 minutes

Alcohol 99% (absolute)— 60 + minutes

Bacillus anthracis (three-day culture)

Alcohol 25%
Alcohol 50%
Alcohol 70%
Alcohol 80%
Alcohol 99%

survived more than

1200 HOURS

in all concentrations

Figure 35   Time required for alcohol to kill *Bacillus anthracis* and *Mycobacterium tuberculosis*. (Based on McCulloch and Smith.)

increases. Temperatures below 20° C. (68° F.) are undesirable because they slow the reactions.

Organic Materials   The presence of organic matter, such as protein, interferes with the process of disinfection since a part of the disinfectant will combine with the protein. (See Tables 9 and 10.) The product is often an insoluble substance which by coating the microorganisms decreases the surface contact between the disinfectant and the microorganism. Such organic matter seems to protect the bacterial cell from ready contact with the disinfectant. Some chemicals combine with the complex substances and become inert, while other agents

Table 9   RELATIVE EFFICIENCIES OF DISINFECTANT SOLUTIONS AGAINST *Micrococcus pyogenes* VAR. *aureus* AFTER IMMERSION OF THERMOMETER SECTIONS

IMMERSION TIME OF THERMOMETER IN TEST DISINFECTANTS	DISINFECTANTS TESTED						
	IODINE SOLUTION 2% I_2	IODINE TINCTURE 2% I_2	ETHYL ALCOHOL 95%	ETHYL ALCOHOL 70%	ETHYL ALCOHOL 50%	ISOPROPYL ALCOHOL 70%	ISOPROPYL ALCOHOL 50%
Control thermometer	+	+	+	+	+	+	+
100 sec.	+	0	+	+	+	+	+
120 sec.	0	0	+	+	+	+	+
3 min.	0	0	+	+	+	+	+
4 min.	0	0	+	+	+	0	+
5 min.	0	0	+	+	+	0	+
10 min.	0	0	+	0	0	0	0

+ = growth in 48 hours.
0 = no growth in 48 hours.
(From Gershenfeld, L., and others: J. Am. Pharm. A. (Scient. Ed.), *40*: 459.)

Table 10   RELATIVE EFFICIENCIES OF DISINFECTANT SOLUTIONS AGAINST *Micrococcus pyogenes* VAR. *aureus* AFTER IMMERSION OF THERMOMETER SECTIONS COATED WITH A 25% CITRATED HUMAN PLASMA CULTURE MIXTURE

IMMERSION TIME OF THERMOMETER IN TEST DISINFECTANT	IODINE SOLUTION 2% I_2	IODINE TINCTURE 2% I_2	DISINFECTANTS TESTED			
			ETHYL ALCOHOL 50%	ETHYL ALCOHOL 70%	ISOPROPYL ALCOHOL 70%	ISOPROPYL ALCOHOL 50%
Control thermometer	+	+	+	+	+	+
3 min.	0	+++	+++	+++	+++	+++
5 min.	0	++	++	+++	++	++
10 min.	0	+	+	+		

+ = growth in 48 hours.
0 = no growth in 48 hours.
(From Gershenfeld, L., and others: J. Am. Pharm. A. (Scient. Ed.), *40*: 460.)

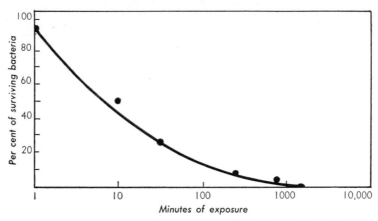

Figure 36   Zephiran 1:50,000 aqueous solution—the effect on *Escherichia coli.* (Redrawn from Price: The Meaning of Bacteriostasis.)

may be so strongly attracted to the particles of organic material that they are no longer equally distributed in the solution. For this reason, feces, sputum, and pus are difficult to disinfect. Table 10 shows the influence of organic matter upon the efficiency of several germicides. Observe that the organic matter interferes with disinfection. For this reason it is necessary to remove organic matter from thermometers and other equipment before placing them in disinfectant solutions. Furthermore, the addition of soaps or inorganic salts will sometimes increase and at other times decrease the effectiveness of the agent. Such additions are not desirable unless one knows that they will increase the destructive action. When soap solutions are used to cleanse objects before disinfection, it is important that these objects be rinsed carefully to remove all soap.

EFFECTIVE DISINFECTION

Effective disinfection depends upon an intimate contact between bacterial cells (in vegetative state) and the suitable chemical agent for a period of time more than adequate to kill all nonspore-formers present. This is facilitated if the chemical agent is also a "wetting agent," i.e., one that lowers the surface tension of the cell and spreads evenly over the surface of the bacterial cells. Because of the many variables in the disinfection process, it is desirable to have a large factor of safety. That is, if laboratory tests indicate that there are no living typhoid bacilli in material exposed to a given disinfectant after one-half hour, a routine disinfection procedure should allow one hour, in order to be doubly sure that it has been effective. The selection of the drug, the concentration, and the time used in the disinfection procedure should be based upon the advice of an expert.

The chemical reactions which destroy bacterial cells are not definitely and completely known. From the nature of the disinfectants it seems probable that one or more of the following chemical actions are involved: oxidation (oxidizing agents), hydrolysis (strong acids and alkalies), or the formation of protein salts (oxidizing agents). Enzymes and cells are so complex in structure that it is difficult to know which of the many substances present react with the chemical disinfectant. It seems likely, however, that an effective disinfectant injures a bacterial cell by destroying or inactivating some essential cell constituent such as the genes (heredity bearers), cell membranes, or other boundaries within the cell or enzyme proteins.

Antibacterial substances may be used on inanimate articles, such as thermometers and utensils, or they may be applied to the human body. Many good disinfectants are quite unsuited to use on wounds or on the skin because they are toxic and injure body cells, thereby interfering with healing. The ideal antiseptic is one that destroys bacteria without doing harm to body cells. Few antiseptics meet these requirements. (See Chapter 18.)

PROBLEMS IN DISINFECTION

Inanimate objects which are free from cracks and crevices and free from organic materials are relatively easy to disinfect because bacteria on their surfaces are quite unprotected from the disinfectant. For instance, a thermometer which has been washed with green soap and alcohol and rinsed well can be disinfected by a solution of alcohol and iodine in ten minutes. (See page 163.) Careful cleansing to remove organic matter is an essential step in disinfection.

Skin and Mucous Membranes   It is almost impossible

to disinfect the tissues of the skin and mucous membranes. The protoplasm which composes the cells is very much like that of the bacteria, so that most substances which injure the bacteria will also harm the human cells. As bacteria live in the gland structures of the skin and mucous membranes, even if one succeeded in sterilizing the upper layer, the secretions would soon bring more bacteria to the surface.

The following table shows the results of experiments designed to sterilize the skin with different antiseptics. The skin was shaved and then painted with the disinfectant. Then a small piece of the skin was removed for culture. The results were as follows:

Table 11   SKIN STERILIZATION[2]

COMPOUND	NUMBER OF SKIN GRAFTS	PER CENT STERILE
Merphenyl nitrate tincture 1:1500	100	0
Merthiolate tincture 1:1000	30	6
Metaphen tincture 1:200	50	80
Mercurochrome tincture 1:50	40	10
Phenol (2% aqueous)	20	0
Alcohol acetone solution	30	0
Iodine, tincture 7%	40	80

This experiment demonstrates the difficulty of killing all of the bacteria present on the skin. Even the best antiseptics failed in 20 per cent of the tests. Since the organisms which make up the normal flora are relatively harmless, the aim of skin preparation before surgery and of washing and scrubbing the hands is to remove the transient bacteria which may be harmful. (See page 310.)

The oral cavity, which normally supports a huge bacterial population, is very resistant to disinfection. Mouthwashes, contrary to the extravagant claims of advertising, produce little effect on the luxuriant bacterial flora of the mouth. For the most part, they are pleasant-tasting solutions whose chief virtue is that they are harmless. The same principle applies to antiseptics designed for use on other mucous membranes. Either they are harmless and useless or they may depress the natural defenses of the tissues involved. Therefore, the disinfection of normal mucous membranes is not only difficult but is often undesirable as well.

Stools and Body Discharges   Feces from persons ill with diseases such as typhoid fever often contain large numbers of disease-producing bacteria. Such stools must be disinfected before disposal* to prevent the organisms from reaching a water supply and thus spreading the disease. This constitutes a difficult problem because the bacteria are well protected by large quantities of organic material. The stool should be broken up and thoroughly mixed with a disinfectant, such as compound cresol† solution or household lye, and allowed to stand for thirty minutes or more.[3]

Surgical Instruments   Many surgical instruments would be injured by steam sterilization. Chemical sterilization of such instruments involves four steps: (1) thorough cleaning of the instrument to remove all blood and pus, (2) prolonged soaking in the disinfectant solution, (3) thorough rinsing in sterile water, and (4) drying under sterile conditions. A variety of chemicals will kill nonspore-forming bacteria under these conditions. However, the spore-forming tetanus organism (*Clostridium tetani*) can survive for eighteen hours or more in solutions of alcohol (70 per cent), cresol (5 per cent), Metaphen, Bard-Parker solution, and benzalkonium chloride (Zephiran).

Clinical Thermometers   A recent study reported by the Communicable Disease Center of the United States Public Health Service reveals that many methods used to disinfect thermometers are unsafe because they permit the survival of tubercle bacilli (*Mycobacterium tuberculosis*) and various mouth organisms. The method described below was found to be effective against bacteria commonly found in the mouth.‡

* Where there is a good municipal sewage disposal system which will insure the destruction disinfection may not be required.

† Compound cresol solution, 1 part to 10 parts of fecal material—or household lye, 1 heaping tablespoonful for each stool with enough water to cover.[3]

‡ This procedure is demonstrated in a film strip *Disinfection of Clinical Thermometers* produced and distributed by the Communicable Disease Center, United States Public Health Service, Atlanta, Georgia.

1. Wipe the thermometer carefully with a large pledget of dry cotton to remove mucus. Place the thermometer in a container provided for contaminated thermometers.

2. When all temperatures have been taken, cleanse each thermometer carefully with a solution composed of equal parts of alcohol (95 per cent) and green soap, using a large cotton pledget for the purpose.

3. Rinse the thermometer under cold running water to remove all soap.

4. Place thermometers in a tray; immerse thermometers completely in an alcohol-iodine solution (ethyl alcohol [70 per cent] and iodine [1 per cent] or isopropyl alcohol [70 per cent] and iodine [1 per cent]). Allow to stand for ten minutes.

5. Hold pan with thermometers and disinfectant under cold water tap. Permit a slow stream of water to float off the disinfectant solution.

6. Rinse thermometers carefully with running water. Dry with paper towel. Store in clean, covered container until needed.

SOME COMMON ANTISEPTIC AND DISINFECTANT SOLUTIONS

Acids and Alkalies   The chemistry student who has seen the effects of strong acids or bases on human skin will not be surprised to learn that they will destroy bacteria. Acids and alkalies inhibit the growth of most bacteria within the pH range below 5 and above 9. With mineral acids, the injurious effect is proportional to the hydrogen ions in solution. In the case of the organic acids, which do not ionize readily, the whole acid molecule seems to be toxic. In practice, acids and alkalies are seldom used, because they are injurious to tissues.

Alcohols   Ethyl alcohol has long been used as an antiseptic solution. Isopropyl alcohol, though less well known, is equally effective and has the advantage of being less volatile and cheaper. Both act by denaturing proteins and are unusually effective against tuberculosis organisms (*Mycobacterium tuberculosis*) found on mouth thermometers. (See page 157.) Against other organisms, ethyl alcohol (absolute— 95 to 99 per cent) is practically worthless as a germicide

Seventy per cent water solutions of ethyl alcohol are mildly antiseptic if continued for a long time. P. B. Price[4] reported that ethyl alcohol—70 per cent *by weight*—is much more effective than the usual solutions which are 70 per cent by volume. Ethyl alcohol and ether are useful in preparing skin for operation because they remove fatty substances which protect bacteria from contact with the disinfectant to be applied subseqently. Ethyl or isopropyl alcohol combined with iodine has been recommended for the disinfection of mouth thermometers. (See page 163.)

Two of the higher alcohols, triethylene glycol and propylene glycol, are being used experimentally for disinfecting air.

Surface-Active Agents   Surface-active agents disrupt cell membranes by combining with proteins and lipids. These agents migrate to and accumulate on the surface of bacterial cells because they contain a water-soluble group (hydrophilic) and a water-insoluble group (hydrophobic). The initial contact changes the permeability of cell membranes. Further injury is produced when the chemical enters the cell and combines with enzymes and other cell proteins. The surface-active agents include the phenols, cresols, soaps, and the anionic and cationic detergents.

PHENOL AND CRESOLS   Like other surface-active agents, phenol and cresol injure the membrane of the bacterial cell. In addition they inactivate enzymes and denature proteins. Phenol (carbolic acid), an effective disinfectant in 5 per cent solution, kills vegetative cells quickly. The cresols are close relatives and are more effective germicides than phenol. As they are insoluble in water, they are usually used mixed with soap solution—compound cresol solution, 2 to 5 per cent. Both phenol and cresol are relatively effective in the presence of organic matter.

SOAPS   Soaps have some germicidal power, but their influence varies with different organisms. For example, many gram-positive and acid-fast organisms tend to be inhibited by the action of soaps. However, *Micrococcus pyogenes* (gram-positive skin organism) and the gram-negative organisms are resistant to its action. Although soap has some germicidal power, the time allowed for its action is frequently too short to kill the organisms present. Its chief value lies in its effect as a mechanical agent which, with the aid of friction, removes bacteria from contaminated hands and utensils. Hot water increases the efficiency of cleaning with soap. Germicidal soaps have little value because of the brief period in which they are in contact with the organisms.

DETERGENTS   In recent years many synthetic detergents have been developed. These fall into two groups: the *cationic* and the *anionic*. In the anionic detergents the anion (negatively charged group) is the detergent part of the molecule, while in the cationic detergents the cation (positively charged group) contains the water-insoluble group (hydrophobic). Anionic detergents are effective against gram-positive bacteria but not against the gram-negative. Soaps and anionic detergents are commonly used as cleansing agents.

Cationic detergents in aqueous solutions are effective against both gram-positive and gram-negative bacteria but are not active against tuberculosis organisms (*Mycobacterium tuberculosis*). Most cationic detergents are effective in alkaline solutions. They are inactivated by fats, proteins, soaps, and anionic detergents. Cationic detergents in common use include: alkyldimethylbenzyl ammonium chloride (Roccal, Zephiran) and cetyl pyridinium bromide and cetyl trimethyl ammonium chloride.

Oxidizing Agents   Oxidizing agents combine with and inactivate enzyme proteins. In some instances this combination merely prevents cell activity (bacteriostatic action) while in others it causes the death of the cell (bacteriocidal action). The oxidizing agents used as disinfectants include: hydrogen peroxide, iodine, chlorine, and the salts of heavy metals such as mercury and silver.

HYDROGEN PEROXIDE   Hydrogen peroxide in a 3 per cent solution is a mild, harmless antiseptic which is rapidly decomposed by an enzyme produced by human beings and also by many bacteria. It is not very effective, especially in the presence of organic matter.

IODINE   Iodine rapidly kills both gram-positive and gram-negative bacteria. It is widely used as a skin disinfectant but has the disadvantage of blistering when moisture is present.

It is effective as a disinfectant of drinking water and has been recommended in combination with alcohol for disinfecting clinical thermometers. (See page 163.)

CHLORINE   This is a useful disinfectant for water that is used for drinking and for swimming pools.

SALTS OF HEAVY METALS   Although virtually all salts in *sufficiently* low concentrations appear to stimulate the growth of bacteria, the same salts in higher concentrations will inhibit or kill bacteria. Unlike other cells, most bacteria are very resistant to changes in osmotic pressure. The chlorides of sodium and potassium are relatively harmless, while the salts of the heavy metals, such as silver and mercury, are toxic. The bivalent salts of the heavy metals are usually more toxic than the monovalent; for example, bichloride of mercury (mercuric chloride, $HgCl_2$) is more toxic than mercurous chloride (calomel, $HgCl$). These salts combine with the SH of the enzyme proteins thus causing the enzyme to become inactive.

$$HgCl_2 + enzyme \begin{cases} S\text{-}H \\ S\text{-}H \end{cases} \xrightarrow{\quad} \xleftarrow{\quad} enzyme \begin{cases} S \\ Hg \\ S \end{cases} + 2HCl$$

mercuric chloride	active enzyme	inactive enzyme	+ hydrochloric acid

Since this action is reversible, bacterial cells are likely to survive contacts with solutions of heavy metals for considerable periods of time. High concentrations and prolonged exposure will bring about irreversible changes resulting in the death of the cell.

Mercury compounds are highly effective bacteriostatic agents which combine with bacterial proteins and prevent multiplication of the organisms. Laboratory experiments have shown that it is possible to revive bacteria after long contacts with mercury compounds. One should therefore question statements to the effect that *mercuric chloride* (1:500 or 1:2000) will kill bacteria in a few minutes. The organisms will eventually die, but probably not in a few minutes or even in a few hours. Mercuric chloride has no special affinity for bacterial protein, but combines readily with any protein. Therefore the presence of body fluids or excreta markedly decreases its efficiency. The drug has several other disadvantages: namely, it is very poisonous to man, it is irritating to tissues, and it corrodes metals. Chemists have worked for years to develop mercury compounds that are nontoxic and nonirritating. As a result, a number of complex organic compounds of mercury, such as merbromin (Mercurochrome), Merthiolate, and Metaphen, have appeared on the market.

Merbromin (*Mercurochrome*), *Metaphen,* and *Merthiolate* are commonly overrated. Well-controlled laboratory tests show that these compounds are more toxic for embryonic tissues and for white blood cells than they are for *Micrococcus pyogenes* (*Staphylococcus aureus*). Furthermore, cultures of virulent streptococci exposed for ten minutes to merbromin, 2 per cent; Merthiolate, 1:1000; or to Metaphen, 1:500, were still capable of causing fatal streptococcus infections in mice. The results indicate that these compounds are not germicidal, nor are they sufficiently antiseptic to prevent streptococcus infections in mice.[5]

Silver nitrate and the organic compounds of silver—Argyrol and strong protein silver (Protargol)—are used as disinfectants for mucous membranes of the eyes, nose, and throat. They are effective against bacteria, but are also injurious to body tissues.

Dyes   Many coal-tar dyes used to stain bacteria will also inhibit or kill them by uniting with cell proteins. Basic dyes are usually more effective than acid dyes. In general, the gram-negative bacteria such as the colon bacillus and the typhoid organisms are more resistant than are those that take Gram's stain. For example, methyl violet or gentian violet, 1:1,000,000 to 1:5,000,000, will prevent the growth of gram-positive organisms, the micrococci (staphylococci) and streptococci, but do not inhibit colon bacilli. The fact that dyes are rapidly adsorbed on plasma proteins and tissues limits their usefulness as bacteriocidal agents.

Miscellaneous Compounds   A variety of substances recently discovered have proved of value in combating bacterial infections. These include numerous antibiotics and the synthetic drugs such as the sulfonamides and isonicotinic acid compounds. These will be discussed in Chapter 18.

SUMMARY

1. Microorganisms can be controlled or destroyed by introduction of toxic agents into the surrounding medium.

2. Disinfection is a gradual process which requires time. The effectiveness of any disinfectant solution is influenced by many variables such as time, temperature, the presence or absence of body fluids, the concentration of the drug, the amount of water present, and the pH of the medium.

3. Bacterial spores are more resistant than vegetative cells. Likewise, bacteria in organic material are more resistant than those in water or in a saline solution. Bacterial cells present in dried material are more difficult to destroy than moist cells. The same disinfectant may vary greatly in its effectiveness toward different species of bacteria.

4. Disinfection procedures should be planned to secure a large measure of safety by providing adequate contact between the bacteria and the chemical agent.

5. Many disinfectants are unsuitable for use on body surfaces because they injure human cells as well as bacteria.

REFERENCES

1. Smith, R. C.: Alcohol as a Disinfectant against the Tubercle Bacillus. Pub. Health Rep., *62:* 1285–1295, 1947.
2. Burrows, W.: Jordan-Burrows Textbook of Bacteriology. 15th ed. Philadelphia, W. B. Saunders Co., 1949, p. 77.
3. McCulloch, E. C.: Disinfection and Sterilization. 2d ed. Philadelphia, Lea & Febiger, 1945, p. 422.
4. Price, J. B.: Ethyl Alcohol as a Germicide. Arch. Surg., *38:* 528–542, 1939.
5. Morton, H. E., and others: The Bacteriostatic and Bactericidal Actions of Some Mercurial Compounds on Hemolytic Streptococci. J.A.M.A., *136:* 37–41, 1948.

SUPPLEMENTARY READINGS

BOOKS:

Davis, B. D.: Principles of Sterilization. In Dubos, R. J.: Bacterial and Mycotic Infections of Man. 2d ed. Philadelphia, J. B. Lippincott Co., 1952.
Salle, A. J.: Fundamental Principles of Bacteriology. 3d ed. New York, McGraw-Hill Book Co., 1948.
Smith, D. T., and Conant, N. F.: Zinsser's Textbook of Bacteriology. 10th ed. New York, Appleton-Century-Crofts, Inc., 1952.

Walter, C. W.: The Aseptic Treatment of Wounds. New York, The Macmillan Co., 1948.

Wyss, O.: Chemical Factors Affecting Growth and Death. in Werkman, C. H., and Wilson, P. W.: Bacterial Physiology. New York, Academic Press, Inc., 1951.

PERIODICALS:

Frobisher, M., and Sommermeyer, L.: A Study of the Effect of Alcohols on Tubercle Bacilli and Other Bacteria in Sputum. Am. Rev. Tuberc., *68:* 419–424, 1953.

Gershenfeld, L., and others: Disinfection of Clinical Thermometers. J. Am. Pharm. A. (Scient. Ed.), *40:* 457–460, 1951.

Notter, L. E.: Disinfection of Clinical Thermometers. Nursing Outlook, *1:* 569–571, 1953.

Price, P.: The Meaning of Bacteriostasis, Bacteriocidal Effect, and Rate of Disinfection. Ann. New York Acad. Sci., *53:* 76–90, 1950.

Robinson, E.: Quaternary Ammonium Compounds—What Are They? The Sanitarian, *13:* 49–55, 1950.

Sommermeyer, L., and Frobisher, M.: Laboratory Studies on Disinfection of Oral Thermometers. Nursing Research, *1:* 32–35, 1952.

Sommermeyer, L., and Frobisher, M.: Laboratory Studies on Disinfection of Rectal Thermometers. Nursing Research, *2:* 85–89, 1953.

Suggested Laboratory Experience for Unit II

A. Favorable Temperature for Growth

THE DETERMINATION of the optimum temperature for the growth of any organism requires considerable equipment, but the effects of some of the temperatures that favor growth can easily be demonstrated.

EXPERIMENT A

Materials: One or more of the following cultures:
> *Escherichia coli*
> *Micrococcus pyogenes* (*Staphylococcus aureus*)
> *Bacillus subtilis*
> *Proteus vulgaris*
> Slants of sterile agar

Method:
1. Label tubes 1, 2, 3, date, name of organism.
2. Inoculate tubes 1, 2, 3, with the test organism selected.
3. Incubate tube 1, in the icebox; 2, at room temperature; 3, at 37° C. (98.6° F.).
4. Observe at the end of 24 and 48 hours; record results.

EXPERIMENT B

Materials: Tubes of raw or pasteurized milk (1, 2, 3).
Method:
1. Label tubes as indicated above.
2. Incubate tubes 1, in the icebox; 2, at room temperature; 3, at 37° C. (98.6° F.).
3. Observe in 24 and 48 hours.
4. Have any changes occurred? Explain. Conclusions? Recommendations for storing milk?

EXPERIMENT C

Materials: 3 tubes containing 1 gm. of powdered milk, flour or dehydrated eggs
> Sterile water and pipettes or teakettle containing cool boiled water

Method:
1. To tubes 1, 2, add about 10 cc. of sterile water, to tube 3 add nothing.

2. Incubate tube 1 at 37° C. (98.6° F.); incubate tube 2 at room temperature, incubate tube 3 at room temperature.

EXPERIMENT D

Materials: 1 pkg. commercially frozen fruit or vegetable (keep in freezing unit until ready for use)

Sterile knives or forceps

3 sterile containers with covers—1, 2, 3

Method:

1. Using a hot knife or forceps transfer a small piece of the food to each container. Cover. Label.
2. Replace unused portion in freezing unit at once.
3. Place container 1 in the icebox (not in the freezing compartment); 2 at room temperature; 3 at 37° C. (98.6° F.).
4. Observe the appearance of the three samples in 24 and 48 hours. Compare with the portion which remained in the freezing unit. Make smears from samples, 1, 2, and 3. Stain with methylene blue. Observe with oil-immersion lens.

Comment on the results obtained in these experiments. Do these observations confirm the statements found in text and reference books regarding the influence of environment on bacteria? What practical applications can be made?

B. *Thermal Death Time*

The destruction of bacteria is a complex process. The kind of bacterium, the kind of environment, and the time that any agent acts, are all important variables. The expression "thermal death time" emphasizes two important factors in the killing of bacteria.

EXPERIMENT

Materials: 7 tubes of 1 cc. of 1:100 dilution *Bacillus subtilis** in broth

7 tubes of 1 cc. of 1:100 dilution of *Micrococcus pyogenes* (*Staphylococcus aureus*) or other nonspore-former in broth (cultures to be placed in bottom of tube with a pipette, without touching the side of the tube)

14 sterile petri dishes

14 tubes melted agar

Autoclave

Oven

* Preferably a seventy-two-hour culture.

Waterbaths, 60°, 70°, and 99° C. (140°, 158°, and 210.2° F.) (pans or beakers may be used)

Unsterile tube containing 1 cc. water for temperature control

Thermometer

Method:

A. Control of temperature in waterbath.
   1. Heat waterbath to 60° C. (140° F.) (or 70° C. or 80° [158° or 176° F.] or boiling).
   2. Place in the waterbath at the same time the tube of culture and the tube containing thermometer in 1 cc. of water. Notice when the temperature of the water reaches the desired point.
   3. Heat for 2, 5, or 10 minutes as directed.

B. General directions:
   1. Label tubes.
   2. Heat tube 1 in the autoclave (121° C.), tube 2 in the oven (dry heat—121° C.), tube 3 in boiling water (temperature inside tube approximately 99° C.), tube 4 in waterbath at 80° C., tube 5 in waterbath at 70° C., and tube 6 in waterbath at 60° C.; tube 7, the control, do not heat.
   3. Pour the contents of tubes into appropriately labeled petri dishes. Cover with melted agar approximately 45° C. (113° F.). Allow to solidify. Invert and incubate at 37° C. (98.6° F.) or room temperature. Observe in 24 hours and also after 1 week. (Watch for air contaminants.)
   4. Record results.
   5. Any unusual or unexpected results? Can these be explained? Are spore-formers and nonspore-formers equally resistant? Do these results confirm the statements found in textbooks? How can the results of these experiments be applied to nursing practice?

EXPERIMENT

Materials: 4 blunt forceps (sterile)

Culture of *Micrococcus pyogenes* (*Staphylococcus*) in shallow container

Waterbaths 50° C., 70° C., and 100° C. (122°, 158°, and 212° F.)

Agar plates

Method:
   1. Contaminate the end of the forceps by dipping it ½ inch below the surface of the culture, allow to dry for 1 minute.

2. Heat forceps no. 1 for 1 minute ⎫
         no. 2 for 2 minutes ⎬ at 50° C., 70° C., or 100° C.
         no. 3 for 5 minutes ⎪
         no. 4 for 10 minutes ⎭

3. Inoculate ¼ of a sterile agar plate by streaking the forceps gently over the surface of the agar. *Label with care.*

4. Incubate for 48 hours, observe and record results.

5. What are the limitations of this experiment? Conclusions? Significance of the observations? How should the equipment used for this experiment be sterilized?

C. The Effect of Drying

Drying in air increases the death rate of bacteria. As would be expected, different species differ in their ability to resist drying.

EXPERIMENT

Materials: Culture of *Escherichia coli* (dilute 1:100 or 1:1000) in broth or milk

Culture of *Bacillus subtilis* (dilute 1:100 or 1:1000) in broth or milk

10 petri dishes

10 tubes of melted agar

Method:

1. Place a loopful of *Escherichia coli* in the center of each of five sterile petri dishes (1, 2, 3, 4, 5); spread smear to the size of a dime. Repeat using *Bacillus subtilis* for plates 6 to 10.

2. (a) Use plates 1 and 6 for controls by covering with melted agar without drying. Incubate 48 hours at 37° C. (98.6° F.).

   (b) Store plates 2 to 10 as follows:

   2 and   7—dry at room temperature for 2 days ⎫ Cover with
   3 and   8—dry at room temperature for 4 days ⎪ m e l t e d
   4 and   9—dry at room temperature for 6 days ⎬ agar. Incu-
   5 and 10—dry at room temperature for 8 days ⎪ bate at 37°
                                                  ⎭ C.   (98.6° F.)

3. When plates have been incubated for 48 hours, record the number of colonies. Preserve plates in a cool place until the experiment is completed.

4. Study the results.

5. Is drying equally effective against the two test organisms?

Would you expect the results to be the same if the bacteria had been dried in a vacuum or in an atmosphere of nitrogen?

SUPPLEMENTARY READINGS

Salle, A. J.: Fundamental Principles of Bacteriology. 3d ed. New York, McGraw-Hill Book Co., 1948.
Salle, A. J.: Laboratory Manual on Fundamental Principles of Bacteriology. 3d ed. New York, McGraw-Hill Book Co., 1948.

Unit III   PARASITES
AND THE HOST

LIVING THINGS fall into two fairly distinct groups: those that are capable of maintaining an independent existence and those that cannot live apart from other forms of life but are directly dependent upon them for shelter and food. The latter are called *parasites* and their characteristic mode of life is referred to as *parasitism*. The animal or plant supporting them is called the *host*. Many parasites are relatively harmless while others produce disease and still others may be of benefit to the host. Harmless parasites are commonly called *commensals* and their way of life *commensalism* (eating together). Many of the organisms which live in the gastrointestinal tract of man or animals are in fact commensals sharing the food of the host. A parasite that contributes to the welfare of its host is called a *symbiont* and its way of life *symbiosis* (living together). Symbiotic organisms within the intestine of man synthesize vitamin B and secrete enzymes which digest fibers (cellulose) of fruits and vegetables. Grazing animals such as the sheep

177

and the cow depend entirely upon enzymes secreted by yeasts, bacteria, and protozoa to digest the cellulose of the food they eat. In contrast, many parasites may be potentially harmful although they may be present at times without injury to the host. Since it is difficult to determine with certainty the exact relationship of a particular organism to a healthy host, there is a tendency to use the word parasite to describe any organism that characteristically lives in or on a host.

In order to understand parasitism as a mode of life, it seems advisable to consider all types of living forms which show parasitic tendencies. Heretofore, the descriptions of structure and of the life activities of living forms were confined solely to microorganisms and dealt with only the protozoa, molds, yeasts, and bacteria that live in the soil or decaying matter. Many similar protozoa and fungi are adapted to living as parasites within the body of a living plant or animal. In addition, there are still smaller organisms called rickettsias and viruses that habitually live as parasites. These unique organisms and their characteristics will be discussed in some detail. Parasitism as a mode of life is characteristic of many microorganisms and also of some relatively large forms, including certain worms and arthropods, such as lice, ticks, and fleas. Since the mode of life is essentially the same for parasites both large and small, the multicellular organisms will be mentioned from time to time even though they cannot be classified with the microorganisms.

The word parasite is derived from two Greek words meaning *beside food*. In reality, the parasite has solved its food problem by living in or on the body of a living animal or plant. Its behavior differs from that of the animal of prey in that the parasite derives its food from an organism larger than itself, whereas the latter devours smaller animals. Most living forms, including some parasites, serve as hosts for other living forms that differ widely in character and in the degree of their dependence. Many parasites are essentially commensals or food robbers, living as saprophytes in body secretions or other dead material. As would be expected, these hardy organisms are well equipped with enzymes for utilizing food, and grow readily on a wide variety of laboratory media; others grow reluctantly or not at all outside of the animal body. In fact, this dependence may be so highly developed that a certain organism is restricted to life within one species or even to a single organ of one host. For example, the bacteria that live in the human nose and mouth usually cannot grow in the intestine; those that are adapted to the human body are usually unsuited to living within dogs and cats. In other words, parasites are specialists with very definite growth requirements that can be met by only a small number of hosts. As a rule, they produce few enzymes for digesting food, since they live in areas where simple nutrients are readily available.

Many parts of the living body encourage the growth of microorganisms by supplying food, moisture, warmth, and a medium that is approximately neutral in reaction. Parasites are constantly present in the intestine and on the skin and mucous membranes of the nose, mouth, and genitalia. The colon of the average mammal is populated with a great collection of round worms, flat worms, protozoa, and bacteria; that of man always contains great numbers of bacteria and some protozoa and worms. The latter are likely to be numerous in people who live where sanitation is primitive. Many bacteria are always present in the mouth, a smaller number in the nares, and only a very few on the eye. Although the blood stream, the internal organs, and the interior of individual cells are usually free from parasites, these too are sometimes invaded by them.

TYPES OF PARASITES

Dependent organisms vary greatly in size, structure, and behavior. All are alike, however, in that each obtains food or shelter, or both, from another living organism.

Arthropods   Bloodsucking organisms are distinctly parasitic in their food habits. Some of them, such as mosquitoes and flies, live apart from the host except at feeding time, while others, such as fleas and lice, remain in the fur or hair of the larger animals where they mature, mate, and lay eggs. Since the former have wings and the latter are equipped with legs, both are quite capable of migrating from one animal to another. Certain arthropods carry parasites (bacteria, protozoa, rickettsias, or viruses) that cause disease in man and animals.

Worms   Most worms that are dependent upon other organisms are adapted to life within the intestinal tract. As a rule, they are ingested as microscopic eggs and develop into the mature forms in the intestine. As an adaptation to parasitism, these organisms often possess no digestive system, an unnecessary structure for an animal surrounded by food that is ready for use. Although some are sexually differentiated and others contain both male and female organs within the same animal, all produce enormous numbers of eggs, which leave the body in the feces. The many species vary in size from minute organisms to roundworms that are from 6 to 8 inches in length or the tapeworms which attain a length of several feet.

Other worms migrate to skeletal muscle or to the blood vessels of the bladder, intestines, or liver. Infection with worms often disturbs body function of the host by producing injury at the portal of entry or exit, or in the deeper tissues. Such injury may be the result of (1) mechanical trauma, (2) obstruction of hollow organs or circulatory channels, (3) utilization of food, (4) depletion of blood, (5) toxin formation, or (6) displacement of tissues. A warm climate and the use of raw foods and untreated water favor the survival and transfer of many worm parasites.

Protozoa   Protozoan parasites are one-celled organisms which live as individuals, not as colonies. Some fifty-six species are capable of causing disease in man or animals. Most forms are actively motile and are therefore capable of foraging for solid food which they ingest and digest. They usually obtain energy by anaerobic respiration, although they are capable of living in the presence of oxygen. They commonly inhabit the blood, lymph, intestinal, or genitourinary systems of the host. Those that live in the blood require a second host—a blood-sucking arthropod which transfers parasites from one host to another. Certain protozoa are thought to produce toxins, but as yet such toxins have not been isolated.

Fungi   Some of the yeasts and molds are capable of living as parasites. In structure, they resemble the free-living fungi. However, many of them resemble both yeasts and molds since they develop spherical yeastlike cells at one stage of growth and a threadlike network, or mycelium, at other times. Parasitic fungi are usually transmitted to their hosts by direct or indirect contact or by inhalation. Some fungi attack superficial structures such as the skin, hair, and nails, causing low-grade chronic disease. These infections may be the source of discomfort, but they seldom endanger life. Other fungi invade the lungs or other viscera. These infections also are chronic in nature, but they tend to progress slowly until they eventually cause death. Fungous diseases are more common in the tropics than in regions with a temperate climate.

Parasitic Bacteria   In contrast, many bacteria are well adapted to living in the human body and are found in varying numbers on body surfaces, in secretions, and excretions. Most parasitic bacteria remain outside of cells (extracellular) living in secretions or excretions of the host. Some disease-producing organisms (those which cause typhoid fever, undulant fever, and tuberculosis) characteristically grow within cells. Some grow well in blood and lymph of internal organs when they are introduced into those areas. For example, a gunshot wound in the abdomen permits intestinal bacteria to enter and to grow in the body cavity, which is usually sterile. Likewise, a wound in the skin or mucous membrane makes possible the entry of bacteria from the outside. Microorganisms that live in the body, with few exceptions, do not form spores and are therefore not difficult to kill. As a rule, parasitic bacteria produce fewer enzymes than free-living organisms and hence are limited in the foods they utilize. Whereas free-living organisms produce all the enzymes required to carry on life processes, parasites depend upon the host to supply growth factors such as essential amino acids and vitamins. When pathogenic bacteria grow within the host, they produce metabolic products which cause direct injury to body cells. The body responds to this injury by a complex reaction called *inflammation,* which will be discussed in detail in Chapter 13.

Rickettsias   Rickettsias are minute cells ($0.3-0.5$ x 0.3μ) that look like small rods or cocci; they are commonly found *within* the cells of an arthropod or other animal host. These organisms are very fastidious in their requirements, since they grow only within living cells and usually only in one type of living cell. They differ from bacteria in that they do not produce the necessary enzymes which would enable them to grow on artificial media. They are, therefore, difficult to culture. When suitable methods are used, they will grow in laboratory animals (arthropods, mice, or guinea pigs) or in the cells of a developing chick embryo. After a fertile egg has been incubated for several days, the rickettsias can be introduced into the egg through a window cut in the shell; there they grow as incubation continues. Many rickettsias have been observed within the cells of fleas, lice, and ticks, and appear to be so well adjusted that they do not injure the host even when present in large numbers. These same organisms, when they are transferred to the human host may, however, cause serious disease, e.g., typhus or Rocky Mountain spotted fever.

Viruses   Viruses, sometimes called filtrable viruses, are particles so small ($0.01-0.25\mu$ or 10–250 millimicrons in diameter) that they pass through filters fine enough to remove most bacteria. Most viruses are too small to be seen with the light microscope (magnification from 1000 to 2000 times), but pictures taken with the aid of the electron microscope show them to be spheres or rods. The smaller viruses resemble protein molecules and apparently produce no enzymes and carry on no metabolic activities, although they enter into and modify the metabolism of the host cell. The larger viruses do produce some enzymes, and in composition and organization are like bacterial cells. Like the rickettsias, they lack the enzyme systems which would enable them to grow on artificial media, but most will grow in the living cells of a laboratory animal, or of a chick embryo. They may also be induced to grow in tissue cultures consisting of animal cells growing in a sterile nutrient medium. As viruses multiply within cells, they either stimulate the invaded cells to proliferate or they induce changes which result in destruction of those cells. When certain viruses are present, small round or oval masses called *inclusion bodies* appear within the cytoplasm or nucleus of the cell. Inclusion bodies are often larger than bacteria and can readily be seen through the microscope. Although their exact na-

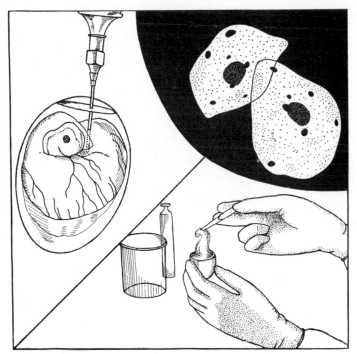

Figure 37   Diagram showing inoculation of a chick embryo with rickettsias or viruses (*left*). The collection of the embryo after rickettsias or viruses have grown within it (*right*). Two epithelial cells showing numerous inclusion bodies (*inset*). (Redrawn from Therapeutic Notes, Parke, Davis & Co.)

ture has not been determined, it is thought that they may consist of masses of virus particles. As invisible bacteria form visible colonies, so viruses, too small to be seen through the microscope, may form masses that are large enough to be seen when magnified 1000 times. Viruses are important because they often cause disease in the host.

For convenience, viruses may be placed in three groups: (1) those which invade plant cells, (2) those which invade animal cells, and (3) those which attack bacterial cells. Viruses can be separated from bacteria and cell fragments by filtration.

FILTRATION   Filters of porous, unglazed porcelain or fine clay (diatomaceous earth) remove bacteria and larger particles from a suspension.

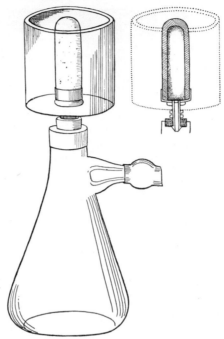

Figure 38   The Berkefeld filter. (The inset shows the internal structure of the filter.) The fluid to be filtered is placed in the upper chamber of the sterile Berkefeld filter. In response to gentle negative pressure applied on the side arm by means of a water-suction pump, the fluid passes through the filter into the flask, leaving the bacteria on the filter. Viruses, if present, will pass through the filter into the filtrate.

Such filters are in no sense simple sieves, since they sometimes hold back bacteria that are smaller than the pores of the filter. It is thought that electrical charges are responsible for this. Since bacteria in a suspension carry a negative charge and the filters a positive charge, the bacteria are attracted to and held on the surface of the porcelain, while the fluid passes into the collecting flask. (See Figure 38.) It is often desirable to hasten filtration by using gentle negative pressure supplied by a water-suction pump, because prolonged filtration may permit bacteria to grow through the pores; excessive pressure should not be used lest it force microorganisms into the filtrate. Such filters may be used to sterilize fluids that will be injured by heat, and are especially valuable as a means of obtaining viruses free from bacteria.

BACTERIOPHAGE   Bacteriophages are virus particles which are capable of multiplying within young bacterial cells and thus causing their disintegration. (See Figure 39.) Bacteriophages are commonly present in old cultures of bacteria and in sewage, and may be obtained by filtration. Sewage filtrates when tested with various cultures of bacteria often exhibit the ability to lyse or dissolve young bacterial cells. The potency of a phage (bacteriophage) obtained in this way can be increased by day-by-day transfer to fresh cultures of susceptible bacteria. The addition of bacteriophage to an eight-hour culture causes the bacterial cells to dissolve and disappear, but old cultures are immune to this action. The inoculation of an agar plate with organisms and the specific bacteriophage leads to the formation of ragged colonies that have a moth-eaten appearance. (See Figure 40.)

Bacteriophages are sometimes used in the treatment of diseases, such as cholera, bacillary dysentery, and wound infections. Their usefulness, however, is definitely limited because they are seldom effective against more than a few strains of an organism. Because bacteriophages are highly specific in their action, they can be used to distinguish between different strains within a species of bacteria which in all other respects appear to be identical.

THE NATURE OF VIRUSES   There is no general agreement as to the nature of viruses. Some investigators consider them the smallest and the most fastidious of parasites, since they grow only within actively growing cells, and in fact may be restricted to only one type of cell. Like bacteria, they may be present without producing visible injury, but generally they are potentially harmful. In fact, some viruses, such as the virus that causes cold sores (*herpes labialis*), are thought to remain in the host's tissues indefinitely, causing chronic or recurrent symptoms. There is some evidence that cells invaded by viruses are so changed that they synthesize virus protein instead of cell proteins.

Tissues which are invaded by viruses (if capable of multiplying) respond by cell growth or proliferation (for example, warts, rabbit papilloma), or by degeneration with or without complete destruction of the cell or by a combination of cell growth and cell degeneration. In cells that cannot multiply, for example in nerve cells, virus invasion causes cell destruc-

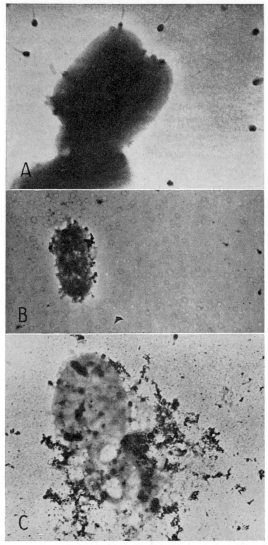

Figure 39   Bacteriophage particles and bacterial cells (*Escherichia coli*) as shown by the electron microscope (magnification 6000 to 22,000 times). A, Bacteriophages migrating toward the bacterial cells. B, Bacteriophages entering cell. C, Bacterial cell twenty minutes after the invasion by bacteriophages. Observe that the cell is completely disintegrated. (Courtesy, RCA Corporation.)

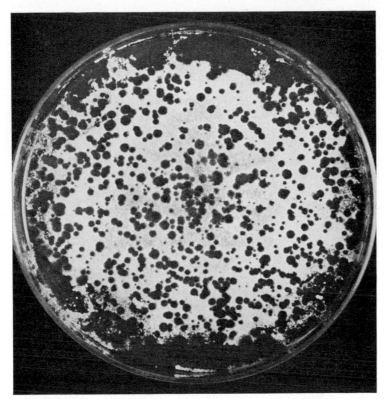

Figure 40   A culture of *Actinomyces griseus* which has been attacked by a specific phage. Note the motheaten character of the growth. (Woodruff, H. P., and Nunheimer, T. D.: J. Bact., 54.)

tion without evidence of cell growth. The cold sore, or fever blister, is a good example of virus activity. First there is inflammation characterized by redness, swelling, heat, and pain. This stage is followed by death of the superficial cells. A similar process is observed in smallpox and chickenpox, where the virus causes extensive destruction of epithelial cells. Obviously the character of a virus disease will depend upon the type of cells which are invaded and the extent of the damage done.

Viruses are adapted to living in specific tissues of the body. For example, the measles virus attacks the epithelial cells of the skin and mucous membranes, the yellow-fever virus grows in liver cells, and the poliomyelitis virus (infantile paralysis) invades nerve tissue. It has been suggested that these organisms are incomplete cells that require the enzymes of the host cell to enable them to grow and to reproduce, thus presenting an extreme degree of parasitism. Their method of reproduction is still in question. Some authorities hold that viruses divide by fission as do many bacteria. Others are sure that they break up into smaller fragments which recombine to form new virus particles. The subject is complicated by the fact that certain viruses that cause plant diseases, such as tobacco mosaic, have been crystallized without losing their ability to invade and multiply in living cells. Naturally the question arises, are viruses living organisms or are they nonliving particles that have some of the characteristics of living things? That question is hard to answer in terms of the accepted definitions of living and nonliving matter, which do not provide a place for borderline or intermediate forms. It is probable that the viruses consist of a large and varied group of organisms, ranging from organized cells that are essentially like bacteria to particles resembling the protein molecules of egg albumen or hemoglobin. For practical purposes, they may be considered as living parasites that behave like bacteria; that is, they enter and leave the host by the same routes. Futhermore, they can be destroyed by physical and chemical agents, although usually they are more resistant to drying and to disinfection with phenol, formaldehyde, and glycerin than the bacteria without spores. They are unique in that they multiply only when they are within active living cells.

LIFE PATTERNS

Entry and Exit   The preceding discussion has included some parasites that are relatively large (insects and worms), some that are microscopic (protozoa, molds, yeasts, bacteria, and rickettsias), and some that are ultramicroscopic (viruses). These diverse forms are alike in their need for a host; their success as parasites depends upon their ability to enter and to leave the body of a suitable host. Man commonly acquires new parasites through his contacts with other human beings, animal vectors, or inanimate materials. From these sources, parasites may be introduced by way of the mouth, the nose, the eyes, the genital tract, or the skin. Those parasites that enter through the mouth usually establish themselves in the digestive or respiratory tracts, and those entering through the skin may remain at the point of entry or spread to other areas. The site invaded depends to a large extent upon the kind of organism, because the latter often have growth requirements that are met by only a few tissues or organs. For example, both the measles virus and the pneumococcus enter the body through the respiratory tract, but the former causes extensive destruction of epithelial cells while the latter may grow in the nose, throat, or lungs.

Parasites usually escape from the host in body fluids or excretions: (1) saliva, sputum, or the secretions of the nose or eye; (2) feces, urine; (3) secretions or pus from lesions; and (4) blood. There are only a few exceptions to this rule; for example, certain intestinal worms, such as trichina and tapeworms, encyst in the muscles of the infected host and are transferred only when the meat is eaten by another animal.

Life Cycles   Though parasites may differ markedly in size and complexity of structure, they have certain common problems. To maintain their own life, they must reach a suitable host and migrate to an area where they can grow and reproduce. To maintain the life of the species, some of the offspring must escape from the host and reach a second host. The mechanisms by which different parasites solve this problem are numerous and varied. The stages in the development or maturing of any organism are spoken of as a *life cycle*. In the case of a parasite, the life cycle may take place within one or more animal forms.

Although most parasites depend upon passive transfer to reach a new host, a few show remarkable ability to migrate within the tissues of the host. The immature hookworm and the trichina actually burrow through the tissues. Life cycles of varying complexity are suggested by the following diagrams of the trichina, the hookworm, the malaria parasite, and the Chinese liver fluke.

(*a*) LIFE CYCLE OF THE TRICHINA

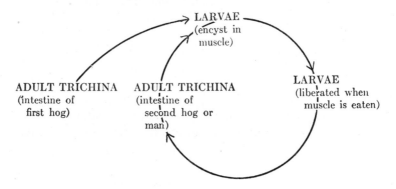

(*b*) LIFE CYCLE OF THE HOOKWORM

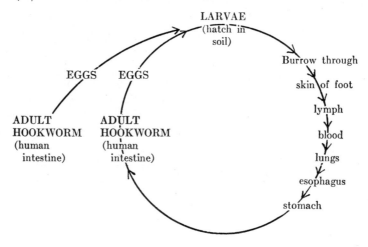

(*c*) Lɪꜰᴇ Cʏᴄʟᴇ ᴏꜰ ᴛʜᴇ Mᴀʟᴀʀɪᴀ Pᴀʀᴀsɪᴛᴇ

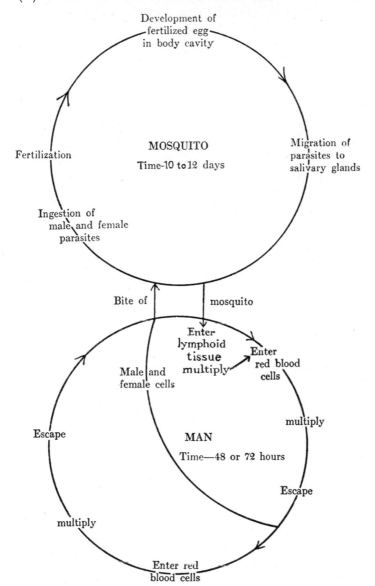

(*d*) Life Cycle of the Chinese Liver Fluke   This is
an example of a parasite dependent upon three different
species—man, snail, and fish.

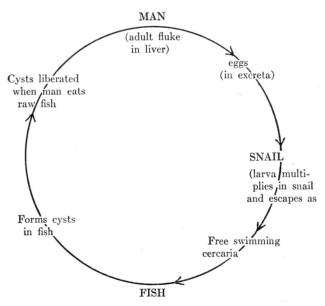

Examples of complex life cycles could be cited almost indefinitely; those of the animal parasites are often very complicated,
whereas the life pattern of fungi appears much simpler. One
unique example of effective parasitism occurs in the life of the
rickettsia which causes Rocky Mountain spotted fever. The
organism which lives in the tick invades the tick eggs before
they are laid and in this way the offspring of the tick is infected
generation after generation. As a rule, parasites depend upon
less direct and certain means of finding new hosts and the
hazards of transfer are offset by the production of tremendous
numbers of offspring.

PARASITES IN HUMAN HOSTS

Permanent Residents   Although before birth the body
is usually free from microorganisms, after birth its contact with
its environment brings bacterial parasites that promptly colo-
nize the virgin territory. These constitute the *normal flora* of the

body. The bacteria that inhabit the different regions of the body vary greatly in number and kind. Few are found on smooth surfaces of the skin or eye or in areas bathed by acid secretions (stomach, urinary tract, vagina). Many are found in the moist areas of the skin, mouth, nose, and pharynx. Most of these are relatively harmless and some may even be beneficial. The duodenum, like the stomach, is usually free from bacteria. The lower part of the small intestine contains intestinal cocci (enterococci) and colon bacteria (*Escherichia coli*). The large intestine supports a tremendous population of microorganisms, chiefly bacteria. It has been estimated that about one third of the weight of feces is due to the presence of dead and living bacteria. This bacterial population is extremely complex and varied, and changes its character in response to diet and other factors. It usually includes a large number of gram-positive and gram-negative organisms, both aerobic and anaerobic. The administration of certain antibiotics produces marked changes in the character of the bacterial flora. These changes are usually temporary. (See page 281.) Table 12 (page 194) lists some of the organisms commonly found on or in the human body.

Transients   Besides the normal bacterial flora on or in the human body, other more or less harmful organisms come and go without making the host aware of their presence. Sometimes, however, they disturb body functions and give rise to signs of disease or infection. The consequences following the entry of bacteria into the body will depend in part upon the *kind* of organisms, their *number* and their *disease-producing ability* or *virulence*.

Parasitism is definitely a two-way adjustment: the successful parasite must avoid destruction by the cells and secretions of the host; the host that is to survive must protect himself against the secretions of the invader. Often there develops a high degree of tolerance which permits both host and parasite "to live and to let live."

Bacteria are the most numerous parasites of man. Some are transient, others permanent residents appearing soon after birth and remaining through life. The latter may be termed *efficient parasites,* since they establish themselves without dis-

Table 12   PARASITES OF THE HEALTHY HUMAN BEING

AREA	ORGANISMS	RELATIVE NUMBER	REMARKS
Conjunctiva of the eyes	*Bacteria*—rods or cocci	Very few	Removed by constant washing of tears which are somewhat antiseptic
Skin	*Bacteria* Micrococci (Staphylococci) Diphtheroids	Many Few	Hands are often contaminated by organisms from the mouth, nose, soil
Mouth	*Bacteria* Micrococci (Staphylococci) Streptococci Diplococci Rods Spirilla Spirochetes *Amebas* (sometimes)	Very many	The number and kinds tend to increase with age of the person Saliva is mildly antiseptic for some organisms
Pharynx	*Bacteria* Micrococci (Staphylococci) Streptococci Pneumococci *Neisseria catarrhalis* Various rods	Many	
Nose	Same types as in pharynx	Few	Secretions are mildly antiseptic for some organisms
Stomach	No constant flora	Few or none Some organisms pass through	Gastric juice is acid (pH 1 to 2)
Duodenum	No constant flora	Few or none	
Jejunum and ileum	Enterococci Colon bacteria (*Escherichia coli*) Micrococci	Many	

Table 12—(*Continued*)

AREA	ORGANISMS	RELATIVE NUMBER	REMARKS
Large intestines	Sarcinae Lactobacilli Yeasts *Bacteria* Colon bacillus (*Escherichia coli*) Other gram-negative rods Gram-positive rods and Cocci	Millions	The colon has been called one large culture tube of microorganisms
	Yeasts, molds Protozoa Worms	Variable	Number and variety depend upon the sanitation of food and water

turbing the structure or function of the host. At times when resistance is lowered or when the external barrier is broken, some of these usually harmless organisms may invade the tissues and cause disease. Such bacteria have been called *opportunists.* Other organisms, called *pathogens,* are more likely to produce injury and call forth a response from the body of the host that is likely to end either in the death of the invaders or of the invaded. There is growing recognition that many factors contribute to the host's state of health or disease. The presence of the pathogen alone does not always result in disease. Other injurious agents or conditions (stress) commonly reinforce the action of the pathogen or set up conditions that enable organisms that are usually harmless to produce disease. (See Chapter 14.) The host's defenses and his response to pathogens will be discussed in Chapter 13.

SUMMARY

1. Parasitism as a way of life is so common that virtually all multicellular organisms serve as hosts for many dependent forms.

2. In size and structure, parasites vary from relatively large

complex insects and worms to unicellular fungi and protozoa and the still smaller organisms—the rickettsias and viruses. The latter represent an extreme degree of parasitism since they grow only within living cells.

3. Successful parasitism depends upon the ability of the smaller organism to reach a suitable host, multiply, and to produce offspring that in turn escape, and then reach another host. Certain organisms pass through very complicated cycles involving development in two or more hosts of different species.

4. Microorganisms differ in their ability to establish themselves temporarily or permanently in the human body and also in their power to produce disease.

SUPPLEMENTARY READINGS

BOOKS:

Burnet, F. M.: Virus as Organism. Cambridge, Mass., Harvard University Press, 1945.

Burrows, W.: Jordan-Burrows Textbook of Bacteriology. 15th ed. Philadelphia, W. B. Saunders Co., 1949.

Dubos, R.: The Bacterial Cell. Cambridge, Mass., Harvard University Press, 1946.

Dubos, R. (Ed.): Bacterial and Mycotic Infections of Man. 2d ed. Philadelphia, J. B. Lippincott Co., 1952.

Rivers, T. (Ed.): Viral and Rickettsial Infections of Man. 2d ed. Philadelphia, J. B. Lippincott Co., 1952.

Smith, D. T., and Conant, N. F.: Zinsser's Textbook of Bacteriology. 10th ed. New York, Appleton-Century-Crofts, Inc., 1952.

CHAPTER 13

Infection

DISEASE or infection may follow the entrance of microorganisms into the body. When this occurs, it is due to the interaction between the host cells and the parasite population. The consequences of such invasion depend upon the character of the organisms, the number of organisms, and the effectiveness of the host responses which protect against invasion and also the presence of other bacteria. For example, the invasion and destruction of cells by the influenza virus favors bacterial infection whereas the normal flora in the normal healthy nose and throat appears to discourage the growth of a variety of microorganisms. The throats of persons receiving penicillin are often colonized by the colon bacteria (*Escherichia coli*) and other gram-negative organisms. These organisms do not establish themselves when the normal flora is present. As in a military battle, when the defense is adequate, the invasion fails, but when the defense is weak and the invaders are both well equipped and numerous, the microorganisms win the first contest. The character and the severity of the resulting infection will depend upon the ability of the organisms to multiply freely, to disrupt body structure and function (*virulence*), and to spread from the original site (*invasiveness*).

PATHOGENS

Some parasites (pathogens) are so ill-adapted to life within the host that they injure the cells of the host. Injury to the host is incidental to the life processes of the parasite and is of no real value to the organism since it may destroy both host and parasites.

The prime requisite of a disease-producing organism (*pathogen*) is the ability to survive and multiply within the tissues of the host. Usually this means that the organisms must enter the body through a suitable portal of entry (skin, mouth, respiratory tract, genital organisms, blood). Failure to reach a suitable portal of entry commonly results in the death of the

197

organism. Just how invading organisms avoid destruction by the host is not fully known, but among bacteria, this ability is often associated with the secretion of polysaccharide capsular material. Some virulent bacteria produce discrete capsules which protect them against the host cells and secretions. There is some evidence that others may be protected by the presence of soluble capsular material which is excreted into the medium. Still others appear to resist body defenses because the bacterial cell contains substances which repel or destroy the body cells which engulf bacteria (*phagocytes*).

The entrance of the parasite into the tissues with subsequent colonization constitutes *infection*. When this occurs with little or no evidence of injury, it is known as a *latent* or *subclinical* infection. Often bacterial growth in the tissues is accompanied by evident injury resulting in obvious infection or disease. The contribution of the microorganisms to the disease process is always the same—injury to body cells. It is thought that bacteria may injure the cells of the host in one or more of the following ways:

1. By changing the fluid medium in which the cell lives.
   a. by competing with the cell for essential nutrients.
   b. by excreting relatively harmless substances which combine with enzymes or in other ways interfere with the metabolism of the cell.
2. By secreting substances which speed up or slow the life processes of the host cell.
3. By secreting enzymes or other substances which change cell structure as, for example, by changing permeability of cell membranes.

Some of the injurious substances produced by bacteria have been recognized and studied in the laboratory. They include filtrable substances (*exotoxins*) which are excreted from the cell, and poisonous substances forming an integral part of the bacterial cell and liberated only when the cell dies or is artificially broken (*endotoxins*).

Endotoxins   Endotoxins are found within the cells of virulent gram-negative bacteria. Endotoxins derived from different kinds of bacteria appear to be similar and are capable of poisoning a large variety of laboratory animals. An hour or two after injection with an endotoxin the animal develops tremors, difficult breathing, diarrhea, prostration, and sometimes paralysis. After death the body reveals widespread damage to capillary walls with evidence of hemorrhage and clotting. The endotoxins appear to cause direct injury to nerve tissue and to the thin walls of blood capillaries. In naturally occurring infections this action would be most pronounced at the stage when body cells were destroying large numbers of the invaders. Endotoxins are formed by the following organisms:

ENDOTOXIN-PRODUCING ORGANISM	DISEASE
Salmonella	Typhoid and typhoid-like infections
Shigella	Bacillary dysentery
Brucella	Undulant fever
Neisseria	Meningitis, gonorrhea

Exotoxins Exotoxins are, as a rule, secreted by gram-positive bacteria. They can be obtained by growing the bacteria in a nutrient broth and then removing the bacteria by filtration. The toxins contained in the filtrate are composed of proteins. Some can be denatured by heat, chemicals, and the action of proteolytic enzymes. Since chemically they resemble bland proteins such as egg white, their mode of action remains a mystery. It has been suggested that exotoxins may function as enzymes which attack some essential component of the animal cell or stop some essential process. For example, diphtheria toxin interferes with cell respiration and thus is capable of damaging all types of cells. Relatively few bacteria and certain viruses and rickettsias are known to produce exotoxins; they include the more pathogenic strains of the following organisms:

TOXIN-PRODUCING ORGANISM	DISEASE
Corynebacterium diphtheriae	Diphtheria
Clostridium botulinum	Botulism
Clostridium tetani	Tetanus
Clostridium perfringens	Gas gangrene
Micrococcus pyogenes	Wound infection
Streptococcus pyogenes	Wound infection
Shigella dysenteriae	Bacillary dysentery
Viruses	Influenza, psittacosis
Rickettsias	Various typhus infections

Some of the toxic secretions are called toxins, as, for example, diphtheria toxin, tetanus toxin. Others are described by their action or by a name which suggests what they do, as, for example:

(a) destroy white blood cells (*leukocidins*).

(b) destroy red blood cells (*hemolysins*).

(c) clot blood plasma (*coagulase*).

(d) dissolve the fibrin of clots (*fibrinolysin* or *streptokinase* and *streptodornase*).

(e) make the tissues more permeable to bacteria or their products (*spreading factor* or *hyaluronidase*).

It is unlikely that any one type of microorganism would produce all of the known injurious substances. Further study may prove that some of the substances listed are identical in character. In fact, toxin formation is variable even among bacteria of the same species. For instance, only a few strains of *Micrococcus pyogenes* var. *aureus* (*Staphylococcus aureus*) produce hemolysin* or fibrinolysin. Some exotoxins have the ability to combine with and destroy tissues of the nervous or circulatory systems, while others destroy phagocytes or red blood cells, or change the character of body tissues or fluids. The extent and the location of the damage partially determine the character of the disease produced. The signs of disease are, however, in large part the result of the defense processes of the host.

BODY DEFENSES

The preceding discussion has emphasized the activities of the invader and its ability to protect itself and to injure the host. It is well to remember that the prospective host is no passive victim.

In spite of the fact that body cells are essentially good nutrient medium, invasion of the internal structures of the body seldom occurs. There are many reasons for this. The body as a whole or a particular organ may fail to provide the conditions required for the growth of various microorganisms. For example, the body temperature may be too high or too low, an

---

* Hemolysins are sometimes named for the organism that produces them; as, for example, *streptolysin* is the toxin produced by a streptococcus, and *tetanolysin* is that produced by **Clostridium tetani**.

essential food substance may be lacking, or the oxygen content of the tissue may be too high or too low. In addition, the host has an active defense system designed to exclude microorganisms or to inactivate and destroy them once they have gained entrance. Body defenses are of three types: cellular barriers which exclude microorganisms, phagocytic cells, and protective substances in body fluids or tissues.

Cellular Barriers   The unbroken skin, the mucous membrane with its sticky secretion, and the various layers of connective tissue constitute mechanical barriers against bacterial invasion. (See Figure 41.) The epidermis, or outer skin, consists of many layers of scalelike epithelial cells, and its structure is such that the active growing cells are protected by an outer coat of dry, dead, toughened (cornefied) cells. Bacteria are constantly present in this nonliving portion of the skin, although some observers report an active germicidal action when certain pathogens are placed on the unbroken skin. Such action may be due in part to the effect of drying and to the action of the acid secretion (sweat). It is important to realize that the skin does not sterilize itself; micrococci and other organisms are constantly present and therefore may gain entrance through a break in the skin.

The mucous membranes are somewhat similar to the skin in structure except that the epithelial layer is much thinner. This tissue is bathed by a stringy, sticky fluid (mucus) that may serve as a mechanical barrier to bacteria. In the respiratory tract (posterior nares and trachea), the waving of hairlike cilia keeps the mucus moving toward the pharynx. Furthermore, wandering cells (phagocytes) capable of engulfing and destroying bacteria are normally present on these surfaces. These cells and the upward movement of the mucus propelled by the microscopic cilia are so effective in removing dust and bacteria that the lungs and trachea generally contain few microorganisms. The anterior portion of the nasal cavity too is kept remarkably free from bacteria by the combined action of hairs, mucus, cilia, and an enzyme (*lysozyme*) that destroys many common forms of bacteria. The grime which appears on the handkerchief for days after a visit to a smoky city gives evidence of the work of the cilia in removing larger particles

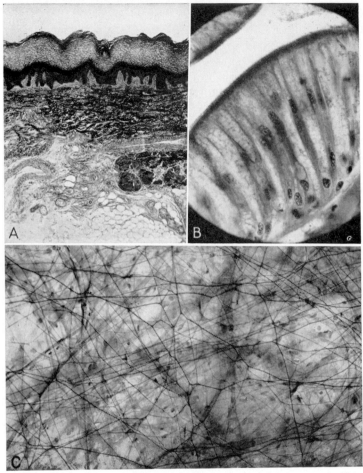

Figure 41   Cell walls protect against bacterial invasion. A, Skin;
B, Mucous membrane; C, Connective tissue. A, 70 ×; B, 400 ×; C,
85 ×. (Courtesy of General Biological Supply House, Chicago.)

from the nasal passages. It is now recognized that only small
particles (the size of a single bacterium, a mold spore, or a
virus particle) are likely to reach the tiny air sacs in the lungs.
Larger masses fall on the mucous coating and then are carried
upward and swallowed.

The connective tissues, made up of cells in a viscous matrix,
also constitute a further barrier to the penetration of bacteria

and their products. Certain bacteria overcome this obstacle by secreting spreading factor, a substance capable of digesting the jelly-like ground substance of the connective tissue. When this happens, the connective tissue serves as a pathway rather than a barrier.

In health, the urinary tract, except the urethra, is free from bacteria. The acid reaction of the urine and the outward flow of that excretion prevents deeper penetration. The vaginal secretions also are usually acid and effectively prevent the growth of all but a few species of bacteria.

In contrast, a large part of the digestive tube affords favorable conditions for parasitic life; the mouth, the ileum, and the colon support large bacterial populations, whereas the acid secretions of the stomach (pH from 1 to 2) and the duodenum (pH from 5.7 to 6) inhibit or kill many of the organisms which enter. Just how the thin mucous membrane of the intestine keeps the hordes of bacteria from penetrating its structure is not clear. It is known that wandering cells called macrophages (see page 217) are present and migrate freely through the intestinal wall. It is probable that they usually stop bacterial invasion. Occasionally they may actually transport pathogens such as the typhoid bacillus and the tuberculosis organism to the nearest lymph node where these organisms are capable of multiplying and producing disease. It is possible that a few bacteria do pass through the walls and are filtered out by the lymph nodes or the liver. Nevertheless, this wall is remarkably effective as long as the host is alive, but bacterial invasions of the tissues take place very promptly after death or perhaps just before. There is evidence to suggest that bacterial invasion causes the irreversible changes that lead to death. It is thought that poor circulation with lack of oxygen injures the intestinal wall so that it permits the intestinal flora to invade freely.

Protective   Cells   and   Fluids   Phagocytic   Cells The body is equipped with certain primitive cells called *phagocytes* that resemble amebas in that they ingest bacteria and other particles. Certain of these cells are actively motile, while others, called *fixed phagocytes,* are firmly attached to connective tissue or the endothelial cells lining the capillaries of the

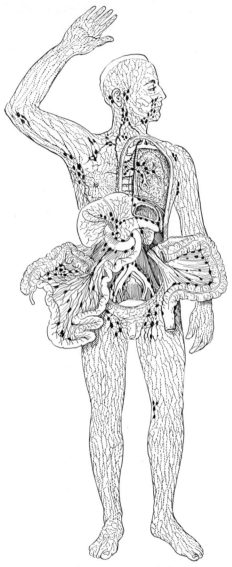

Figure 42   Diagram showing some of the important lymph nodes.

lymph nodes, spleen, liver, bone marrow, and lungs. The organs containing phagocytic cells belong to the *reticulo-endothelial* system. These constitute fixed or stationary defense organs that remove foreign bodies from the blood or lymph stream. The liver, spleen, and bone marrow serve as blood filters, while the lymph nodes remove bacteria and foreign bodies present in the lymph as it flows from the tissues toward the large veins. Lymph nodes are strategically distributed along the lymph channels in various parts of the body. (See Figure 42.) Some of the important lymph nodes and their locations are listed below. The fixed phagocytes are especially important in combating infection since they remove bacteria from the circulating fluids of the body, namely, the blood and lymph.

The motile cells consist of the granular leukocytes of the blood and the wandering cells of the connective tissue (histiocytes). The former are often called *microphages* (small phagocytes) in contrast to the larger wandering cells and the fixed phagocytes that are known as *macrophages*. Both are

LOCATION OF SOME OF THE LYMPH NODES	AREA SUPPLYING LYMPH TO NODES
Neck—Posterior cervical	Scalp
Anterior cervical	Head, nose, throat, sinuses
Deep	
Superficial	
Bronchial tree	Lungs
Popliteal space	Foot, leg
Groin—Superficial	Foot, leg, thigh
Deep	Pelvis
Anticubital space	Hand, forearm
Axilla	Hand, forearm, arm
	Chest wall, including breast
Mesentery	Intestines

active in removing foreign bodies including bacteria. Macrophages are active not only in engulfing and destroying bacteria but also in disposing of dead leukocytes and other cellular debris. (See Figure 47, page 218.) Furthermore, they take an active part in the repair of tissues during the healing process. Following an injury, the motile leukocytes increase in number, leave the tissue spaces and blood vessels, and migrate to the site of injury where they surround and engulf invading bacteria. This migration is apparently a response to chemical stimuli given off by injured body cells and invading bacteria; microorganisms of high virulence repel and those that are less virulent attract leukocytes and are engulfed by them. Such organisms are usually digested by the enzymes of the leukocyte and disappear. Certain virulent or resistant bacteria may live or even multiply within the phagocytes. For example, there is some evidence that the organism that causes tuberculosis can resist destruction by the leukocyte, live and travel with it, and when the phagocyte dies, can escape none the worse for the encounter. In fact, certain gram-negative bacteria characteristically live within phagocytic cells during chronic infections.

BLOOD PLASMA OR SERUM   Blood serum, the fluid remaining after a clot has formed, thereby removing the blood cells and fibrin, is moderately bactericidal even in the absence of phagocytes. This is especially true of the serum taken from an immune person or animal (person or animal that has recovered from a specific infection). In addition, blood serum contains substances called *opsonins* that combine with the bacterial cells and prepare them for engulfment. When bacteria serum from an immune animal, and leukocytes from the blood are mixed in fluid or on a smooth surface, phagocytosis (engulfing of microorganisms) proceeds rapidly; whereas in the presence of normal serum, the process takes place more slowly, and in the absence of blood serum almost no phagocytosis takes place. In contrast, on membranes or on rough surfaces, leukocytes appear to be able to engulf virulent bacteria without the aid of serum. A detailed account of specific protective substances will be found in Chapter 15.

Local Infection   The internal defense structures function only after the organisms have penetrated the skin or mucous membrane. Often these invasions are combated so promptly that there is little evidence of the process, but sometimes they result in a local or in a general infection.

Suppose that a group of micrococci (staphylococci) is introduced into the deeper layers of the skin by a cut or pinprick. There they begin to multiply in the cell fluid of the finger. At first there will be no evidence of infection, but later, signs and symptoms may appear. This interval between the time bacteria enter and the first signs of disease appear, is called the *incubation period*. As the invaders increase in numbers, their secretions injure the surrounding cells. The resulting infection is caused by the interaction between the cells of the host and the invaders. Some of the signs of disease are due to injury to cells; others are evidence that the body defenses are in action.

Body tissues respond to injury in one or more of the following ways:

1. Cell changes which result in degeneration and death.
2. Cell changes which increase the tissue response, and thereby increase the susceptibility to local injury by the same agent.
3. Cell changes which protect against present and future injury by the specific agent.

The latter response is of special interest and is commonly associated with *fever, inflammation,* and *antibody formation.* Substances derived from the bacterial cell, in this case the micrococcus, stimulate special cells to form antibodies. (See Chapter 15.) In contrast, fever and inflammation are due to products liberated by body cells that have been injured.

Fever is so definitely associated with illness that it is likely to be considered as an unfavorable sign. High fever may be undesirable because of its destructive action on the more delicate body cells, but moderate fever during infection is a desirable response to invasion because it provides a temperature that tends to inhibit bacterial growth, thus limiting the number of organisms to be disposed of by phagocytes. In fact, fever may actually kill invading organisms, since few pathogens can long survive temperatures of 38° to 40° C. (102° to 104° F.). There is growing evidence that fever is caused by a chemical substance (*pyrexin*) liberated by injured cells.

Inflammation, the direct local response to severe cellular injury, is characterized by *redness, swelling, heat,* and *pain,* and is often associated with some loss of function or with local destruction of tissues. Anyone who has had a pimple, boil, or burn has had first-hand experience with this process. The cells, injured by trauma or bacterial products, liberate substances which cause profound changes in the local capillaries. First, the blood supply to the area is augmented by increasing the number of functioning capillaries and by dilation of those vessels. This is accompanied by a marked permeability of the capillary walls, which permits plasma to leak into the surrounding tissues. As a result of this plasma leakage, therefore, bacterial products are diluted and protective substances called *antibodies* are brought in close contact with the invading organisms.

The plasma clots form a fibrin network in the intracellular spaces, thereby blocking the return flow of lymph which might otherwise carry bacteria to other areas. Instead, the coagulated fluid forms a wall which is strengthened by the multiplication of connective tissue cells in the area. This wall tends to limit the spread of bacteria until the phagocytes have time to engulf and digest* the invaders.

The permeable capillaries permit the escape of white blood cells and sometimes also of red blood cells. As the blood stream becomes slower and slower, the leukocytes (microphages) attach themselves to the walls and squeeze through into the surrounding tissues. At the same time, the blood-forming organs of the bone marrow increase the manufacture and output of leukocytes, so that the white cell count may increase from 8000 to 20,000 or 30,000 per cu. mm. in a few hours. In the early response to injury, leukocytes (polymorphonuclear) by the thousands migrate into the fibrin network. Then follows a period of active phagocytosis resulting in the destruction of many bacteria and some leukocytes. The leukocytes are short lived, and do not multiply in the tissues. As time goes on, they are replaced by the macrophages from connective tissues and blood. In this way, the bacteria (micrococci, in the case of the pinprick) are surrounded by a deep wall of fibrin and phagocytes. If the bacteria are not too numerous or too virulent, they are engulfed and digested by the leukocytes, the debris is cleared away by the macrophages, and circulation returns to normal. The relation of the external signs of inflammation to the internal process is fairly obvious. The increased blood supply to the area accounts for the redness and heat.

---

* When an insoluble body or a group of bacteria which cannot be digested is introduced into the tissues, macrophages join to form a permanent wall which with a supporting layer of connective tissue separates the foreign mass from body tissues. Such a nodule is called a *tubercle.*

The entrance of fluid into the tissues causes swelling with pressure on nerve endings, resulting in pain.

If the struggle results in the death of many leukocytes, the debris may be too great to be cleared away by the phagocytes. Then enzyme action transforms the dead cells into a central mass of fluid. Pressure from this mass destroys more cells and the digestive process continues until a channel is formed to the outside. Through this channel is poured the thick, creamy white exudate called *pus*. Pus consists of cell fluids and debris, together with phagocytes and bacteria in various stages of disintegration. This process of pus formation with its subsequent drainage to the outside is called *suppuration*. It protects the body as a whole from bacteria by destroying and eliminating the body cells that are in direct contact with the invading organisms. During and following suppuration, the phagocytes clear away the debris and begin the repair process by laying down a network of new cells to form new capillaries while skin cells from nearby areas migrate to form growing islands of new skin.

Two varieties of local infection have been described. When the invading forces are especially numerous or virulent, they may break through the local defenses. Furthermore, certain bacteria characteristically produce so little irritation that no local inflammation occurs. In either case, the bacteria may spread to nearby tissues or to remote areas. Bacteria that reach the lymph or blood stream acquire direct transportation to distant areas, and once in the vessels, they may be carried passively or they may actually injure the walls of the lymph vessel. When inflamed lymph vessels lie near the skin, they appear as red streaks on the surface of the arm or leg. As the infection spreads, these red lines lengthen along the course of the lymph vessels. Their appearance always means that the local defenses have failed and that the infection is spreading.

Spreading Infection   Although bacteria have escaped the local defenses, their progress can still be checked. At strategic points, the lymph passes through special organs called lymph nodes. These spongelike filters contain phagocytic cells which remove bacteria. Like the leukocytes, these cells may be overwhelmed by the bacteria. Infection may develop within the nodes, resulting in inflammation and sometimes suppuration. For example, tender, swollen masses (inflamed lymph nodes) are often observed in the neck of a person who is suffering from a cold or sore throat. These structures perform the important function of removing bacteria from the lymph before it reaches the large ducts which lead to the blood stream (see Figure 42, page 204).

Blood Stream Infection (Bacteremia or Septicemia) When bacteria gain access to the blood stream, causing *bacteremia* or *septicemia*, they have the advantage of transportation to all parts of the body. This often leads to colonization and the development of secondary infections. This condition is serious, but is not necessarily fatal. If the phagocytic cells of the liver, spleen, and bone marrow can remove the bacteria from the blood stream before too much damage is done, the host will recover.

The outcome of infection, its character, and its severity will always depend upon both the host and the parasites. If the invading organisms are numerous, virulent, and aggressive, the resulting infection will be short and acute, and will usually end with the death of the host or of the parasites, whereas a long-standing chronic infection results when the forces of the host and parasite are so well matched that neither gains much advantage. Pneumonia is an acute infection, while many sinus infections are chronic in nature. Some infections are so mild that they go unrecognized; these are termed *latent* or *subclinical* infections. Infections may also be classified as *local,* that is, restricted to one area, or *general,* when they involve many parts of the body. A general infection, bacteremia, or septicemia is recognized by finding bacteria in the blood stream.

Tissue Response to an Inert Foreign Body   Some stress agents injure cells and call forth a prompt tissue response called *inflammation.* Other agents produce little initial injury. Nevertheless their presence calls forth macrophages from the connective tissues which if possible engulf the foreign particles. If the agent is living, this contact may result in (1) the death of the parasite, (2) the death of the macrophage, or

(3) a condition of intracellular parasitism in which the parasite continues to live and perhaps to multiply within the phagocyte. If the foreign body resists digestion and removal, the macrophages change their character and build a wall around the object. This wall consists of giant cells, epithelial-like cells, and connective tissue. This mass may be called a *nodule,* a *tubercle,* or a *granuloma.* The center of the mass may at times become necrotic or it may contain calcium deposits. A variety of agents may call forth this macrophage walling-off response. They include objects such as fat, sand, wood, carbon, and living organisms such as the spores of molds and the bacteria which cause tuberculosis (*Mycobacterium tuberculosis*), undulant fever (*Brucella*), typhoid fever (*Salmonella typhosa*), and syphilis (*Treponema pallidum*). Diseases characterized by this macrophage walling-off response tend to be chronic and are relatively resistant to treatment.

EXPERIMENTAL EVIDENCE

The defense mechanism just described includes: (1) the exclusion of bacteria by the unbroken skin and mucous membranes; (2) the localization of the invader by walls formed by wandering phagocytes and fibrin threads; and (3) the removal of bacteria by the phagocytic cells of the lymph nodes, liver, spleen, and bone marrow. How can one know that phagocytes from the capillaries and connective tissues migrate to the point of injury and surround and destroy bacteria? How can one know that the spleen and liver remove foreign bodies from the blood stream? These questions have been answered by putting together pieces of evidence gained from thousands of experiments with animals. Only a few simplified experiments will be described here to show how one can demonstrate at least a part of the evidence for the statements made concerning body defenses.

Inflammatory Response WHAT HAPPENS The early stages of inflammation can be observed by removing a small piece of epithelium from the web of a frog's foot and mounting the web under the microscope. Soon one observes that the capillaries dilate and the blood flows rapidly. (Stage

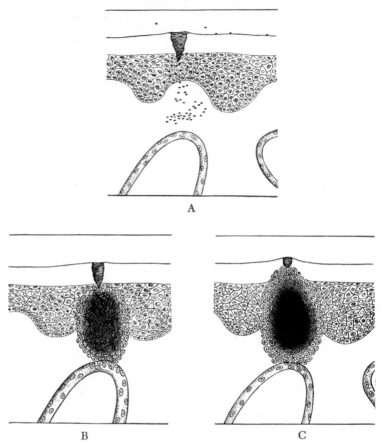

Figure 43   Schematic drawings of the skin showing: *A*, A break in the skin that permits the entrance of bacteria; *B*, a dilated capillary with phagocytes migrating to the point of injury where a wall of fibrin and phagocytes is formed; *C*, an accumulation of pus in the invaded area. (Redrawn from Erpi Classroom Films "Body Defenses Against Disease.")

of increased blood flow, or hyperemia.) After an hour or more, the blood vessels remain fully dilated, but the rate of flow becomes progressively slower until the blood flows with a pulsing movement. At this time, leukocytes can be observed clinging to the vessel walls, and if one has the time and patience, one may observe single cells squeeze through the walls. This process may take from ten to thirty minutes. The later changes are not readily observed by direct examination of even a thin membrane. However, phagocytes and fibrin threads can be demonstrated in thin sections of inflamed tissue.

The same process (inflammation) occurs when cell injury is due to bacterial products. To demonstrate the events that occur in a local infection, ten mice may be inoculated under the skin with virulent micrococci. Then by killing the mice at appropriate intervals and making thin, stained sections of the injured area, it is possible to obtain a progressive record of the infection. A study of hundreds of such slides will demonstrate that the body cells in contact with the bacteria are destroyed, that blood vessels are dilated, and that plasma, leukocytes, and macrophages find their way into the tissues. Certain of these events are illustrated in the simplified drawings shown in Figure 43. They are as follows:

EVENTS SUGGESTED IN FIGURE 43	EVENTS NOT REPRESENTED IN FIGURE 43
A. The entrance of bacteria through the broken skin.	The multiplication of the bacteria and the subsequent injury to cells and the liberation of chemical substances that stimulate changes in the capillary walls.
B. The migration of phagocytes through the walls of a dilated capillary and the formation of a wall of fibrin and phagocytes.	The escape of blood plasma and the migration of phagocytes from the connective tissues.
C. The destruction of the phagocytes, resulting in pus formation.	The escape of pus from the suppurating area and the rebuilding of the damaged tissues by phagocytes from the connective tissue.

WHY IT HAPPENS   Obviously any process as complicated and important as inflammation would raise questions concerning its origin. Experiments using laboratory animals indicate that active substances derived from the inflammatory exudate are responsible for many of the changes described above. To date, five distinct factors have been isolated and studied, and a sixth is now being investigated. They are:

FRACTION OF INFLAMMATORY EXUDATE	EFFECT OF SUBCUTANEOUS INJECTION ON LABORATORY ANIMAL
Permeability factor	Increases permeability of capillaries promoting the escape of plasma and the early migration of leukocytes from the capillaries.
Leukocytosis-promoting factor	Stimulates blood-forming organs to discharge immature leukocytes into the blood stream.
Cell-destroying factor (necrosin)	Causes local swelling and redness of tissues, accompanied by blockade of lymph vessels and injury to epithelial and muscle tissue. (Intravenous injection causes destruction of cells in the liver, spleen, and kidneys.)
Fever-promoting factor (pyrexin)	Causes a rise in body temperature of from two to three degrees Fahrenheit in the rabbit.
Leukopenia factor	Causes a decrease in the circulating white blood cells, owing to the trapping of these cells in the walls of lungs, liver, and spleen.
Growth-promoting factor (?)	May encourage repair processes. Present evidence is incomplete.

It will be noted that the injection of substances found in cell exudate will bring about most of the changes associated with inflammation. At present, the healing process is not well understood, and almost nothing is known concerning the stimulus which brings about the migration of the macrophages into the injured tissues.

Blood Filters   REMOVAL OF FOREIGN BODIES   TO demonstrate the function of the liver and spleen in removing foreign bodies from the circulating blood, a rabbit may be injected intravenously with India ink—a suspension of black carbon particles. A half hour later, the animal is killed and dissected. Upon examination, all tissues appear normal except the liver, spleen, and some patches in the lungs which are jet black. (See Figure 44.) India ink is used because it produces immediate and visible results. That the same structures remove bacteria could be shown by a similar experiment. However, it would be necessary to make microscopic and cultural examinations to demonstrate the presence of bacteria.

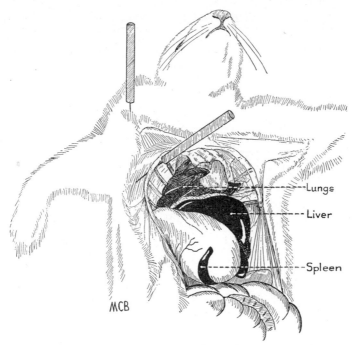

Figure 44   The organs of a rabbit a few minutes after an intravenous injection of India ink. Observe that the spleen, liver, and certain patches in the lungs are jet black, while the other organs appear normal.

REMOVAL OF BACTERIA   The removal of bacteria from the circulating blood can be demonstrated by inoculating three rabbits intravenously with three different cultures of pneumococci—the first, harmless (avirulent); the second, slightly virulent; and the third, highly virulent. Samples of blood from each animal may be collected at intervals and transferred to agar plates. After incubation, the colonies on the plates can be estimated. As would be expected, the avirulent bacteria are promptly removed from the blood stream, while the virulent bacteria show a primary reduction followed by an increase in numbers when the bacteria begin to multiply in the rabbit. The results shown in Figure 45 are typical of those that may be expected in an experiment of this kind. Observe that the avirulent bacteria were promptly and finally removed from

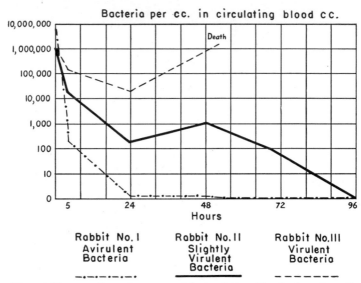

Figure 45   Bacteria per cc. of circulating blood at various time intervals. Rabbit No. I was injected intravenously with avirulent pneumococci. Rabbit No. II was injected with slightly virulent pneumococci, and Rabbit No. III was injected with highly virulent pneumococci.

the circulation and that both virulent cultures demonstrated some ability to multiply in the body before they were finally disposed of by the reticuloendothelial system of rabbit number 2 and before they caused the death of rabbit number 3. A substantial increase or decrease in the number of virulent organisms administered may be expected to change the outcome of the experiment.

Phagocytes   IN A TEST TUBE   The function of the leukocytes can be demonstrated by obtaining cells from a fresh specimen of citrated blood by removing the creamy layer of leukocytes that appear over the red cells after they have been settled by centrifugation. The living cells collected in this manner can then be added to tubes containing (1) avirulent pneumococci, (2) virulent pneumococci, and (3) virulent pneumococci and specific serum obtained from an immune animal. After two hours, incubation at 37° C. (98.6° F.), stained smears will demonstrate that phagocytes have engulfed most of the avirulent pneumococci and also those

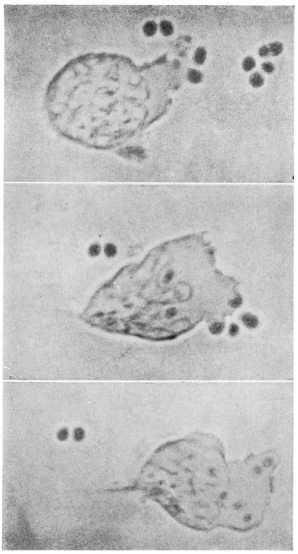

Figure 46   Phagocytosis of pneumococci in hanging drops of gelatin Locke's solution containing type specific antiserum (× 3350). *Upper,* Observe phagocytes and eight pneumococci with swollen capsules (swelling is due to the union of specific antiserum with the antigen of the capsule). Time: 3:51 P.M. *Middle,* Two minutes later—four organisms have been engulfed and two others are in contact with the phagocyte. Time: 3:53 P.M. *Lower,* Four minutes later—six pneumococci have entered the cytoplasm of the phagocyte. Time: 3:55 P.M. (Wood, B. W.: J. Exper. Med., 84.)

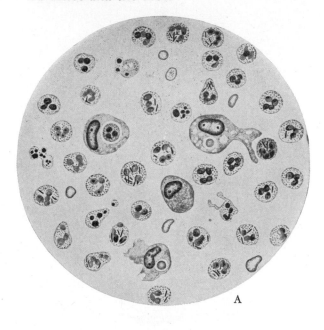

A

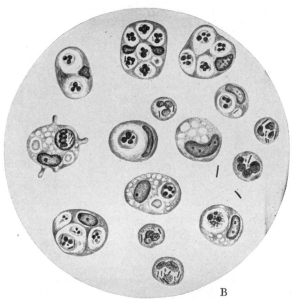

B

Figure 47   See opposite page for legend.

virulent bacteria which were exposed to serum from an immune animal, whereas most of the virulent organisms not exposed to serum have remained outside of the phagocytes. However, recent experiments show that phagocytic cells function more effectively on rough surfaces and cellular membranes than they do on glass. These observations suggest that in the body, phagocytes probably engulf virulent bacteria with or without the aid of specific substances. Figure 46 shows the rapid phagocytosis of eight pneumococci in the presence of serum from an immune animal. Figure 47 shows phagocytic cells in inflammatory exudate.

IN THE BLOOD   The number of leukocytes in the circulating blood can be estimated by placing a measured quantity of diluted blood in a special ruled chamber and, by the aid of the microscope, counting the cells seen in a given area. The number of white cells in a normal, well person varies at different times of the day but usually ranges from 5000 to 9000 per cubic millimeter of blood. During infection, reserves from the blood-forming organs often augment this number to 15,000 or 20,000 per cubic millimeter. This increase in the number of white cells is called *leukocytosis*. A high leukocyte count is evidence not only that there is infection but also that the body defenses are active; like fever, a moderate increase in the number of white blood cells may be considered a favorable host response. Certain infections caused by microorganisms that destroy leukocytes are usually accompanied by a low leukocyte count, i.e., *leukopenia*.

SUMMARY

1. Among the parasites that reach the body, certain organisms called pathogens are able to invade and injure body structure. The invasion of the host by microorganisms may result in a latent, a chronic, or an acute infection.

Figure 47   Phagocytes in inflammatory exudate after a culture of bacteria was injected into peritoneum of rabbit. *A,* Inflammatory exudate from peritoneum of rabbit 24 hours after introduction of bacteria. Observe evidence of phagocytosis by leukocytes (microphages). *B,* Exudate 48 hours after introduction of bacteria. Observe the presence of large macrophages which have engulfed leukocytes containing bacteria. (Dibble, J. H., and Davie, T. B.: Pathology—An Introduction to Medicine and Surgery. J. & A. Churchill.)

2. The body of the host has a well-developed defense mechanism and is protected by four lines of defense: (a) the external walls and their secretions, (b) the mobile defenses—phagocytes and blood proteins, (c) the fixed phagocytic cells of the lymph nodes, and (d) the fixed phagocytic cells of the liver, spleen, and bone marrow.

3. Laboratory experiments provide a means of demonstrating many of the defense mechanisms that protect the animal body against invaders.

SUPPLEMENTARY READINGS

BOOKS:

Boyd, W. C.: Fundamentals of Immunology. 2d ed. New York, Interscience Publishers, Inc., 1947.

Burnet, F. M., and Fenner, F.: The Production of Antibodies. London, The Macmillan Company, 1949.

Burrows, W.: Jordan-Burrows Textbook of Bacteriology. 15th ed. Philadelphia, W. B. Saunders Co., 1949.

Dubos, R.: The Bacterial Cell. Cambridge, Mass., Harvard University Press, 1946.

Dubos, R. (Ed.): Bacterial and Mycotic Infections of Man. 2d ed. Philadelphia, J. B. Lippincott Co., 1952.

Forbus, W. D.: Granulomatous Inflammation. Springfield, Ill., Charles C Thomas, Publisher, 1949.

Forbus, W. D.: Reaction to Injury. Baltimore, Williams & Wilkins Co., 1952.

Frobisher, M.: Fundamentals of Microbiology. 5th ed. Philadelphia, W. B. Saunders Co., 1953.

Langmuir, A. D.: Air-borne Infection. In: Maxcy, K. F.: Rosenau Preventive Medicine and Hygiene. 7th ed. New York, Appleton-Century-Crofts, Inc., 1951.

Menkin, V.: Biochemical and Physiological Mechanisms in Inflammation. In: Alexander, J.: Colloid Chemistry. New York, Reinhold Publishing Corporation, 1944, Vol. 5.

Pappenheimer, A. M., Jr. (Ed.): The Nature and Significance of Antibody Response. Symposium of the Section of Microbiology New York Academy of Medicine. New York, Columbia University Press, 1953.

Smith, D. T., and Conant, N. F.: Zinsser's Textbook of Bacteriology. 10th ed. New York, Appleton-Century-Crofts, Inc., 1952.

PERIODICALS:

Burrows, W.: Endotoxins. Ann. Rev. Microbiol., 5: 1951.

Harrell, G. T., and Aikawa, J. K.: Alteration in the Permeability of Membranes during Infection. J.A.M.A., 147: 232–238, 1951.

Kahn, R. L.: The Tissues in Infection and Immunity. Scient. Monthly, 67: 162–172, 1948.

Nungester, W. J.: Mechanism of Man's Resistance to Infectious Disease. Bact. Rev., 15: 105–129, 1951.

CHAPTER 14

Parasites As Stress Agents

THE preceding chapter dealt with the body's defenses and with the role of microorganisms in infection. It is all too easy to look upon microorganisms as a primary and direct cause of disease. In reality, human illness is not so simple. There is growing evidence that parasitic microorganisms, though important, are often a secondary cause of illness; that is, they become active only after body functions and structures have been disturbed by other stress agents.

Stress and Stress Agents   In recent years the term "stress" has been used to refer to the pressures or forces which act upon a human being in such a way that they disturb body function. In its milder forms, stress represents the wear and tear of living. Mild degrees of stress, as, for example, work and play, are pleasant and contribute to well-being. Stresses vary in degree of severity and also in duration. They may be sudden and severe as in an automobile accident or they may be prolonged as in chronic starvation. Events, conditions, or substances which initiate or contribute to disease or distress may be considered stress agents. The following commonly produce general injury to the body and may therefore be considered as stress agents:

Stresses that act on the person:
    Situations that arouse prolonged anger, anxiety, resentment, fear, panic
Stresses which destroy cells directly:
    Burns, pathogenic organisms, trauma, surgical operations
Some stresses that deprive cells of optimum conditions for living:
    Fluids—too little, too much, wrong kind
    Food—too little, too much, wrong kind
    Hormones—too little, too much
    Oxygen—too little, too much

LOCALIZED RESPONSE TO INJURY AND INSULT

Illness may be present without microorganisms, and pathogenic microorganisms may be present without illness. Disease (lack of ease) represents a failure on the part of the body to adapt itself and to function with ease or comfort. This ability to function with ease and comfort can be disturbed by a variety of situations and agents—both living and nonliving. For example, the signs and symptoms of the common cold may be caused by infection with viruses or bacteria, by contact with chemical irritants or common proteins (pollens, house dust, goosefeathers), or by emotional disturbances.[1] There is considerable evidence that man responds to unhappy social situations, or to symbols or threats of danger, as he would to actual injury or danger. His responses may therefore at times be appropriate and afford considerable protection or they may be useless or even harmful. For example, if one is exposed to the fumes of ammonia, it can be predicted that the nasal mucous membranes will respond to this insult by dilation of blood vessels, increased secretion, and obstruction of the nasal passages. This is a protective response since it tends to shut out the irritating agent. When, however, an individual who is hurt, angry, or resentful responds to a social situation by closing off his nasal passages, that is obviously an inappropriate response since it does not help him to deal effectively with an arrogant boss, mother-in-law, or disobedient child. In fact the engorged or anemic condition of the nasal mucous membrane which results may permit or invite invasion by the bacteria or viruses that are present in the nose. As a result the individual may develop a real infection—a common cold. In this instance the microorganisms would invade only after an inappropriate response (changed blood supply, swelling, secretions) had rendered the tissues susceptible to invasion.

Different individuals, in adapting to their culture, to the people around them, and to external agents, develop characteristic patterns of response. When confronted by a threat or insult to the cellular structure or to the person (the "I"), one individual may react with changes in the function of the nose, another with disturbances of the intestine (vomiting, diarrhea, spasm, constipation), still another may react by dilation of the blood vessels of the head (result—*headache*) or by increased blood pressure or increased tension of skeletal muscles. In some of these reactions, microorganisms may play a part in making the person feel sick. Table 13 suggests some responses and the relation of microorganisms to them. Anyone who has experienced worry or anxiety (and who has not?) has had experience with one or more of the inappropriate reaction patterns. When stimuli (especially cultural and social pressures) are prolonged, inappropriate reactions may lead to more or less chronic illness. In contrast, severe injury regardless of the cause calls forth a complex general response—sometimes called the *general adaptation syndrome*.

GENERAL OR SYSTEMIC RESPONSE TO INJURY

Response to Stress—The Alarm Reaction   Local injury to cells usually results in a prompt local connective tissue reaction called inflammation. (See page 207.) Severe or extensive injury from any cause starts a complex response that is called the *alarm reaction*. The alarm reaction is followed by either recovery and resistance or exhaustion and death. The sequence is as follows:

$$\text{Stress (Cell Damage)} \rightarrow \text{Alarm Reaction} \left\langle \begin{array}{l} \text{Recovery and Resistance} \\ \text{or} \\ \text{Exhaustion and Death} \end{array} \right.$$

The alarm reaction has two parts: (1) *shock** or the effects of injury to cells and (2) countershock—a complex process that tends to prevent or repair cell damage. This discussion will be limited to shock and countershock in tissues.

SHOCK   Injury due to trauma, burns, cold, or severe infection causes profound changes in body function. Inadequate food, prolonged anxiety, or chronic infection also disturbs body function but usually at a lower rate. Tissue shock is characterized by damage to all tissues at the site of injury including the walls of capillaries. Injury to cells renders the capillary walls more permeable thus permitting plasma pro-

---

* The term "shock" refers to tissue damage as well as to extreme general circulatory failure—known as surgical and medical shock.

Table 13   RELATION OF MICROORGANISMS TO SELECTED BODY RESPONSES TO INSULT OR INJURY

RESPONSE	APPROPRIATE WHEN IT OCCURS IN RESPONSE TO	INAPPROPRIATE WHEN IT OCCURS IN RESPONSE TO	RELATION TO MICROORGANISMS
Inflammation	Physical damage to cells or presence of microorganisms	Relatively harmless or non-living agents	Tends to localize infection and prevent further invasion
Increased capillary permeability	Physical blow; Mosquito bite	Social situations; Various allergies* including hay fever and hives	May favor infection
Hypo- or hyperactivity of the intestine	Noxious agent living or nonliving	Social situation	May favor infection
Dilation of blood vessels in the head (headache)	?	Social situations	Uncertain
Increased activity of heart and blood vessels (often greater in degree and prolonged beyond the period of physical activity)	Situation which calls for fight or flight	Social situations in which the individual cannot fight or run	Uncertain—perhaps none
Decreased activity of large bowel	Strenuous physical exertion	Social situation which makes the individual tense, worried or sad	Prolonged changes in motility, secretions, and blood supply may decrease resistance of the lining cells—thus permitting bacteria to cause secondary infection

* Many individuals who are sensitive to various pollens or other proteins can remain symptom-free while things go well for them. Situations which are disturbing emotionally either bring on an attack or cause symptoms to become more severe.

teins to leak into tissue spaces. Plasma tends to clot in lymph vessels and intercellular spaces, and blood circulation to the area is impaired. This provides an abnormal medium for the cells in the injured area—one which deprives them of optimal amounts of food, oxygen, and hormones. Thus the original stresses of injury and pain may be reinforced by lack of nutrients. If they are prolonged, death of tissues may be expected.*
Some of the important changes occurring in tissue shock are summarized on page 226.

When tissue injury is sudden and severe as in a burn or trauma the signs of injury (shock) and those of restoration (countershock) are readily distinguished. When stress is relatively moderate and prolonged the signs of damage (shock phase) and restoration (countershock) are, however, so intermingled that they cannot be readily separated.

COUNTERSHOCK   Countershock, sometimes called systemic defense, is a complex series of reactions which tends in part to reverse the circulatory changes described above. Both the nervous system and hormones are involved in these reactions. It is known that severe stress in laboratory animals brings about predictable visible changes. These include: (1) enlargement of the adrenal cortex, (2) marked destruction of lymphoid tissue, and (3) gastrointestinal ulcers. In man, stress is associated with varying degrees of prostration, malaise, weakness, apathy, and loss of appetite. The reader will recognize these signs as common to many illnesses. On these, the common signs of illness, may be superimposed other changes that are characteristic of the particular stress agent. Specific injury by tetanus toxin, for example, will be shown by disturbed nerve function resulting in muscular contractions; poliomyelitis virus acting on nerve cells may cause paralysis of muscles. These actions are specific in that they are commonly associated

---

* Local tissue shock, if severe, often gives rise to systemic shock characterized by progressive failure of the cardiovascular system which if not promptly reversed results in the death of the individual. There is evidence to suggest that microorganisms from the intestines contribute to irreversible shock and death by passing through the intestinal walls (made more permeable by an inadequate oxygen supply) into the portal blood stream and liver and possibly into the general circulation.

SHOCK (CELL DAMAGE) PHASE OF THE ALARM REACTION
FOLLOWING A SEVERE INJURY

First stress: Damage to large area of skin (example: wounds, burns)
                              ↓
Second stress: Pain, fear
                              ↓
                   Damage to cell membranes
                              ↓
                   Damage to adjacent capillary networks
                              ↓
                   Loss of cell fluid into tissue spaces
                              ↓
                   Loss of plasma proteins into tissue spaces
                              ↓
                   Various chemical changes in cells and surrounding fluid
                              ↓
Third stress: Diminished oxygen to cells (hypoxia)
                              ↓
Other stresses: Lack of food and hormones
                              ↓
                   Lack of oxygen (anoxia)
                          ↙   ↘
                                              (Countershock)

Possible invasion of bacteria
            ↓
Death of cells (irreversible damage)*   Restoration of normal con-
            ↓   ditions for cells
                                                                          ↓
Death of individual   Repair of cells
                                                                          ↓
                                                             Recovery of individual

with a single kind of agent, in contrast to the general signs of illness that are common to many illnesses.

It is thought that these general signs of illness and the predictable changes in experimental animals occur in response to pituitary and adrenocortical hormones. This area is currently under investigation but as yet there is not full agreement regarding the specific functions of each hormone—or, for that matter, about the number of hormones involved in the alarm reaction, or the source of the original stimulus. It seems

* Refer to footnote on page 225.

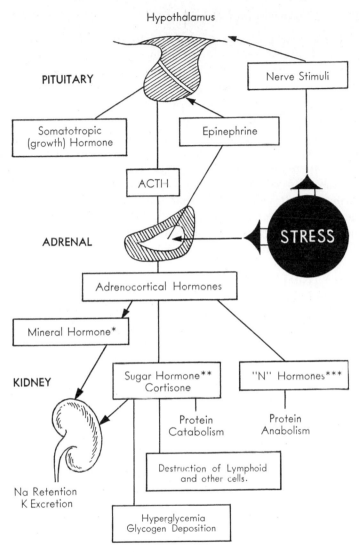

Figure 48   Schematic diagram showing pathways which are probably involved during the alarm reaction. Both nervous and hormonal controls are active in adapting the body to injury. Some of the effects of hormones are suggested although there is not complete agreement regarding hormones and their action.

° Desoxycorticosterone (DOCA).

°° Cortisone.

°°° Probably some of the sex (gonadotropic) hormones (testosterone, progesterone (?) and adrenosterone).

probable that the cells responding to stress send (nerve or chemical) stimuli to the lower brain (hypothalamus) and also to the adrenal (medulla) gland causing it to increase its secretion of epinephrine. Epinephrine and nerve impulses from the hypothalamus act on the anterior pituitary causing it to pour out additional amounts of ACTH (adrenocorticotropic hormone) and possibly also STH (somatotropic [growth] hormone). The ACTH in turn stimulates the adrenal cortex to secrete increased amounts of sugar hormone (cortisone) and possibly also mineral and sex hormones (gonadotropic or N hormones). It seems likely that the changes which occur in the early phase of the alarm reaction occur in response to the sugar hormone (glucocorticoid or cortisone). Increased amounts of the sugar hormone are associated with (1) increased destruction of lymphoid and other cells (muscle and connective tissue) (catabolism) with liberation of cell proteins and antibody globulin into the blood stream, (2) inhibition of inflammatory response, and (3) the retention of sodium chloride and water in the intracellular spaces. It has been called the sugar hormone because it transforms proteins into glucose which is either used or stored as glycogen. As a result of this activity the glucose level in the circulating blood commonly rises and at times glucose may be excreted in the urine. Mineral hormones promote inflammatory processes and wound healing, and also favor the retention of sodium chloride and water in the intracellular spaces. The gonadotropic hormone is thought to be mildly anabolic, favoring tissue building. The somatotropic hormone is thought to increase the inflammatory response and also to maintain normal cell growth and nutrition (anabolism). It will be noted that these hormones are to some extent antagonistic. For example, the sugar hormone decreases inflammation while the mineral hormone and the somatotropic hormone promote it. Likewise the sugar hormone favors cell and protein destruction while the gonadotropic and somatotropic hormones seem to favor cell building and repair. It is obvious that the response to stress may bring some fairly drastic changes in the inflammatory response and also in cell structure and the composition of body fluids. These responses though drastic and somewhat destructive are thought to have evolved to protect the body in case of severe injury. Undoubtedly these changes were especially important to man living under primitive conditions where severe injury meant cutting off his supply of food and water. Under these circumstances, survival depended upon the ability of the body to conserve water and to maintain itself at the expense of its own tissues. And this is essentially what the pituitary and adrenal cortical hormones enable it to do.

Response to Stress—Resistance   It is well known that certain diseases such as measles increase the resistance of the host to a second infection of the same kind. This ability to avoid a second infection is due in large part to the fact that body cells have developed the ability to produce specific protective substances (antibody globulins). (See page 241.) Recent experiments with animals suggest that some specific resistance is developed to stress produced by nonliving agents and (nonantigenic) stress agents. For example, a rat that has recovered from shock associated with long exposure to ice water will after complete recovery be able to stand cold water better than a litter-mate which has not previously been exposed to cold water. That is, it can endure a lower temperature for a longer time before showing signs of shock. Its ability to stand other stresses such as infection or starvation may be definitely diminished. The development of resistance to stresses, other than microorganisms or complex antigens, is not understood. However, this does seem to occur and may possibly account for the fact that native populations are usually better able to cope with stresses of climate than are strangers from abroad.

Response to Stress—Exhaustion   Exhaustion may be defined as that state at which the body has no further ability to adapt to stress. Exhaustion and death occur when the body's adaptation to injury proves inadequate to prevent irreversible changes in cells. In some individuals this occurs at the hour of birth while for others it occurs after a life-span of eighty or ninety years. Selye has suggested that aging is the cumulative effect of many stresses.

IMPORTANCE OF THE STRESS CONCEPT
The stress concept, although of recent origin, has profound

significance for members of the helping professions (teachers, social workers, nurses, doctors, dentists), since frequently these individuals deal with persons who are under stress. While mild stress (locomotion, work, play) is essential to health and *mild* concern or anxiety probably facilitates learning, severe stresses are definitely harmful. Significant is the fact that many stress agents are capable of disturbing function and thus causing disease. While some diseases are due to microorganisms the nature and severity of the infection will often depend on other stresses which precede or accompany the infection. Some parasites cause typical recognizable disease in all susceptible persons—as, for example, those responsible for measles or smallpox. In contrast, the organisms which cause tuberculosis, for example, infect many persons with little or no evidence of disease. Other stresses such as malnutrition, crowding, and various insecurities appear to be determining factors in the production of illness. Galdston has stated the concept in this manner: "more commonly, the particular individual is *not sick because he has tuberculosis but rather he has tuberculosis because he is sick.*"[2]

There is growing recognition that stresses reinforce one another and that several may be involved in making a person sick. Consider the situation of a two-year-old child suffering from pneumonia following an attack of measles. Assume that he is taken to a hospital, promptly separated from his parents, and treated by strangers, while being surrounded by the gadgets and ceremony of modern medicine (oxygen tents, tube feeding, hypodermic injections). In view of the fact that man responds to threats and symbols of danger as he would to real danger, the stresses inherent in this and many hospital situations can readily be surmised. In situations like this, professional people may really be creating stress for the one whom they are trying to help. Those who work with persons who are under stress have a responsibility for developing an awareness of the nature of stress situations remembering that the stress in a situation depends not on the situation *per se* but upon *what it means to the individual* in terms of his culture and past experience. Many common life experiences are very threatening to certain individuals. The trip to the dentist's or doctor's office, diagnostic tests, and the so-called minor operations (minor for whom?) are typical examples. Too often these are routine matters for medical personnel but they may represent stress of the first magnitude to the client or patient. Many routine procedures in clinics, hospitals, and other agencies may have been developed for the convenience of admininstration or of personnel rather than for the comfort of clients. An understanding of stress and its effects may provide a basis for critical evaluation of nursing and medical procedures and of office, clinic, and hospital practice. The basic questions are: *What does this situation mean to the client? Can I make this situation less threatening to him?*

MULTIPLE CAUSES OF INFECTIOUS DISEASE

The foregoing may have given the impression that microorganisms play a minor role in disease production. Actually many are potent stress agents but whether or not they cause injury depends to a considerable degree on the other stresses which may be acting at the same time. Since many kinds of microorganisms reach relatively few types of body structures, one might reasonably expect the illness caused by different organisms might be similar. To some extent this is true. While certain organisms always cause a specific disease—as, for example, measles virus causes measles—groups of organisms are able to cause infections of wounds, lungs, nasal passages, and joints—to mention only a few. Some of these are suggested in Table 14.

The examples given in the table suggest that there is no one organism or agent that injures a specific tissue but rather that numerous different agents are capable of producing injury to a particular tissue or organ and that the injury produced by different agents may be quite similar in nature.

SUMMARY

1. Man is constantly exposed to bodily injury by a variety of stresses. His response is at times protective and at other times may be inadequate or even harmful.

2. Stress may be produced by a variety of agents which harm or deprive cells or threaten the prestige of the person.

Table 14   STRESS AGENTS CAPABLE OF DISTURBING
FUNCTIONS OF SELECTED TISSUES

| | STRESS AGENTS | |
TISSUE RESPONSE	NONLIVING	LIVING
Common cold, rhinitis, pharyngitis	Various threats, pollens, chemical irritants	Various bacteria Various viruses
Inflammatory changes in lung tissue	Chemical irritants, dusts, oils	Larvae of intestinal worms Mold spores Various bacteria Various rickettsias Various viruses
Inflammatory changes in joints (arthritis)	Injury, aging, serum, and unknown agents	Various bacteria
Gastroenteritis and other disturbances of the digestive tract	Emotional stresses Chemical poisons Irritant foods Bacterial toxins in foods	Various bacteria and certain protozoa and possibly certain viruses

3. Severe injury, regardless of cause, calls forth the alarm reaction—a series of complex changes directed by the lower brain and the hormones of the pituitary and adrenal glands.

4. The severity of infection caused by microorganisms is often influenced by other stresses such as malnutrition, exposure, and emotional disturbances.

5. Numerous stress agents, including microorganisms, may give rise to rather similar signs of illness.

6. Professional workers have a need to learn to deal helpfully with persons who are under stress.

REFERENCES

1. Osmun, P.: Are You Sure You Have a Cold? Am. J. Nursing, 52: 168–173, 1952.
2. Galdston, I.: A Philosophy for Today's Doctor. United Nations World, 6: 59, 1952.

SUPPLEMENTARY READINGS

BOOKS:

Apperly, F. L.: Patterns of Disease. Philadelphia, J. B. Lippincott Co., 1951.
Elman, R.: Surgical Care. New York, Appleton-Century-Crofts, Inc., 1951, Chapter 2, pp. 18–41.

Selye, H.: Physiology and Pathology of Exposure to Stress. Montreal, Canada, Acta, Inc., 1950.

Selye, H.: The First Annual Report on Stress. Montreal, Canada, Acta, Inc., 1951.

Selye, H.: The Second Annual Report on Stress. Montreal, Canada, Acta, Inc., 1952.

Selye, H.: Story of the Adaptation Syndrome. Montreal, Canada, Acta, Inc., 1952.

Stackpole, C., and Leavell, L.: Textbook of Physiology, The Activities of the Living Body. New York, The Macmillan Co., 1953.

Wolff, H. G.: Stress and Disease. Springfield, Ill., Charles C Thomas, Publisher, 1953.

PERIODICALS:

Editorial: The Way the Hospital Appears to the Patient. Canad. M. A. J., *67:* 363–365, 1952.

Galdston, I.: A Philosophy for Today's Doctor. United Nations World, *6:* 58–59, 1952.

Lehmann, H. E.: Stress Dynamics in Psychiatric Perspective. Psychiatry, *15:* 387–393, 1952.

Stone, H. M.: Psychological Factors in Infantile Eczema. Am. J. Nursing, *53:* 449–451, 1953.

PEOPLE differ in their ability to resist infection, and further-more, the resistance of the same person varies from time to time. For example, an individual's susceptibility to certain childhood diseases is low during infancy and adult life, and high from ages one to ten years. Recovery from a disease con-fers the ability to resist that particular infection for varying periods of time. In certain diseases, such as the common cold, the protection is of short duration, whereas one attack of measles usually gives lasting protection against the disease. This increased resistance is called *immunity*. The term is un-fortunate, since it implies that the immune person is exempt from all risk. In reality, virtually all immunity is a relative factor that permits infection whenever virulent organisms are present in sufficient numbers to overcome the defenses of the host.

Varying degrees of immunity markedly influence the char-acter and outcome of infection. Where there is complete lack of immunity, all or almost all of the infected persons develop a fatal systemic infection characterized by widespread cellular damage. When some degree of immunity exists, the infections are more likely to be local, with bacteremia and death less common. Subclinical and latent infections may also occur. Where there is a high degree of resistance, latent infections are common and when disease occurs, it is apt to be mild. In contrast, complete immunity, a very rare state, enables those possessing it to resist all attacks by the infectious agent. The degrees of immunity may be arranged on a scale ranging from complete susceptibility to complete immunity. (See Table 15.)

The character and severity of the disease process is further influenced by hormones (ACTH and cortisone) and other factors which tend to counteract the effects of cell damage. This is a nonspecific defense (see page 223), in contrast to immunity which is specific for the particular organism which caused the original infection.

234

Table 15   RELATION OF THE CHARACTER OF DISEASE TO THE
DEGREE OF IMMUNITY OF THE HOST

COMPLETE SUSCEPTIBILITY	MODERATE IMMUNITY	HIGH DEGREE OF IMMUNITY	COMPLETE IMMUNITY (VERY RARE)
Severe Stress Characterized by Widespread cell damage Bacteremia High mortality	*Moderate Stress* Characterized by Less cell damage Local and latent infections Bacteremia and death less common	*Milder Stress* Characterized by Limited cell damage Local and latent infections No deaths	*Little or No Stress* No infection

During and after recovery from a specific disease, a person acquires an ability to withstand further attacks by the same organism. This increased resistance appears to be due to an increased sensitivity of the body cells to injury by the infectious agent, resulting in a prompt and effective inflammation, phagocytosis, and antibody formation. It has been suggested that the skin and mucous membranes may be altered in a way which prevents the entrance of the infectious agent. The evidence on this point is quite incomplete, whereas the influence of inflammation, phagocytosis, and antibodies is easily demonstrated.

The early experiments of Jenner and Pasteur proved that immunity could be produced by artificial means. Jenner observed that milkmaids who had had cowpox were resistant to smallpox. In 1798 he inoculated a child with material from a cowpox lesion and later demonstrated that the boy was immune to smallpox. Later, in 1881, a French scientist, Louis Pasteur, conducted well-controlled experiments in which he protected sheep from anthrax by inoculating them with weakened (attenuated) cultures of anthrax organisms. These experiments served as a stimulus to other scientists to try to prevent disease by increasing the resistance of the host.

KINDS OF IMMUNITY

Immunity appears to be of two kinds: first, that which is *natural,* or innate; and second, that which is *acquired.* Natural immunity is usually associated with species and race. Dogs and cats are immune to measles and mumps, and cold-blooded animals are resistant to the diseases of the warm-blooded. Furthermore, white mice are highly susceptible to pneumococci, while man is relatively resistant to them. Just what it is that makes the body of one animal unsuited to become the habitation for parasites that are pathogenic for another species is not clear. The chemical composition of the invading organism or its capsule may be a factor if one or both consist of proteins or carbohydrates that resist digestion by enzymes of the host tissues. In the case of the cold-blooded animals, temperature may be a factor. Pasteur's early work showed that frogs inoculated with anthrax were immune at ordinary temperatures but developed the disease and died when the water in the tank was heated to 35° C. (98.6° F.) (thermal stress).

In general, man does not provide a suitable environment for the parasites of lower animals and is therefore immune to most animal diseases. There are several outstanding exceptions, however; for example:

PARASITE	PRIMARY HOST	OCCASIONAL HOST
Bacteria causing bovine tuberculosis . .	Cow	Man
Rabies virus	Dog, fox, skunk	Man
Bacteria causing undulant fever	Cow, goat, or hog	Man

Heredity is undoubtedly of some importance in determining susceptibility and resistance to disease. In well-controlled laboratory experiments, it has been possible to develop strains of mice and rabbits which were either very susceptible or very resistant to specific infections or to poisons. Different racial and cultural groups in the human population vary markedly in their ability to cope with certain infections. For example, the natives of isolated regions are more likely to die of measles than are people of European stock, and tuberculosis death rates for Negroes are from two to four times those of the white population. It is difficult, if not impossible, to determine to what extent the observed differences are due to heredity, because of the many variable environmental factors involved.

Individual differences too are noted in all races. These may well be related to the efficiency of the alarm reaction in response to stress, nutrition, and experiences which influence general health as, for example, physical and psychological trauma, starvation, and infection or chronic illness.

ACQUIRED IMMUNITY

Active Immunity Acquired immunity may be either *active* or *passive*. Active immunity, the increased resistance which results from reacting with the disease-producing agent, is developed in one of three ways: by having and recovering from the disease, by having unnoticed or latent infection, or by artificial inoculation or vaccination. Thus the reader may be immune to smallpox either because he has had the disease or has been vaccinated recently. He may be resistant to diphtheria because he has recovered from the disease, he has had a mild or latent infection, or he has been inoculated with products of the diphtheria organism (diphtheria toxoid). This active resistance developed in response to the invading organism or its products often lasts for years, although it is sometimes more transient.

The process of increasing the resistance of a person to a particular infection by artificial means is called *immunization.* Immunization procedures are designed to stimulate the normal response of the tissues in such a way that the person will develop an artificial active immunity without the risk or inconvenience of having the infection.

The immune animal disposes of the invading parasite by prompt and effective tissue response, resulting in inflammation and phagocytosis, and the formation of specific protective substances called antibodies. The immune response is sometimes only partly effective, permitting the organism to persist in the body without producing disease. An apparently healthy person who harbors pathogenic organisms is known as a *carrier* and is an important source of infection. The ability of the body cells to form protective substances is an important factor in developing immunity and will, therefore, be considered at length.

Passive Immunity   Blood serum* or gamma globulin obtained from an immune person or animal contains substances which can increase the resistance of the susceptible person. This increased resistance is called *passive immunity*. It may be conferred naturally by the transfer of protective substances from the blood of the immune mother to the fetus by way of the placenta. For example, most infants are passively immune to measles, diphtheria, and poliomyelitis provided the mother had circulating antibodies against these diseases. (Passive immunity acquired from the mother lasts from three to six months.) A passive immunity can also be induced artificially by injecting blood serum containing specific protective substances called antibodies. For example, diphtheria antitoxin (horse serum containing antibodies which combines with diphtheria toxin) may be used to protect a susceptible person who has been exposed to diphtheria. Passive immunity thus acquired is temporary, and usually lasts about three weeks. Gamma globulin derived from animal serum is completely destroyed in two or three weeks. In contrast, human gamma globulin is destroyed more slowly and may persist for months. In contrast to an active immunity where a person forms his own antibodies, a passive immunity is conferred by the administration of protective substances developed by another person or animal.

THE NATURE OF ACQUIRED IMMUNITY

In the course of recovering from an infection, a living body develops a degree of resistance which protects it against further attacks by the same organisms. This process can often be incited by inoculating the person with appropriate complex substances obtained from the specific agent of disease.

Living cells are apparently able to distinguish proteins or carbohydrates which are native and those that are alien and probably harmful. Host enzymes are constantly changing

* The liquid part of blood which remains after the clot has formed. Blood serum contains the proteins, serum albumin, and serum globulin. Globulin is composed of several fractions including the antibody carrying gamma globulin. Since blood serum lacks fibrinogen it will not clot. In contrast, blood plasma will clot because it contains fibrinogen as well as albumin and globulin.

native plasma proteins to amino acids and rebuilding them into tissue proteins or plasma proteins.

Plasma proteins ⇌ Amino acids ⇌ Tissue proteins

Foreign proteins are thought to resist this process so that it goes on at a very slow rate. Persistent foreign proteins which resist digestion stimulate phagocytic cells to form specific protective substances against them. For example, if a rabbit is bled and then injected with his own blood cells (native protein), no change occurs. On the other hand, the repeated inoculation of red blood cells of another species—as for example, the sheep—will cause the character of the rabbit's blood serum to change so that it will dissolve (hemolyze) the red cells of sheep but not those of other species. In like manner, the injection of bacterial cells, soluble bacterial toxins, or complex natural proteins such as enzymes, egg whites, or horse serum causes the host to respond by forming substances (antibodies) which react with the injected material. The product formed by body cells is called *antibody globulin* (gamma globulin), while the stimulating foreign substance is called the *antigen.*

Antigens   Any substance which will cause the host cells to form antibody globulin and which will combine with that antibody may be considered a complete antigen. In contrast, a substance which will combine with the antibody but which has no ability to incite antibody formation, is called a *partial antigen,* or *hapten.* In the example mentioned, the sheep's cells were the antigen, and the solvent for those cells (hemolysin) was the antibody. Antigens are always foreign substances; usually they are complex colloids* consisting of unaltered proteins, carbohydrates, or combinations of proteins with carbohydrates or with fats. Animal and plant cells contain many cell-stimulating substances, and consequently, the injection of foreign cells leads to the formation of antibodies against each antigen contained in the cells. Antigens are thought to act as enzymes or catalysts that speed up the formation (synthesis) of antibody globulin in such a way that the

---

* Simple crystalloids, such as glucose and sodium chloride, and the altered or incomplete proteins, such as gelatin or the various amino acids, are not antigenic.

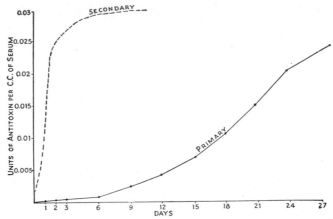

Figure 49   Curves showing rate of antitoxin production following a primary injection and following a secondary injection. Note that
after the secondary injection antitoxin production is much more rapid
and extensive than after the first or primary stimulus. (Frobisher: Fundamentals of Microbiology.)

globulin molecule is an exact mirror image of some part of the
antigen. In other words, antigen and antibody are so arranged
that in regard to structure and electrical changes they fit one
another as a lock fits a key.

Antigens given by mouth stimulate little antibody formation
because they are likely to be destroyed by the enzymes of the
stomach and intestine. Antigens are more effective when injected directly into the tissues; and multiple doses injected a
week or more apart are more effective than a single large dose.
The body response to the introduction of an antigen is usually
twofold: (1) there is an increase in the amount of antibody
in the blood and tissues and (2) there is an increase in the
ability of the cells to form the specific antibodies quickly and
in large quantities, and (3) increased ability to localize the
antigen. The antibody output resulting from the first contact
with an antigen is small in comparison with that produced by
later contacts, which, if properly spaced, are followed by
marked antibody production. (See Figure 49.) In practice,
immunizing materials such as typhoid vaccine are commonly
given in three doses spaced a week or more apart. Six months
or a year later, a single dose of the antigen, called a *stimulating*

(or *booster*) *dose,* may be given to maintain the antibody content at a high level.

Antibody Globulin   Antibody globulin (antibody) is the protective protein formed by various phagocytic cells (and possibly by plasma cells) in response to stimulation by an antigen. If the antigen is thought of as an enzyme the antibody may be considered as an enzyme inhibitor (antienzyme) capable of blocking or interfering with the action of the antigen. For example, diphtheria toxin (*antigen* or *enzyme*) when injected into the skin causes redness and swelling of the area. Diphtheria antitoxin (enzyme inhibitor) mixed with the toxin or present in body fluids prevents this action. Antibody globulin may be present within cells, on the surface of cells, and in the circulating fluids, lymph and blood plasma. A convenient source for antibodies is the blood serum.* Blood serum contains water, salts, and the proteins, serum *albumin* and serum *globulin.* The globulin fraction, called *antibody globulin* (*immune globulin*),† is the protective substance in blood. Serum from an immune animal differs from normal blood serum in that it contains more globulin and this protein (globulin) has been modified so that it readily combines with the specific antigens which stimulated its production. The specific antibody globulin formed in response to a particular antigen is called a *homologous* (like) antibody or antiserum in contrast to a *heterologous* antibody which was formed in response to a different antigen. For example, Type I pneumococcus antiserum is homologous for Type I pneumococcus and is heterologous for Type II pneumococcus, or typhoid antigen. Recent experiments show that antibody formation is directly related to the protein intake of the person forming the antibodies. Animals living on diets deficient in protein show, therefore, a decreased ability to form antibodies and also to resist infection.

There are several theories regarding antibody formation. One theory suggests that the antigen in contact with the cell acts

---

* The straw-colored fluid that remains after clotting has occurred. It differs from blood plasma in that it contains no fibrinogen and therefore will not clot.

† The term immune serum or immune globulin is not accurate. The animal not the globulin is immune.

as a die or pattern around which the antibody globulin (one molecule after another) is formed. Another supposes that through contact with the antigen, a cell enzyme (a proteinase) becomes so modified that it synthesizes molecules of antibody globulin which exactly fit over the antigen because they are mirror images of the antigen in regard to electrical charges and the shape of the molecule. The latter theory seems more plausible, although definite proof is lacking. Antibodies, in common with other body proteins, are constantly destroyed and rebuilt.

Plasma globulin ⇌ Amino acids ⇌ Tissue proteins

Consequently, the antibody content of the blood varies from time to time. Immediately after recovery from disease or after immunization, the specific antibody globulin is formed more rapidly than it is destroyed. After the passage of months or years, antibody destruction takes precedence over its formation. At that time, a single dose of the antigen is of value in increasing resistance by stimulating antibody formation.

The word "antibody" is not well chosen because it suggests a body, particle, or mass. Obviously this is not the case. Antibodies, like other enzymes, are recognized by what they do— that is, by their ability to unite and react with the antigen that caused their formation. The results of that union are predictable and can often be used as the laboratory tests and experiments. Although a vast amount of experimental work has been done, antigen-antibody reactions are not completely understood. Nevertheless, antigens and antibodies have proved of value in research, diagnosis, and disease prevention.

Antigen-Antibody Reactions   By definition an antibody is a substance which will react with the specific antigen which caused its formation. This combination with antibody can be expected to inhibit the action of the antigen. For example, in a test tube, antigen alone can be expected to stay in solution or suspension. The addition of specific antibody (in suitable amounts) causes the antigen particles to precipitate or clump. This is the basis for precipitation and agglutination tests. (See page 339.)

In many (but not all) instances the presence of antibodies resulting from infection or inoculation will give protection against disease in man and animals. It is common knowledge that persons who recover from measles are usually immune, and that vaccination will protect against smallpox. Immunization sometimes gives only partial immunity which, though unable to prevent infection, modifies its character so that a mild form of the disease occurs. As laboratory animals show a similar response to infection and to immunization, they can be used in tests to determine the presence and identity of an antigen or antibody. These are commonly called "animal protection tests" or "neutralization tests."*

Animal-Protection Tests Animal-protection tests are performed by injecting one group of animals with specific immune serum and a lethal dose of toxin, bacteria, or virus, while a second group (the controls) are given the pathogen with no immune serum. Specific antibody globulin when present will give partial or full protection. This type of test can be used to demonstrate (1) the identity and virulence of an organism or toxin, and (2) the presence of specific antibody globulin. For example, if blood serum taken from a convalescent person protects ferrets or mice against influenza A virus but not against influenza B, this constitutes evidence that the infection was of the A type.

The following experiment could be carried out to demonstrate the resistance of immune animals to disease. One hundred and fifty mice (alike in age, sex distribution, size, living conditions, diet) may be placed in three groups and treated as follows:

Group I—Immunize by inoculation with killed plague bacilli.

Group II—Immunize by injecting blood serum from an animal that is immune to plague.

Group III—The controls, not immunized.

It is customary to determine and use a standard dose for animal experiments. The minimum lethal dose (MLD) or more

---

* Neutralization is not a good term since it is commonly associated with acid-base relationships. Inactivation might be a better term since the antibody inactivates or inhibits the ability of the antigen to injure or infect.

commonly the dose which will kill 50 per cent of the animals (LD_{50}) is used. Thus if all the test animals were injected with plague bacilli (LD_{50}) the following results are likely to occur:

Table 16   RESULTS OF INJECTING ANIMALS WITH
PLAGUE BACILLI (LD_{50})

TEST ANIMALS	NUMBER TESTED	NUMBER ALIVE	NUMBER KILLED
Group I (active immunity)	50	49	1
Group II (passive immunity)	50	48	2
Group III (unprotected controls)	50	25	25

Such results are typical for many diseases and indicate that the presence of antibodies will either prevent or modify the course and outcome of the disease. Animal-protection tests can be used to determine the antibody content of blood serum; for example, to determine whether the reader's serum contains antibodies (antitoxin) against diphtheria toxin, measured quantities of the serum could be given to a group of test animals and withheld from the controls. If lethal doses of toxin killed the controls but not the test animals, it would indicate that antibodies were present in the blood in sufficient quantity to protect the animals, but if a lethal dose killed both the controls and the test animals, one may assume that the blood serum contained few or no antibodies against diphtheria toxin.

Immune animals are more prompt and effective in removing bacteria from the blood stream and in avoiding or overcoming infection. The relative resistance of the normal and the immune animal to bacterial infection can also be demonstrated by inoculating one normal and two immune rabbits with virulent pneumococci intravenously and then at intervals collecting samples of blood and estimating the number of bacteria per cubic centimeter. Figure 50 shows typical results obtained in such an experiment. Notice that both active and passive immunization protected the animals against large doses of virulent organisms, and also that the immune rabbits removed the invaders from the circulating blood about as rapidly as

BACTERIA PER C C. CIRCULATING BLOOD AT VARIOUS TIME INTERVALS

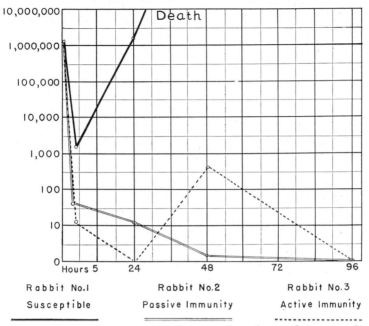

Figure 50   Immune animals respond to bacterial invasion by active and prompt phagocytosis. Note how quickly bacteria are removed from circulating blood.

a normal rabbit removes harmless or avirulent organisms (see page 216).

Just how antibodies act to protect against disease is not fully known but there is considerable evidence that they combine with toxic substances and render them harmless, that they prevent bacteria from multiplying, and that they change the exterior of the foreign substance so that phagocytic cells can attack it. It seems likely that an antigen, upon entering the blood stream or tissues of an immune animal, is changed by the antibody so that it is easily removed by the phagocytes. Not all antigen-antibody reactions are protective in nature. It is likely that in diseases caused by organisms forming endotoxins that injury to cells and the signs of the disease occur at the time when antibodies are uniting with the antigens of bacterial cells. In fact, certain contacts with antigens make the person more susceptible to further injury by the antigen. This state of increased susceptibility is called *hypersensitivity*. It is thought that both hypersensitivity and immunity are due to the same mechanism, but that immunity results when sufficient antibodies are formed to combine with the antigen before it reaches the cells, whereas, in hypersensitivity, the combination of antigen and antibody takes place in the cells with consequent damage to the cells. The injured cells in turn probably give off substances (acetylcholine, histamine, or proteolytic enzymes) which cause smooth-muscle contraction and damage to the capillary walls.

ALLERGY   Allergy or hypersensitivity is a state of increased susceptibility (of cells) due to the formation of antibodies which combine with the antigen under conditions which produce cell damage. Hay fever, pollen asthma, hives (urticaria), and serum sickness are all examples of allergy. In these conditions the antigen-antibody reaction constitutes a severe stress agent. It is thought that antigen unites with antibody that is fixed to cells (instead of circulating free in body fluids). This sometimes results in widespread injury to cells and symptoms of profound shock (see page 226) which may be rapidly fatal. This extreme form of allergy is known as *anaphylaxis* or *anaphylactic shock*. This extreme sensitivity can be induced in a laboratory animal such as a guinea pig by injecting one dose of egg albumin or horse serum (*sensitizing dose* of antigen); after an incubation period of eight to fourteen days, the pig forms antibodies and becomes sensitive although the animal appears normal. Then, if a minute dose of egg albumin is injected, the animal becomes restless and shows signs of respiratory difficulty and may develop convulsions and die. In other species, this method will produce a similar shock although the symptoms may be different. However, shock reactions appear to be of two types: those associated with the contraction of smooth muscles (bronchi, blood vessels, or intestine), and those which cause increased capillary permeability resulting in hemorrhage, edema, or urticaria (hives). In other words, a single dose of a relatively harmless foreign protein can, after a suitable incubation period, make the animal sensitive to that protein; this sensitivity can be transferred to a second animal by injecting blood serum from a sensitive person. A person who has been sensitized can be temporarily *desensitized* by the slow administration of minute doses of the antigen. The common forms of hypersensitivity observed in man are *serum sickness* and a variety of allergies; fortunately anaphylactic shock is rare among human beings.

SERUM SICKNESS   This is seen in certain persons several days after the injection of antitoxic or antibacterial serums. The symptoms include urticaria, swelling, and pain in the joints, swelling in the glands, and fever. This reaction is a response to the proteins in horse serum rather than to the specific antibodies contained in the serum. It may occur after the first as well as after a second dose of the foreign protein and is thought to be due to the formation of antibodies against horse serum proteins. When this antibody appears on cell surfaces, it reacts with the antigen (horse serum) present in the body fluids. This process injures the cells, which in turn calls forth the typical symptoms.

SOME COMMON ALLERGIES   Allergy is so common that the reader must have encountered at least one person who is sensitive or allergic to strawberries, horse hair, house dust, chicken feathers, eggs, fish, pollen, or certain drugs such as penicillin. Normally these antigens (called *allergens*) are changed to simpler substances before entering the cells, or they may be completely excluded. In the susceptible person, however, these allergens appear to pass through the cell barriers unchanged and then stimulate limited antibody formation within the cells. In the sensitive person, circulating antibodies (called *reagins*) formed against the allergen are present in very minute quantities, and therefore fail to protect the cells from injury by the foreign protein. It would seem then that the difference between allergy and immunity is only one of degree. When generous quantities of antibody globulin are formed against an antigen, the two combine before the latter can reach the cells, but when antigen and antibody combine within the cells they cause injury and allergic symptoms. In this way, the dusts and pollens irritate the cells of the respiratory tract, causing hay fever, and certain foods injure the capillaries (of the sensitive person) so that they permit the escape of fluid into the tissues with the formation of large, red, itching welts on the skin (hives or urticaria). Although allergy depends on an antigen-antibody reaction in cells, cell damage and allergic symptoms may be profoundly influenced by resulting emotional stresses. A person sensitive to ragweed pollen may remain free from symptoms when exposed to the antigen (pollen) until he encounters a situation which causes anger or resentment. Discussing or thinking about something which calls forth anger may be sufficient to bring on a full blown attack of hay fever.

It is possible to detect sensitivity by scratching the skin and applying small quantities of antigen to the tissue. The person who is sensitive responds by developing a red, inflamed area at the point of contact. Certain antigens contained within bacterial cells, for example, tuberculosis organisms, leave the person sensitive to them. The tuberculin reaction, the skin test, used to determine sensitivity to the protein of tuberculosis organisms, is discussed on page 417.

Both hypersensitivity and antibody formation often occur together following infection or inoculation. For example, a child inoculated with multiple doses of pertussis vaccine forms specific antibody globulin and also becomes sensitive to pertussis antigen. In some instances, antibody formation is the dominant response; for example, the formation of antitoxin in response to diphtheria or tetanus toxoid. With other antigens, little or no circulating antibody is formed but infection causes marked hypersensitivity, as in tuberculosis, syphilis, and various mold infections.

Test-Tube Reactions   Antibody globulin obtained from the serum of an immune animal will react with the specific antigen outside the body. When a bacterial toxin is mixed with its specific antibody (antitoxin), the toxin is inactivated (neutralized) and thus rendered harmless, whereas antigens consisting of soluble proteins are precipitated and bacterial cells are clumped or dissolved. Antibodies have been given names that suggest their action, and it is customary to speak of them as though they were specific entities although it is probable that a single antibody formed against a specific antigen may show a variety of reactions depending upon the conditions of the test. Table 17 summarizes some of the common reactions which occur when suitable quantities of specific antigen and antibody are mixed.

Table 17	REACTIONS OF ANTIGENS AND ANTIBODIES	
ANTIGEN (ENZYME)	SPECIFIC ANTIBODY (ENZYME INHIBITOR)	REACTION
Toxin	+ Antitoxin ————————>	Inactivation (Neutralization)
Protcins	+ Precipitin ————————>	Precipitation
Bacterial cells	+ Agglutinin ————————>	Agglutination (clumping)
Bacterial cells	+ Opsonin ————————>	Preparation for phagocytosis
Bacterial cells	+ Inhibiting antibody ————>	Prevention of cell division
Bacterial cells	+ Bacteriolysins + complement—>	Destruction or lysis of cells
Red blood cells	+ Hemolysins + complement—>	Destruction or lysis of cells
Other cells	+ Cytolysins + complement—>	Destruction or lysis of cclls
Viruses	+ Neutralizing antibodies ————>	Inactivation — i.e., rendering them incapable of producing disease
Red blood cells*	+ Antigen + antibody ————>	Agglutination (hemagglutination)

* Where an antigen and antibody do not readily react with a detectable change, the antigen, such as tuberculin (protein from tuberculosis organism), can be adsorbed on red blood cells. The specific antibody will then combine with the antigen (on the surface of red cells) and clump the red cells.

As these reactions are highly specific, they can be used to identify either the antigen or the antibody. For example, a known typhoid antiserum can be used to identify unknown organisms or proteins because it will combine only with the specific antigen; likewise a known antigen, for example, typhoid bacteria, may be used to detect antibodies against those bacteria. The finding of antibodies in the blood of a patient sometimes aids the physician in making a diagnosis. Such diagnostic tests are discussed in Chapter 21.

SUMMARY

1. Immunity or the ability to resist disease may be either natural or acquired. Natural immunity is associated with species or race, while acquired immunity depends upon the experience of the person.

2. There are two types of immunity: active and passive.

3. An active immunity occurs from one of the following experiences: (a) recovering from the disease; (b) recovering from a latent or mild infection; (c) being inoculated with a suitable antigen.

4. A passive immunity of short duration follows the injection of an immune serum.

5. Antigens are complex foreign substances, usually protein in character, that stimulate the body to form protective substances or antibodies. The body responds to the antigen by increasing and modifying its output of serum globulin and by increasing its ability to localize the antigen. Bacteria, animal cells, plant cells, and complex proteins including enzymes are examples of antigens.

6. Antibody globulin reacts with the corresponding antigen in the animal body and in the test tube. In the animal body, serum containing antibodies often protects against disease or modifies the character of the disease but sometimes its presence makes the animal more susceptible to injury. When suitable amounts of antibody and antigen are combined in test tubes, visible or detectable changes occur. This union of antibody and antigen is the basis of the agglutination, precipitation, complement-fixation tests, and animal protection tests.

SUPPLEMENTARY READINGS

BOOKS:

Boyd, W. C.: Fundamentals of Immunology. 2d ed. New York, Interscience Publishers, Inc., 1947.

Burnet, F. M., and Fenner, F.: The Production of Antibodies. 2d ed. London, The Macmillan Co., 1949.

Burrows, W.: Jordan-Burrows Textbook of Bacteriology. 15th ed. Philadelphia, W. B. Saunders Co., 1949.

Dubos, R.: Bacterial and Mycotic Infections of Man. 2d ed. Philadelphia, J. B. Lippincott Co., 1952.

Pappenheimer, A. M., Jr. (Ed.): The Nature and Significance of Antibody Response. Symposium of the Section of Microbiology. New York Academy of Medicine. New York, Columbia University Press, 1953.

Raffel, S.: Immunity: Hypersensitivity, Serology. New York, Appleton-Century-Crofts, Inc., 1953.

Selye, H.: The Physiology and Pathology of Exposure to Stress. Montreal, Canada, Acta, Inc., 1950.

Selye, H.: First Annual Report on Stress. Montreal, Canada, Acta, Inc., 1951.

Sevag, M. G.: Immuno-Catalysis and Related Fields in Bacteriology and Biochemistry. 2d ed., Springfield, Ill., Charles C Thomas, Publisher, 1951.

Smith, D. T., and Conant, N. F.: Zinsser's Textbook of Bacteriology. 10th ed. New York, Appleton-Century-Crofts, Inc., 1952.

PERIODICALS:

McGuinness, A. C.: Review of Current Trends in Active and Passive Immunization. J.A.M.A., *148:* 261–265, 1952.

Rawlins, A. G.: Hormonal-Connective Tissue Mechanism in Allergy. Ann. Allergy, *10:* 440–444, 1952.

ANTIBODY formation is interesting evidence of the ability of a living body to adjust itself to unfavorable circumstances. During the course of an infection or any contact with foreign proteins, the cells of the host produce protective antibodies that persist in the blood plasma, lymph, and cells for months or years. Antibody formation can also be stimulated by the introduction of artificial antigens prepared from the cells or products of microorganisms so modified that they are incapable of producing disease. These antigens are called immunizing agents or *vaccines;* the word vaccine is derived from the Latin *vacca* (meaning cow) and refers to the fact that the first vaccine (smallpox) was derived from the cow. The organisms used for the various vaccines are either killed or rendered incapable of producing disease, that is, *attenuated.* Viruses may be attenuated by animal passage; for example, the virus of smallpox loses its virulence for man after growing in the tissues of a calf or rabbit. Bacteria are commonly attenuated by prolonged cultivation on artificial media or by growth at an unfavorable temperature.

Attenuated living viruses are commonly used in vaccines because the killed organisms are often ineffective, whereas living bacteria are seldom used to inoculate human beings. Table 18 shows examples of vaccines in common use.

The duration of immunity acquired by vaccination varies with the antigen used, the dose of the vaccine, and the age and general health of the person. As a rule, the exotoxins and some, but not all, viruses are more efficient antigens than the bacterial cells or endotoxins.

VACCINIA OR SMALLPOX VACCINE VIRUS

Preparation   *Vaccinia* (smallpox vaccine virus) is an effective and useful antigen. Since viruses require a living medium for growth, the vaccine virus is grown in the skin cells of healthy calves. The virus seed used to vaccinate the

Table 18   VACCINES IN COMMON USE

ANTIGEN	COMMON NAME	EXAMPLE	DURATION OF IMMUNITY
Living attenuated virus	Vaccine virus	Smallpox vaccine	One or more years
Living attenuated virus	Virus vaccine	Yellow fever vaccine	Six years
Attenuated or killed rickettsia	Rickettsial vaccine	Typhus vaccine	Uncertain
Killed bacteria	Bacterial vaccine	Typhoid vaccine	Six months to two years
Killed bacteria	Bacterial vaccine	Pertussis vaccine	One year
Modified exotoxin	Toxoid	Diphtheria toxoid	Several years
Modified exotoxin	Toxoid	Tetanus toxoid	One or more years
Exotoxin	Toxin	Scarlet fever toxin	Six months or more

calf is obtained from rabbits previously inoculated with the
virus. The calves are kept in ultrasanitary surroundings where
even the bedding is sterilized to kill the spore-forming tetanus
organisms that may be present. Before vaccination, the abdomen and thighs of the calf are shaved and scrubbed thoroughly
with soap, water, and alcohol. After drying, the whole area is
prepared by making hundreds of superficial incisions that expose the living skin cells. Then the virus seed is applied to
the scratches and allowed to dry; no dressing is used, but the
area is sprayed with an antiseptic that inhibits the growth of
bacteria. The virus is allowed to grow until the inoculated area
shows signs of mild inflammation and pus formation. On the
sixth day, the calf is anesthetized and scrubbed vigorously with
soap and water, then the pus and crusts are scraped off and
collected under aseptic conditions. This material, consisting of
pus, epithelial cells, virus, and some bacteria, is crude vaccine
virus. Before it is used, the calf is killed and examined to
determine that it is free from all evidence of disease. Then the
crude vaccine is ground with a mixture of glycerin and phenol
and stored for several months at —12° C. (10.4° F.). This long
storage kills most of the bacteria but does not injure the virus.

Since vaccine virus always contains some bacteria, appropriate laboratory tests must be made to determine that it is free from tetanus organisms and other pathogenic bacteria. Next, its potency as an antigen is tested by inoculating rabbits and susceptible human subjects. If the virus produces a typical vaccination reaction, it is placed in capillary tubes ready for distribution. Vaccine virus may also be cultivated in the cells of developing chick embryos, though this product is still in the experimental stage and is not widely used. It differs from the ordinary virus in that it is injected into the skin and leaves no scar as a tangible evidence of successful vaccination.

Storage   Vaccine virus, like other biological products, must be properly stored if it is to retain its potency. It should be kept continuously at a temperature below freezing until one hour before use and should be packed in dry ice for transportation. The expiration date printed on each package of commercial vaccine is valid only when the product has been kept cold.

Vaccination   A small drop of vaccine is applied to the dry skin of the arm that has been cleansed with soap and water or with alcohol. Then a sterile, sharp needle, held parallel to the arm, is used to pick up some of the superficial cells, thus introducing the virus to the living cells beneath. After the excess vaccine has been wiped away, the area is permitted to dry. The arm should be left *without dressings* or *shields,* which are undesirable because they increase the temperature and moisture of the area, so that the skin softens instead of forming a tough protective scab. Furthermore, experiments performed on rabbits indicate that the application of dressings definitely increases the risk of infection with the tetanus bacillus (*Clostridium tetani*), an organism that thrives on dead tissue in the absence of oxygen. The arm is the preferred site for vaccination because it is subject to less contamination and because the better circulation of blood in the arm favors healing and lessens the risk of infection. When necessary, clothing may be protected by pinning a square of clean gauze or linen

* Some authorities suggest a loose gauze dressing fluffed and applied without pressure to prevent the individual from touching or scratching the area.

to the inside of the sleeve. The arm should be guarded against mechanical injury that would break the scab or contaminate the wound. Vaccinia is not contagious, but the virus can be transferred to eyes or wounds. Therefore, the hands should be carefully washed after contact with the vaccine or the vaccinated area.

RESPONSE TO VACCINATION   For antibody formation to take place it is necessary that the virus actually multiply in the body. The invasion of the skin cells by the living virus brings visible and predictable results. Contrary to popular opinion, no reaction does not indicate immunity; it means that poor vaccine or poor technique was employed.

Local tissue responses to vaccine virus can for convenience be placed in one of four groups: (1) primary vaccinia or primary reaction, (2) early reaction, (3) vaccinoid or accelerated reaction, and (4) failure or no reaction.

In response to the first vaccination, the person develops *vaccinia* or a *primary reaction* (see Figure 51). The virus invades the skin cells, the lymph, and the blood stream. On the third day, a raised papule appears at the site of inoculation and gradually enlarges. On the sixth or seventh day, the papule changes to a white blister or *vesicle* surrounded by a red area— described by Jenner as a "pearl upon a rose leaf"—which becomes larger and fills with pus. This pustule is surrounded by a reddened area 10 to 12 cm. in diameter. A crust forms on the twelfth day and falls off on the twenty-first day, leaving a red scar which gradually fades. This reaction, which ends in the formation of pustule, crust, and scar, indicates that the individual who previously was highly susceptible has developed an immunity to smallpox.

The *early reaction* occurs in persons previously vaccinated who are either allergic or immune to smallpox. This response may be stimulated by dead or living vaccine virus. A red papule, usually 1 to 2 cm. in diameter, appears within three days. A vesicle may or may not appear, but no scar is formed. This response may be assumed to indicate immunity if vaccine from the same lot produces primary vaccinia in susceptible individuals. Persons who have been vaccinated previously should be observed on the third and seventh days, before the evidence of the early reaction disappears. The term *immune reaction* is misleading and therefore should not be used to describe the early response to vaccinia.

The *vaccinoid* or *accelerated reaction* occurs in a person who is partially protected by previous infection or vaccination. A papule appears at the site of inoculation on the third or fourth day, followed by a vesicle on the fifth. The latter may or may not form a pustule, that is, become filled with pus. After the

Table 19   REACTIONS TO SMALLPOX VACCINATIONS

TYPE	DIAMETER OF AREOLA	TIME	COMMENT
Primary	10-12 cm. with vesicle, pustule, and crust	8-14 days	No prior immunity scar present
Accelerated	4-6 cm. vesicle present	4-7 days	Partial prior immunity; scar usually present
Early	1-2 cm.	Less than 3 days	Sensitivity—not necessarily immune
Failure	No reaction		Repeat using another lot of vaccine

Modified from Warnock, G. H.: Current Concepts of Immunization. Merck Report *61:* 9–15, 1952.

sixth or seventh day, the lesion heals rapidly; a small scar is formed but it may be difficult to find. This response is intermediate, since it requires less time than the primary but more time than the early reaction. The four possible responses to smallpox vaccination are summarized in Table 19.

OTHER VIRUS AND RICKETTSIAL VACCINES

Effective vaccines may be prepared to protect against some of those virus and rickettsial diseases in which infection is followed by lasting immunity. The attenuated organisms used in preparing such vaccines must be grown within susceptible living cells. Different viruses have definite preferences for certain species of animals and also for certain types of cells. For example, the rabies virus can be propagated in the nerve cells of many animals, while vaccinia virus grows best in the epithelial cells of rabbits or cattle. The disease-producing abil-

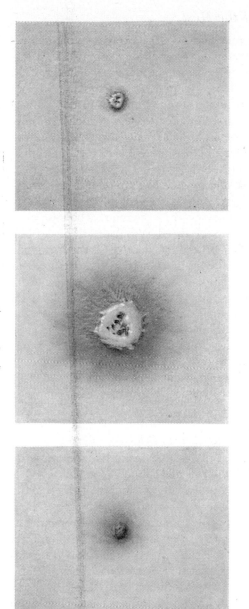

Primary vaccinia—appearance of a normal "take" three or four days following vaccination.

Primary vaccinia — by the ninth or tenth day the reaction has reached a maximum, following which the redness fades and a scab begins to form.

Early reaction — when immunity or allergy is high a prompt and very mild reaction occurs.

Figure 51

ity of the virus may be changed by inoculating it into a laboratory animal or by adapting the virus to development in a different type of tissue. For example, rabies virus when passed
from rabbit to rabbit increases its infectiveness for that animal
but loses its ability to produce severe infection in dogs. Likewise, the virulence of the yellow-fever virus, which normally
attacks liver cells, may be so reduced by growing it in mouse
brains that it is no longer able to injure liver cells. The virulence of some viruses may be decreased by prolonged cultivation in developing chick embryos or in tissue cultures consisting of susceptible cells growing in a sterile nutrient medium.
Still another method was evolved by Pasteur, who prepared
a rabies vaccine consisting of dried spinal cords of rabbits
infected with rabies. This process so decreased the virulence
of the material that it could be inoculated without danger of
causing disease. Like vaccinia, crude virus vaccines prepared
for tissue cultures, chick embryos, or spinal cords must be
tested for sterility and also for their ability to stimulate the
production of antibodies. The potency of the vaccine can be
determined by inoculating suitable laboratory animals and
later determining the antibody content of the blood by means
of animal protection or complement fixation tests. Most virus
and rickettsial vaccines are made by growing the organisms
in chick embryos.

BACTERIAL VACCINES

Bacterial vaccines consist of suspensions of living attenuated
organisms or of killed bacterial cells. BCG (bacillus of Calmette-Guérin) vaccine contains living bovine tuberculosis
organisms which have lost their disease-producing power
through long cultivation on bile medium. As a rule, attenuated
bacteria are too dangerous to use for human beings; therefore,
most bacterial vaccines consist of suspensions of killed organisms. Virulent bacteria are grown on a suitable solid medium
and are then suspended in salt solution and killed by heat,
chemicals, or ultraviolet light. The killing process should be
as gentle as possible to avoid unnecessary changes in the antigen structure. For this reason, a low temperature (from 56
to 60° C. [132.8° to 140° F.] for one hour), or a weak concen-

tration of phenol, tricresol, or Formalin may be used. Experiments with ultraviolet light have proved so successful that it seems likely that this method may replace heat and chemicals as a means of inactivating bacteria without decreasing their value as antigens. Samples of the suspension are inoculated into aerobic and anaerobic cultures and into laboratory animals, to determine that the vaccine is free from living bacteria and is nontoxic. The number of bacteria per cubic centimeter can be estimated either by comparing the turbidity or cloudiness of the vaccine with that of turbidity standards, or by mixing equal quantities of vaccine and fresh blood and determining the ratio of bacteria to red blood cells. Estimates of the number of bacteria per cubic centimeter of suspension can also be made by determining the protein content of the suspension. When this has been done, saline solution can be added to the suspension to dilute it to the required concentration. The label on a vial of bacterial vaccine must include a statement of the kind of bacteria, the approximate number of bacteria in 1 cc. of the fluid, the expiration date, and lot number.

Some bacterial vaccines consist of one type of organism, while others, called *mixed vaccines,* contain several different organisms. The bacteria used for the preparation of vaccines may come from stock cultures or from organisms isolated from the person for whom the vaccine is to be used. The former are called stock while the latter are designated as *autogenous vaccines.* The latter are uncommon; the former include cholera, plague, pertussis, and the mixed typhoid and paratyphoid vaccines. (See Table 20.)

ANTIGENS DERIVED FROM BACTERIAL CELLS

Bacterial cells contain many antigens which stimulate antibody formation. Some of these antibodies have real protective value while others do not. For this reason, it would seem to be desirable when possible to inoculate the effective antigen instead of the whole bacterial cell. This has been done successfully with bacteria exotoxins and is being attempted experimentally with other bacterial antigens such as the purified antigen for typhoid.

Bacterial Antigens   Bacterial antigens extracted from

Table 20   SOME ANTIGENS THAT ARE USED AS VACCINES

VACCINE	ANTIGEN	SOURCE OF ANTIGEN	INOCULATION
Cholera*	Killed bacteria	Culture on artificial medium	Two doses at from 7- to 10-day intervals, followed by one stimulating dose every 4 to 6 months by subcutaneous injection
Diphtheria‡	Toxoid (modified exotoxin)	Broth culture	Three doses at 4-week intervals at age 3 months followed by stimulating dose one year later and then every 3 years if necessary
Gas gangrene (experimental)	Toxoid (modified exotoxin)	Cultures of *Clostridium perfringens* and *Clostridium novyi* on artificial media	Two doses at from 7- to 10-day intervals, followed by stimulating dose in from 6 to 9 months
Influenza	Attenuated virus—strains A and B	Culture in chick embryo	One or two doses subcutaneously
Mumps (experimental)	Attenuated virus	Culture in chick embryo	Two or three doses
Plague*	Killed bacteria	Culture on artificial medium	Two doses at from 7- to 21-day intervals, followed by a stimulating dose every 4 to 6 months
Pertussis (whooping cough)	Killed bacteria	Culture	Three doses at 3-week intervals at age 3 months
Rabies	Killed virus	Culture in rabbit brain	Fourteen doses on 14 successive days
Smallpox†‡	Attenuated virus	Calf inoculation	Introduced to skin cells by multiple puncture at age 6 months and every 5 years thereafter
Tetanus†	Toxoid (modified exotoxin)	Broth culture	Two doses at 4-week intervals at 6 months or later; stimulating dose at 1 year and then every 3 years

Table 20—(Continued)

VACCINE	ANTIGEN	SOURCE OF ANTIGEN	INOCULATION
Typhoid and paraty- phoid†‡	Killed bacteria	Culture on arti- ficial medium	Three doses by subcuta- neous injection at from 7- to 10-day intervals; stimulating dose every 1 to 2 years
Tuberculosis BCG‡	Attenuated bacteria (Bovine strain)	Culture on arti- ficial medium	One dose subcutaneously or by mouth
Irradiated tubercu- losis vac- cine (exper- imental)	Bacteria killed by ultra- violet light		
Typhus*	Killed rickettsias	Culture in chick embryos	Three doses at from 7- to 10-day intervals by sub- cutaneous injection, fol- lowed by one stimulating dose every 4 to 6 months
Yellow fever*	Attenuated virus	Culture in chick embryos	One dose by subcutaneous injection

* Used by the United States Army for personnel stationed in or travel- ing through areas where there is risk of exposure.
† Used by the United States Army for all personnel.
‡ Used by many civilian hospitals for selected personnel.

the cell and purified should prove valuable if and when they can be obtained. A purified somatic antigen of typhoid has been used experimentally. Purified antigens are thought to be identical with endotoxins. Contrary to common opinion, endo- toxins (formed chiefly by gram-negative bacteria) do stimulate antibody formation. The globulin so formed does not, however, counteract their injurious effects. It seems probable that injury occurs when antigen and antibody unite on cell surfaces.

Toxins and Toxoids   Certain bacteria, namely, those that cause scarlet fever, diphtheria, and tetanus, produce solu- ble exotoxins which are excellent antigens. These toxins are present in the filtrate of broth in which the organisms have been grown. Their potency can be determined by injecting measured quantities into suitable laboratory animals and observing the effects. After standardization, the product can be used as an antigen or as a source for toxoid. Unaltered scarlet fever toxin may be used as an antigen, but tetanus and diphtheria toxins are too irritating to be employed. Toxins consisting of two parts—one which stimulates the formation of antitoxin (the antigen) and another that injures the cells (the poison)—can be rendered harmless by the addition of Formalin. This modified toxin, called *toxoid,* is suitable for human use. This product is called "fluid toxoid" and is commonly used for older children and adults. Alum-precipitated or adsorbed aluminum hydroxide toxoids which are absorbed slowly are commonly used for infants and small children. Diphtheria and tetanus toxoids are used to protect susceptible persons against diphtheria and tetanus.

COMBINED ANTIGENS

Two or more immunizing agents may be combined and given at the same time. There is now general agreement that it is desirable for all infants to develop an active immunity against smallpox, diphtheria, tetanus, and pertussis (whooping cough). Smallpox vaccine is commonly given alone whereas the antigens for diphtheria, tetanus, and pertussis may be combined and given in three or more divided doses. The following schedule is recommended by the American Academy of Pediatrics:*

3 months of age—0.5 cc.	alum-precipitated or aluminum hydroxide adsorbed diphtheria and tetanus toxoids containing 15 billion *H. pertussis* intramuscularly, left gluteus maximus
4 months of age	Repeat in right gluteus maximus
5 months of age	Repeat in left vastus lateralis or right deltoid
6 months of age	Smallpox vaccination over left deltoid
12 months of age	Schick test

The intervals between doses may be increased if necessary. Antigens should not be given during the course of respiratory or other acute infections. Fever, drowsiness, or severe local

* Report of the Committee on Immunization and Therapeutic Procedures for Acute Infectious Diseases of the American Academy of Pediatrics, page 4.

reactions following inoculations usually indicate the need for smaller doses. If convulsions or severe reactions (fortunately these are rare) occur, inoculations may need to be postponed for several months or even a year. As a rule, diphtheria, tetanus, and pertussis vaccines are not given during the season when poliomyelitis is epidemic. (See page 368.)

SUMMARY

1. Antigens used to stimulate an active immunity are called immunizing agents or vaccines.

2. Vaccines may consist of living attenuated organisms, dead organisms, or toxins or extracts derived from the organism. Some of these may with advantage be combined and given at the same time.

3. The active immunity following the introduction of vaccines lasts for periods varying from a few months to several years.

4. Vaccines should be stored in a refrigerator and should not be removed more than one hour before use.

SUPPLEMENTARY READINGS

BOOKS:

American Academy of Pediatrics: Report of the Committee on Immunization and Therapeutic Procedures for Acute Infectious Diseases of the Academy of Pediatrics. Evanston, Ill., American Academy of Pediatrics, 1951.

American Public Health Association: The Control of Communicable Diseases in Man. 7th ed. New York, American Public Health Association, 1950.

Boyd, W. C.: Fundamentals of Immunology. 2d ed. New York, Interscience Publishers, Inc., 1947.

Burrows, W.: Jordan-Burrows Textbook of Bacteriology. 15th ed Philadelphia, W. B. Saunders Co., 1949.

Greenberg, M., and Matz, A. V.: Modern Concepts of Communicable Disease. New York, G. P. Putnam's Sons, 1953.

Maxcy, K. F.: Rosenau Preventive Medicine and Hygiene. 7th ed New York, Appleton-Century-Crofts, Inc., 1951.

Raffel, S.: Immunity-Hypersensitivity-Serology. New York, Appleton-Century-Crofts, Inc., 1953.

Smith, D. T., and Conant, N. F.: Zinsser's Textbook of Bacteriology 10th ed. New York, Appleton-Century-Crofts, Inc., 1952.

PERIODICALS:

Benenson, A. S.: Immediate (So-Called "Immune") Reaction to Smallpox Vaccination. J.A.M.A., *143:* 1238–1240, 1950.

Brackett, A. S.: The Importance of Vaccination and Revaccination. Am. J. Nursing, *52:* 847, 1952.
Burrows, W.: Endotoxins. Ann. Rev. Microbiol., *5:* 181–196, 1951.
Editorial: Irradiated Tuberculosis Vaccine. J.A.M.A., *146:* 931, 1951.
Henle, G., and others: Studies in the Prevention of Mumps. J. Immunol., *66:* 535–578, 1951.
Wiener, A. S., and others: Studies in Autoantibodies in Human Sera. J. Immunol., *71:* 58–65, 1953.

THE BLOOD serum from an immune animal can sometimes be used to prevent disease or to modify the course of the disease, but this increased resistance is so transient that the person is often susceptible again within a short time, usually three weeks. In theory, it is possible to develop antiserums against any antigens, but in practice, only a few are distinctly useful while many are of little value in protecting a living host. Antiserums can be obtained from human beings, or from laboratory animals that are actively immune. The antibody globulins contained in such serums are of two types: those which are formed in response to a vaccine consisting of whole bacterial cells (antibacterial serums), and those which are formed in response to specific antigens obtained from bacterial cells (for example, antitoxins).

ANTITOXINS

Antitoxins are the antibody globulins formed against soluble exotoxins. Few antiserums of this type are available because few bacteria form exotoxins. The chief toxin-formers are the organisms which cause diphtheria, tetanus, botulism, Shiga dysentery, and certain strains of the streptococci and micrococci. Diphtheria antitoxin can be used as an example of this type of antiserum. Tetanus antitoxin is similar to that of diphtheria and is useful in preventing the disease (tetanus, lockjaw), but is of little value after toxin has caused damage to nerve cells. Other antitoxins are prepared in a manner similar to that used for diphtheria antitoxin—that is, each is formed by an animal in response to repeated injections of the specific toxin or toxoid and each is useful in combating only the type of toxin against which it was formed. To be effective, it must be given early and in sufficient amounts to prevent the toxin excreted by the invading organisms from uniting with the cells of the host.

Diphtheria   Antitoxin *   PREPARATION   Diphtheria antitoxin is formed by a healthy horse which has been inoculated with diphtheria toxin or toxoid. When the horse has developed a high concentration of antibody globulin, the blood is collected and allowed to clot. The serum remaining after the clot has formed is crude antitoxin which must be refined and concentrated by laboratory procedures (precipitation, enzyme digestion, and dialysis) before it is ready for use. Also, it must be tested for its ability to protect laboratory animals against standard doses of toxin.

STANDARDIZATION   Since diphtheria toxin and antitoxin are not available in the chemically pure state, their potency cannot be measured by weight or by volume but must be determined in terms of units indicating the degree of toxicity for the toxin and the protecting power of the antitoxin as determined by animal tests. This standardization process consists of two steps: (1) the determination of the potency of diphtheria toxin obtained from a culture of virulent bacteria, by testing it against a standard diphtheria antitoxin, and (2) the determination of the protective power of the new antitoxin by testing it against the toxin standardized in step (1). The standard antitoxin, prepared and distributed by the National Institute of Health (U. S. Public Health Service), is used because it is more stable than the toxin. Thus, the initial step in the process is to grow diphtheria organisms in broth to obtain toxin for standardizing the antitoxin. But first the potency of the toxin itself must be assayed by the method outlined below:

1. Standardization of diphtheria toxin
   Materials:
   a. Standard diphtheria antitoxin (from National Institute of Public Health)
   b. Diphtheria toxin (filtrate from diphtheria culture)
   c. Guinea pigs weighing 250 gm.

   Purpose: To determine the smallest amount of toxin which when combined with 1 unit of antitoxin will kill a guinea pig weighing 250 gm. in 4 days, i.e., the L + dose (the dose combined with one unit of antitoxin that is lethal in 4 days).

   Procedure: Administer varying quantities of toxin, mixed with one unit of antitoxin, to a series of guinea pigs.

   Results: The results may be tabulated as follows:

DETERMINATION OF THE L + DOSE OF TOXIN[1]

The standard antitoxin is used in this measurement.

1 unit of antitoxin + 0.2 cc. toxin   no reaction
1 unit of antitoxin + 0.21 cc. toxin   no reaction = L° dose
1 unit of antitoxin + 0.22 cc. toxin   local injury
1 unit of antitoxin + 0.23 cc. toxin   fatal in 17 days
1 unit of antitoxin + 0.24 cc. toxin   fatal in 14 days
1 unit of antitoxin + 0.26 cc. toxin   fatal in 9 days
1 unit of antitoxin + 0.28 cc. toxin   fatal in 6 days
1 unit of antitoxin + 0.29 cc. toxin   fatal in 4 days = L + dose
1 unit of antitoxin + 0.3 cc. toxin   fatal in 3 days
1 unit of antitoxin + 0.31 cc. toxin   fatal in 2 days

Conclusion: The L + dose is 0.29 cc. of toxin. This amount will be used in step "2" to standardize the new antitoxin.

2. Standardization of antitoxin

Materials:
Toxin (standardized in "1")
Antitoxin (blood serum from horse immunized against diphtheria toxin)
Guinea pigs weighing 250 gm.

Purpose: To determine the smallest amount of antitoxin which when mixed with one L + dose of toxin will kill a guinea pig weighing 250 gm. in 4 days.

Procedure: Inject guinea pigs with 1 cc. of various dilutions of antitoxin mixed with one L + dose.

Results:

Table 21   STANDARDIZATION OF AN UNKNOWN SERUM[2]

TEST DOSE		
AMOUNT OF TOXIN SOLUTION (1 L + DOSE) CC.	AMOUNT OF ANTISERUM (CC.)	EFFECT ON ANIMAL
0.29	1/500	lives
0.29	1/600	lives
0.29	1/700	lives
0.29	1/800	dies in 8 days
0.29	1/900	dies in 4 days
0.29	1/1000	dies in 2 days

Conclusion: The antitoxin contains 1 unit in 1/900 cc. or 900 units per cc.

The protecting power of antitoxin is expressed in terms of units of antitoxin per cubic centimeter of fluid. One can always find this information on the label of the box and on the vial of commercial diphtheria antitoxin. The label also gives the expiration date—that is, the last date on which the serum can be used with safety. This is a necessary precaution because diphtheria antitoxin, like other biological products, deteriorates with age.

Use   Diphtheria antitoxin is used to assist an infected person to combat disease and to confer temporary protection on a susceptible person who has been exposed to the disease. The best results are obtained when large doses are given early in the course of the disease before the toxin formed by the diphtheria organisms has united with and injured the cells of the heart, kidneys, or nerve trunks. Antitoxin is almost useless when administered after the cells have been injured.

ANTIBACTERIAL SERUMS

Antibacterial serums are less potent than the antitoxins. Some have little or no protective power, while others if given early may prevent or modify the specific infection. Antibacterial serums are produced by rabbits or horses which have been inoculated with multiple doses of bacterial cells. For example, antipertussis serum is produced by injecting rabbits with pertussis organisms. The serum obtained by bleeding the rabbit is refined, tested, and standardized. Sometimes human subjects are used for antiserum production because globulins of human origin are less rapidly destroyed in the body.

HUMAN SERUM AND GLOBULIN

Human convalescent serum or concentrated globulin is of value in treating certain virus diseases. Gamma globulin, the antibody fraction of globulin, contains antibodies against measles and infectious hepatitis, mumps, poliomyelitis, and certain other childhood infections. Whole blood, serum, or concentrated gamma globulin may be used to modify or prevent measles, mumps (experimental), or infectious hepatitis. Gamma globulin is commonly obtained by fractioning human blood serums or by extracting antibodies from the human placenta. Human globulins are destroyed less rapidly than those produced by animals and therefore give longer protection. The antibody content of any particular gamma globulin depends on the number of individuals who contrib-

Table 22   DISEASES IN WHICH ANTISERUMS HAVE
SOME VALUE

SOURCE	TYPE	DISEASE	PATHOGEN	REMARKS
Serums of animal origin	Antitoxins (in horse serum)	Botulism	*Clostridium botulinum*	
		Diphtheria	*Corynebacterium diphtheriae*	
		Gas gangrene	*Clostridium perfringens*	
		Tetanus	*Clostridium tetani*	
	Antibacterial serums (in rabbit or horse serum)	Anthrax	*Bacillus anthracis*	
		Meningitis	*Hemophilus influenzae*	Used with streptomycin and sulfonamides
		Pertussis	*Hemophilus pertussis*	
	Antiviral serum (in rabbit serum)	Rabies	Virus	
Serums from normal adults or convalescents	Whole blood Concentrated gamma globulin "Immune globulin" (placental) Red Cross gamma globulin (experimental)	Infectious hepatitis	Virus	
		Measles	Virus	
		Poliomyelitis	Virus	
Serums from vaccinated donors	Concentrated gamma globulin	Pertussis	*Hemophilus pertussis*	
	Hyperimmune serum	Mumps	Virus	Experimental

uted blood to the pool. Red Cross gamma globulin, prepared from the blood of some 50,000 persons living in different parts of the United States, contains antibodies against measles, infectious hepatitis, and several strains of poliomyelitis. Table 22 shows some of the diseases in which antiserums are used.

SUMMARY

1. The inoculation of an animal with a bacterial toxin stimulates the body cells to form a specific antitoxin that will combine with and inactivate (neutralize) the toxin. Such antitoxins confer a passive immunity of short duration and can be used to prevent or to modify the course of a disease.

2. The inoculation of an animal with bacterial cells stimulates the formation of specific antibodies against the antigens contained in the cells. Some antibacterial serums also confer passive immunity but they are usually less effective than the antitoxins.

3. Convalescent serum, whole adult blood, and gamma globulin may also be used to confer passive immunity to some of the common diseases of childhood.

REFERENCES

1. Boyd, W. C.: Fundamentals of Immunology. 2d ed. New York, Interscience Publishers, 1947, p. 409.
2. Boyd, W. C.: *Ibid.*, p. 410.

SUPPLEMENTARY READINGS

BOOKS:

American Academy of Pediatrics. Report of the Committee on Immunization and Therapeutic Procedures for Acute Infectious Diseases of the Academy of Pediatrics. Evanston, Ill., American Academy of Pediatrics, 1951.

Burrows, W.: Jordan-Burrows Textbook of Bacteriology. 15th ed. Philadelphia, W. B. Saunders Co., 1949.

Greenberg, M., and Matz, A. V.: Modern Concepts of Communicable Disease. New York, G. P. Putnam's Sons, 1953.

Maxcy, K. F.: Rosenau Preventive Medicine and Hygiene. 7th ed. New York, Appleton-Century-Crofts, Inc., 1951.

Raffel, S.: Immunity: Hypersensitivity, Serology. New York, Appleton-Century-Crofts, Inc., 1953.

Smith, D. T., and Conant, N. F.: Zinsser's Textbook of Bacteriology. 10th ed. New York, Appleton-Century-Crofts, Inc., 1952.

Topley, W. W. C., and Wilson, G. S.: The Principles of Bacteriology and Immunity. 3d ed. Baltimore, William Wood & Co., 1947.

PERIODICALS:

Barondess, J. A.: The Present Status of Gamma Globulin. *Pediatrics,* *10:* 732–742, 1952.
Henle, G., and others: Studies in the Prevention of Mumps. J. Immunol., *66:* 535–578, 1951.
Koprowski, H., and Cox, H. R.: Recent Developments in the Prophylaxis of Rabies. Am. J. Pub. Health, *41:* 1483–1489, 1951.
Wheeler, R. E., and Benenson, A. S.: Criteria of Immunity to Mumps in Young Adults. Am. J. Pub. Health, *41:* 1238–1239, 1951.

MODERN METHODS of combating certain infections include the use of specific antibacterial substances. This approach to therapy is not entirely new, since the folklore of primitive peoples nearly always includes instructions in the use of herbs for treating disease. From this unschooled source have come a few remedies such as opium and digitalis that are useful in treating symptoms. In at least one instance, folk-medicine contributed a drug which acted upon the agent that caused the disease. The Indians of Central and South America treated malaria with cinchona or Peruvian bark, a crude drug containing quinine; quinine is still used today because it destroys malarial parasites without injuring the host. Most poisons combine as readily with the tissue of the infected person as with the invading organism, and are therefore not suitable for use against bacteria that are within the body.

Chemists searched diligently for natural or synthetic compounds that would select and unite with bacterial protoplasm without attacking body tissues. In 1909, Paul Ehrlich, a German scientist, announced the discovery of arsphenamine, an arsenic derivative that is highly toxic for the spirochetes that cause syphilis. This compound, known as "606," was the 606th arsenic compound tested before one was found that would destroy the parasites without injury to the host. In the years that followed, other chemicals proved useful in the treatment of some of the protozoan infections found in the tropics, but bacteria seemed almost completely resistant to this form of attack. Since 1935, several antibacterial substances have been found that are injurious to bacteria and at the same time relatively harmless to human beings. The best known of these are the *sulfonamide* compounds, penicillin, streptomycin, aureomycin, bacitracin, chloramphenicol, and Terramycin. Some of these are synthetic chemical substances, while others are produced by living cells. The latter are called *antibiotics*. The

272

fact that some of these antibacterial agents resemble food
proteins (amino acids and polypeptides) or enzymes suggests
that someday it may be possible to synthesize new antibiotics

Table 23   SOME ANTIMICROBIAL AGENTS

NAME	SOURCE	ACTION	SUSCEPTIBLE ORGANISMS
Aureomycin	*Streptomyces aureofaciens*	Bacteriostatic Bactericidal	Gram-positive organisms Some gram-negative organisms Rickettsias Certain viruses* and *Endamoeba histolytica*
Bacitracin	*Bacillus licheniformis*	Bacteriostatic	Gram-positive organisms
Chloramphenicol (Chloromycetin)	Synthesis	Bacteriostatic	Gram-positive organisms Gram-negative organisms Rickettsias Certain viruses* and *Endamoeba histolytica*
Chloroquine	Synthesis	Bacteriocidal Bacteriolytic	Malaria parasites
Penicillin	*Penicillium notatum*	Bacteriostatic Bactericidal	Gram-positive organisms Gram-negative cocci
p-Aminobenzoic acid	Synthesis	Bacteriostatic	Rickettsias
Streptomycin	*Streptomyces griseus*	Bacteriostatic Bactericidal	Acid-fast organisms Gram-positive organisms Many gram-negative organisms
Sulfonamides	Synthesis	Bacteriostatic	Gram-positive organisms Gram-negative cocci
Terramycin	*Streptomyces rimosus*	Bacteriostatic	Similar to aureomycin

* Virus pneumonia and psittacosis, lymphogranuloma group.

by modifying the chemical structure of amino acids or enzymes. At present, antibodies are derived from cultures of bacteria, molds, or actinomycetes. Some of the antibiotics in common use are listed in Table 23.

Sulfonamides   The sulfonamides inhibit most of the gram-positive rods and cocci, the gram-negative cocci, and also the gram-negative rods that cause dysentery (Shigella). They are thought to prevent growth of susceptible organisms by competing with enzymes which enable the organisms to utilize an essential amino acid (para-aminobenzoic acid). The sulfonamides are inhibited by the presence of blood, pus, and para-aminobenzoic acid. Their action is definitely bacteriostatic. In treatment, therefore, it is essential that they be given in adequate doses and continued long enough for the body defenses to eliminate the invading organisms, otherwise the infection will recur. Persons treated with sulfonamides often develop toxic symptoms.

Streptomycin   Streptomycin is an antibiotic obtained from cultures of *Streptomyces griseus*. Like penicillin, it may inhibit or kill the microorganisms exposed to it. It is thought that streptomycin interferes with the respiration of susceptible cells. It too is rapidly absorbed and rapidly excreted. It is apt to produce toxic symptoms characterized by vestibular disturbances resulting in deafness, ringing in the ears, dizziness, numbness about the face and mouth, fever, rash, coryza, and urticaria. Streptomycin as well as its derivative, dihydrostreptomycin, inhibits the growth of many gram-positive and gram-negative organisms and also of *Mycobacterium tuberculosis*. Unfortunately, if the drug is given repeatedly, microorganisms which were originally susceptible, adapt themselves to the antibiotic and become resistant to it. In fact, some develop enzyme systems for utilizing streptomycin and become so dependent on it that they cannot grow in medium which is free from it. Although it is effective against many organisms, its use is generally limited to those which do not respond to other antibiotics, as, for example, pasteurella, *Hemophilus influenzae* and *Mycobacterium tuberculosis*. (See Figures 52 and 53.)

Penicillin   Penicillin has been widely publicized as Fleming's wonder drug. There are at least five naturally occur-

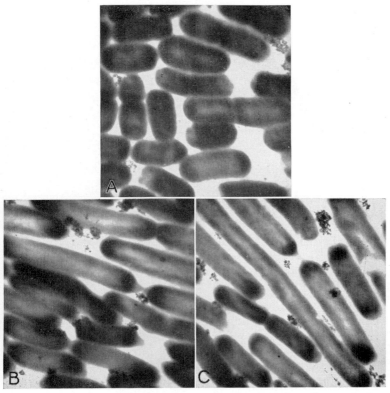

Figure 52   Electron micrographs showing the effects of the antibiotic agent streptomycin on bacteria (*Klebsiella pneumoniae*) × 8850. A, Normal plump rods—some showing cell division. B and C. Organisms after eighteen-hour exposure to streptomycin (0.05 microgram per liter) show typical elongation. Cell growth continues, but normal cell division has been inhibited. Note the extreme length of some of the cells and also the change in cell structure as indicated by lessened density and blurred contours. These cells reach a maximum length and then die of old age. Penicillin also inhibits cell division and encourages the formation of abnormally large cells. Higher concentrations of either streptomycin or penicillin prevent growth or dissolve susceptible cells. (Squibb Institute for Medical Research.)

ring penicillins: penicillin G, which is most commonly used, and penicillin F, X, dihydro-F, and K. All are obtained from *Penicillium notatum*. Most preparations are relatively non-toxic and are rapidly absorbed and excreted. Effective treat-

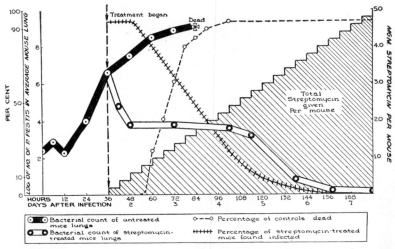

Figure 53   The influence of streptomycin on the number of bacteria in the circulating blood and upon the survival of animals suffering from experimental pneumonic plague (*Pasteurella pestis*). (Meyer, K. F.: Am. Rev. Tuberc., *47.*)

ment depends on multiple doses given at regular intervals (every three or four hours, day and night) or upon large doses of slowly absorbed preparations such as penicillin in beeswax or protamine zinc penicillin. Penicillin apparently interferes with the nutrition* of bacterial cells that are actively growing. Small amounts of penicillin added to growing cultures prevent cell division and cause bacterial cells to increase in size. (See Figure 52, page 275.) Large doses of penicillin kill susceptible organisms while smaller doses prevent cell division (bacteriostatic action). Penicillin is ineffective against resting inactive cells.

Although penicillin is usually not toxic for man, certain individuals will after repeated doses become sensitive to the drug. In these individuals, penicillin acting as a stress agent alters capillary permeability. The usual symptoms are skin rash, hives (urticaria), and fever. A more serious reaction,

* It is thought that penicillin renders susceptible bacterial cells incapable of concentrating one of the amino acids (glutamic). Penicillin-resistant organisms either do not need this compound or are able to manufacture it for themselves.

one which resembles serum sickness, is characterized by hives, edema, itching, fever, and joint pains and swelling. Like serum sickness it usually appears seven to fourteen days after the administration of the agent responsible. Very severe reactions may give rise to shock in twenty or thirty minutes. Fortunately severe reactions are rare.

Skin tests for detecting sensitivity may be made by placing penicillin powder or solution on a scratch. The appearance of a wheal or the occurrence of severe itching indicates that the individual is sensitive to penicillin.

Bacitracin Bacitracin is an antibiotic developed from cultures of the gram-positive spore-forming organism *Bacillus licheniformis,* a close relative of *Bacillus subtilis.* The active culture was isolated from the wound of a patient by the name of Tracy—hence the term "bacitracin." This antibiotic acts primarily on gram-positive organisms and is commonly used on skin, mucous membranes, and wounds. It is somewhat toxic and may cause kidney damage. For this reason, preparations for systemic use bear the label "For Hospital Use Only." It has one distinct advantage over penicillin in that it rarely causes sensitivity. Recent reports suggest that it may be effective in combination with penicillin.

Erythromycin (Ilotycin) Erythromycin is a new antibiotic derived from the moldlike organism *Streptomyces erythreus.* It appears to be effective and is used against gram-positive organisms that are resistant to penicillin.

"Broad Spectrum Antibiotics" The term "broad spectrum antibiotic" is used to describe an antibiotic that is antagonistic to many groups of organisms, as, for example, gram-positive and gram-negative bacteria, rickettsias, and certain viruses (lymphogranuloma psittacosis group) and the protozoan parasite *Endamoeba histolytica.* The broad spectrum antibiotics include: aureomycin, chloramphenicol, and Terramycin.

Aureomycin Aureomycin is a yellow powder obtained from *Streptomyces aureofaciens.* It is usually given by mouth but may be given intravenously if the patient is unable to swallow. Although it is relatively nontoxic it may cause nausea and vomiting.

Aureomycin is used extensively as a supplement to standard diets for growing chicks and pigs. It is said to increase the rate of growth 20 to 40 per cent. Penicillin, bacitracin, streptomycin, and Terramycin produce similar effects. The reason for this growth-stimulating property is not known. Some health authorities warn that the practice of employing antibiotics as diet supplements may encourage resistant forms of pathogens that are capable of causing contact or food-borne infections in man. It is too early to know if their concern is warranted. It is known that the normal flora of the animal fed on antibiotics is replaced by resistant organisms. As yet the disease-producing ability of these resistant organisms is not known.

CHLORAMPHENICOL (Chloromycetin)   This antibiotic was originally obtained from various soil organisms later identified as *Streptomyces venezuela*. Chloramphenicol, a nitrobenzene compound, is now produced commercially by synthesis. It may be given by mouth and is rapidly absorbed. Clinical reports indicate that it is valuable in the treatment of many infections including typhoid fever. Since the action of chloramphenicol is bacteriostatic, relapses are likely to occur especially in infections caused by intracellular organisms, as, for example, undulant fever (Brucella) and typhoid fever (*Salmonella typhosa*). Current reports suggest that chloramphenicol may injure the blood-forming organs thereby causing an aplastic anemia.

TERRAMYCIN   Terramycin (*terra*—earth, and *myces*—fungus) is an antibiotic derived from cultures of *Streptomyces rimosus*. The drug has low toxicity and may be given by mouth. It causes a marked decrease in intestinal organisms including coliforms and other normal inhabitants. Like aureomycin and chloramphenicol it is useful in treating a wide variety of infections.

Isonicotinic Acid Compounds   These drugs have a marked bacteriostatic effect on the growth of tuberculosis organisms (*Mycobacterium tuberculosis*) in cultures and in the animal body. In addition, early reports indicate that their administration to human beings infected with tuberculosis is followed by a decrease in fever and an increase in appetite and general well-being. Resistant strains of tuberculosis organisms have been reported. Toxic symptoms have also been observed. While these drugs seem promising, full evaluation must await further trial.

BACTERIAL RESPONSE

Susceptibility   Microorganisms differ in cell structure and function, and therefore they may be expected to differ in their susceptibility to toxic agents. The gram-positive rods and cocci and also the gram-negative cocci are susceptible to the action of most antibiotics. In contrast, many but not all gram-negative rods are susceptible to aureomycin, chloramphenicol, and Terramycin. *Pseudomonas aeruginosa* and others closely related to free-living organisms have very simple nutritional requirements and produce a variety of enzymes capable of synthesizing cell proteins. This fact probably accounts for their effective resistance to the action of antibiotics. The antibiotics, especially penicillin and streptomycin, have proved useful as inhibiting agents in laboratory procedures designed to isolate gram-negative bacteria, viruses, or rickettsias.

Resistance   Certain strains of susceptible bacteria are naturally resistant to a particular toxic agent and are, therefore, immune to its action. A resistant organism is one that is capable of changing or destroying the antibiotic or is able to carry on all essential life processes in spite of the antagonistic action of the antibiotic. Resistant strains can be developed by growing susceptible bacteria in a medium which contains inactive quantities of the antibiotic. (See page 282.) Bacteria living in the host may become resistant during a course of treatment, especially if the dosage is too small or if the antibiotic is given at irregular intervals.

Antibiotics are sometimes effective when used in combination—as for example penicillin and bacitracin or penicillin and streptomycin. In other combinations one drug may actually interfere with the action of another. Chloramphenicol lessens the effect of penicillin—probably by inhibiting the growth of bacteria. Penicillin seems to act chiefly on active growing cells. Studies are now in progress to determine which combinations of antibiotics are effective against various microorganisms.

Research has revealed many antibacterial agents. Some of

these are toxic to the host as well as to the parasite. Others have proved of great value in the treatment of disease. To date, chemotherapy has proved effective against the parasites listed in Table 24.

Table 24   EFFECTIVENESS OF ANTIMICROBIAL AGENTS

ORGANISM	DISEASE	CHEMICAL AGENTS
Multicellular parasites		
Flatworms (flukes)	Blood fluke infection (Schistosomiasis)	Antimony, stibophen (Fuadin)
Roundworms—*Necator americanus*	Hookworm disease	Tetrachloroethylene, hexylresorcinol
Protozoa		
Endamoeba histolytica	Amebic dysentery	Chloroquine, aureomycin, ipecac, emetine
Leishmania donovani	Kala-azar	Antimony
Plasmodium	Malaria	Quinine, quinacrine hydrochloride (Atabrine), Plasmochin, chloroquine
Trypanosoma	African sleeping sickness (trypanosomiasis)	Arsenic compounds
Bacteria		
Spirochetes		
Borrelia recurrentis	Relapsing fever	Arsenic compounds
Treponema pallidum	Syphilis	Penicillin, arsenic, bismuth
Treponema pertenue	Yaws	Penicillin
Cocci		
Gonococci	Gonorrhea	⎫
Meningococci	Meningitis	Sulfonamides, penicillin, bacitracin, and broad spectrum antibiotics
Pneumococci	Pneumonia	
Micrococci	⎫ Various infections	
Streptococci	⎭	⎭
Rods—Gram-negative		
Brucella	Undulant fever	⎫
Aerobacter aerogenes	⎫	
Escherichia coli		Very resistant
Hemophilus influenzae		More or less susceptible to aureomycin, chloramphenicol, streptomycin, Terramycin
Klebsiella pneumoniae	Various infections	
Pseudomonas aeruginosa		
Proteus vulgaris	⎭	⎭

Table 24—(*Continued*)

ORGANISM	DISEASE	CHEMICAL AGENTS
Pasteurella pestis	Plague	Aureomycin Streptomycin
Pasteurella tularensis	Tularemia	Terramycin Chloramphenicol
Salmonella typhosa	Typhoid fever	Chloramphenicol
Salmonella paratyphi	Paratyphoid fever	(experimental)
Shigella dysenteriae	Bacillary dysentery	Sulfonamides
Rods—Acid-fast		
Mycobacterium leprae	Leprosy	Ethyl chaulmoograte, sulfones
Mycobacterium tuberculosis	Tuberculosis	Isonicotinic acid (experimental), *p*-aminosalicylic acid Streptomycin
Various rickettsias	Typhus, etc.	*p*-aminobenzoic acid Chloramphenicol
Selected viruses	Psittacosis Lymphogranuloma venereum	Aureomycin Terramycin Penicillin Chloramphenicol Aureomycin Terramycin

ADVANTAGES AND DISADVANTAGES

Advantages   Antibacterial agents have proved of great value in the treatment of many infections. The decline in deaths due to pneumococcus penumonia well illustrates this point. (See page 398, Figure 63.) Antibiotics now available are effective against many pathogenic bacteria, rickettsias, and a few viruses. (See Table 24.) They are, however, ineffective against most viruses and against animal parasites with the exception of *Endamoeba histolytica,* the cause of amebic dysentery. Many of the diseases caused by animal parasites respond to treatment with heavy metals (arsenic, antimony) and other chemical compounds. Current research is directed toward finding new antibiotics which will be effective against viruses, animal parasites, and tuberculosis organisms.

Disadvantages   Although the various antibacterial agents have received much well-deserved praise, it is well to recognize that these agents do have some limitations and disadvantages. Laboratory reports indicate that the number of strains of pathogens resistant to one or more antibiotics has increased. For example, in the period from 1941 to 1945 about 10 per cent of the cultures of *Micrococcus pyogenes* (*Staphylococcus aureus*) were resistant to penicillin whereas in recent studies 70 per cent proved to be resistant. Furthermore, there is growing evidence that hospital personnel tend to become persistent (nasal) carriers of resistant strains of *Micrococcus pyogenes* and may therefore be potential sources of infection.

In addition, there have been reports of pertussis, diphtheria, and wound infections in which the causative organisms disappeared in response to antibiotics only to be replaced by a toxin-producing *Micrococcus pyogenes* which then was responsible for typical scarlet fever. Recent investigators studying patients undergoing antibiotic therapy have reported a new disease—staphylococcal dysentery—which is characterized by severe diarrhea associated with blood and pus in the stools. Cultures of these stools revealed large numbers of hemolytic *Micrococcus pyogenes*. Others have reported yeastlike infections of the mouth, pharynx, esophagus, lungs, and intestines. Other diarrheas, usually mild but prolonged, have been attributed to vitamin deficiency due to the suppression of the normal intestinal flora. (These disturbances are said to respond to treatment with liver extract and the B-complex vitamins.) It seems likely that the normal flora of the intestines (coliforms and others) prevents or limits the growth of micrococci and molds. When antibiotics suppress the normal flora, micrococci or molds appear to flourish.

Antibiotics especially if given over a long period of time disturb the "balance of nature" thus permitting the growth of organisms which are potentially harmful. Significant also is the number of reports of persons (patients, industrial workers, nurses) who are sensitive to one of the antibiotics. This fact alone suggests that indiscriminate use of antibiotics in lozenges, toothpaste, and mouthwashes is probably unwise.

SUMMARY

1. Some chemical compounds exhibit a selective action upon the invading parasite and are, therefore, able to injure the invader without doing harm to the host.

2. Chemotherapeutic agents probably act by interfering with some essential life process such as nutrition, reproduction, respiration, or cell division.

3. Antibacterial substances are selective in their action and will, therefore, be very effective against some organisms and of no use against others.

4. Antibacterial substances, such as the sulfonamides, that prevent the growth of bacteria but do not kill them, must be continued until the body defenses have actually destroyed the invaders.

5. Parasitic organisms may adapt themselves to living in the presence of a toxic substance. Some strains are naturally resistant, while others may acquire resistance by contact with the drug.

SUPPLEMENTARY READINGS

BOOK:

Welch, H., and Lewis, C. N.: Antibiotic Therapy. Washington, D. C., The Arundel Press, 1951.

PERIODICALS:

Catron, D. V., and others: Mode of Action of Antibiotics in Swine. Antibiotics & Chemother., *3:* 571–577, 1953.

Dowling, H. F., and others: When Should Antibiotics Be Used in Combination? J.A.M.A., *151:* 813–815, 1953.

Dowling, H. F., and others: Observations on the Epidemiological Spread of Antibiotic-Resistant Staphylococci with Measurements of the Changes in Sensitivity. Am. J. Pub. Health, *43:* 860–838, 1953.

Editorial: Blood Dyscrasia Following the Use of Chloramphenicol. J.A.M.A., *149:* 840, 1952.

Editorial: Fungous Infections Complicating Antibiotic Therapy. J.A.M.A., *149:* 762–763, 1952.

Editorial: Cross Resistance to Antibiotics. J.A.M.A., *148:* 470–471, 1952.

Feinberg, S. M., and others: Penicillin Anaphylaxis—Nonfatal and Fatal Reactions. J.A.M.A. *152:* 114–118, 1953.

Felsen, J., and others: Staphylococcus Infections in Hospital Nurseries and Pediatric Wards. Am. J. Dis. Child., *81:* 534–540, 1951.

Felsenfeld, O., and others: *In Vitro* and *in Vivo* Tests with Newer Antibiotics against *Endamoeba histolytica.* Am. J. Pub. Health, *41:* 1078–1081, 1951.

Finland, M.: The Present Status of Antibiotics in Bacterial Infections. Bull. New York Acad. Med., *27:* 199–220, 1951.

Finland, M.: Antibiotic Resistance of Pathogenic Staphylococci. Arch. Int. Med., *91:* 143–158, 1953.

Finland, M., and Weinstein, L.: Complications Induced by Antimicrobial Agents. New England J. Med., *284:* 220–226, 1953.

Haffner, F. D., and others: Penicillin and Its Effect in Producing a Predominant Gram-Negative Bacillary Flora in the Upper Respiratory Tract of Children. Pediatrics, *6:* 262–268, 1950.

Kligman, A. M.: Are Fungous Infections Increasing as a Result of Antibiotic Therapy? J.A.M.A., *149:* 979–983, 1952.

Long, P. H.: Bacterial Resistance as a Factor in Antibiotic Therapy. Bull. New York Acad. Med., *28:* 809–816, 1952.

Mayer, P. S., and others: Penicillin Anaphylaxis. J.A.M.A., *151:* 351–353, 1953.

Oatway, W. H.: Delays in the Diagnosis of Tuberculosis from the Incautious Use of Antibiotics. Tuberculosis Abstracts, *25:* 1–2, 1952.

Pelner, L., and Waldman, S.: Serum-Sickness Type of Penicillin Reaction Treated with Sodium Dehydrocholate. Postgrad. Med., *11:* 49–55, 1952.

Reinman, H.: Infectious Diseases. Arch. Int. Med., *89:* 115–160, 1952.

Rountree, P., and others: Nasal Carrier Roles of Staphylococcus Pyogenes in Hospital Nurses. J. Path. & Bact., *63:* 313–324, 1951.

Smadel, J. E.: Present Status of Antibiotic Therapy in Viral Infections. Bull. New York Acad. Med., *27:* 199–220, 1951.

Smith, J. W., and others: Absorption Following Oral Administration of Erythromycin. J.A.M.A., *151:* 805–810, 1953.

Smith, M. A.: Rheumatic Fever Prophylaxis. J.A.M.A., *149:* 636–639, 1952.

Starr, M. P., and Reynolds, D. M.: Streptomycin Resistance of Coliform Bacteria from Turkeys Fed Streptomycin. Am. J. Pub. Health, *41:* 1375–1380, 1951.

Sturgeon, P.: Fatal Aplastic Anemia in Children Following Chloramphenicol (Chloromycetin) Therapy. J.A.M.A., *149:* 918–922, 1952.

Wilson, L. P., and others: Aplastic Anemia Following Prolonged Administration of Chloramphenical—A Report of Two Cases, One a Fatality. J.A.M.A., *149:* 231–234, 1952.

Woods, J. N., and others: Monilial Infections Complicating the Therapeutic Effects of Antibiotics. J.A.M.A., *145:* 207–211, 1951.

THE LAST CENTURY has brought to man increased ability to control microorganisms and also a travel speed that makes control very necessary. Competent observers have always noted that epidemics spread rapidly, but usually not faster than the speed of human travel. With air travel becoming common, it is safe to say that today parasites and their hosts are traveling faster and farther than ever before. For the primitive, the disorganized, and the war-torn areas, this may spell disaster because modern methods of transportation can and do introduce new sources of infection. The welfare of a community will often depend upon the application of environmental controls that prevent the organisms from reaching human beings. Since many disease-producing organisms may be carried to man by air, milk, food, water, soil, sewage, and by living animals, each of these agents will be considered in terms of the kinds of organisms transferred, the relative risk, and the means of control.

AIR

Microorganisms do not grow in air because it contains too little food and moisture to support growth. Nevertheless, agar plates exposed to the air usually reveal a transient population of bacteria, yeasts, and molds. The numbers and kinds vary from place to place and from time to time. Samples of air taken at midocean, at high altitudes, in the refrigerator, and in tightly closed rooms or spaces reveal few microorganisms. In contrast, many microbes are likely to be found in the presence of dust, people, and movement. Bacteria, floating free or attached to dust particles or moisture droplets, are heavier than air and tend to settle. A study of streptococci sprayed into a closed room indicated that they settled at a rate of 20 per cent per hour, leaving about 0.5 per cent suspended at the end of twenty-four hours.[1] As air is seldom left undisturbed, one cannot assume that they settle at this or any constant rate;

furthermore, after settling has taken place, a slight breeze can resuspend the bacteria-laden dust. Settling is related to the size of the mass. Relatively large masses (larger than 5 microns), such as dust, lint, flakes of dandruff, and masses of bacteria, tend to settle rapidly whereas extremely small particles (1 to 5 microns), such as a single bacterial cell, remain suspended for long periods of time. Pathogenic organisms, usually growing in masses or chains and mixed with body secretions, tend to form particles that settle. However, a violent sneeze or pressure from a syringe or pipette may release the smaller free-floating particles into the air.

The kinds of bacteria found in the air vary greatly; saprophytes are always present, while parasites from the human respiratory tract are less common. In general, country air is practically free from parasitic microorganisms; city air is relatively free, but occasionally coliform organisms and micrococci may be present. Although free-living yeasts, molds, and bacteria usually predominate, some parasitic and pathogenic organism may be present in dust found in homes, schools, factories, and hospitals. Well-ventilated rooms with few human occupants are remarkably free from bacteria of human origin. In crowded schoolrooms and moving-picture theaters, such organisms are found in proportion to the crowding and to the lack of ventilation. As would be expected, disease-producing organisms may be recovered from the air and the sweepings from hospital wards (see Chapter 20).[2] While it is difficult to assess its importance, air undoubtedly does transfer viruses and bacteria that cause respiratory diseases. Direct and indirect contacts with droplets are probably responsible for introducing the organisms that invade the upper respiratory tract. Air may be important in carrying microorganisms into the lower bronchioles and alveoli. It is now recognized that particle size determines the risk of air-borne infection. Small particles (those less than 5 microns—as, for example, a single bacterium, virus, or rickettsia) are capable of reaching the alveolar spaces of the lung. Larger particles—dust or clumps of bacteria—fall on the ciliated epithelium of the respiratory tract and are promptly engulfed by phagocytes or swept to the external nares or to the pharynx and swallowed. Air-borne infections are hazards of bacteriological laboratories where mixers, grinders, syringes, and pipettes may scatter minute infectious particles into the air.

Numerous experiments indicate that the number of bacteria in the air can be markedly decreased by the use of various methods for the suppression of dust, combined either with ultraviolet light or disinfectant vapors such as propylene glycol (1:50,000,000) and triethylene glycol (1:500,000,000). (See Chapter 20.) Ultraviolet light has proved of some value and may be used to prevent cross infections in pediatric wards and in operating rooms. Ultraviolet light has certain disadvantages which limit its usefulness. Since it has little ability to penetrate, microorganisms in masses or those coated with organic matter may escape destruction. In addition, it is injurious to human skin and eyes and must therefore be installed in the ceiling and screened to protect workers and patients. This position near the ceiling limits the number of organisms exposed to the rays. Furthermore, continuous supervision by competent engineers is required to keep the apparatus functioning properly. The various experiments designed to test the ability of bactericidal lights or vapors to prevent infection have produced inconsistent results. This suggests either that man acquires certain infections in areas that have not been treated or that droplets or direct and indirect contacts are more important than air in transmitting pathogens from one person to another. The problems of air sanitation require further study. At the present time indiscriminate use of either ultraviolet light or germicidal vapors cannot be advocated.

MILK AND MILK PRODUCTS

Milk as a Source of Disease   Milk is a good vehicle for transferring bacteria because it is commonly consumed raw. Before milk reaches the consumer it may be polluted by whatever comes in contact with it. Although it is probably sterile when it is secreted in the milk ducts, by the time it leaves the cow it already contains some bacteria and then it collects more from the body of the cow, the dust of the barn, the hands and clothes of the milker, and from the containers. Large numbers of organisms may be contributed by dung or dirt that falls into the milk pail, and by unclean pails or milking machines. Unless milk is promptly cooled to 10° C. (50° F.), these bacteria multiply rapidly, causing the milk to become sour. Pathogenic bacteria in milk may come from a diseased cow or they may be derived directly or indirectly from infected

Table 25   DISEASES TRANSMITTED BY MILK AND MILK
PRODUCTS

DISEASE	PARASITE	HABITAT OF PARASITE
Diseases of Human Origin		
Diphtheria	*Corynebacterium diphtheriae*	Respiratory tract
Dysentery	*Shigella*—various	Intestinal tract
Food poisoning	Micrococcus (staphylococcus)	Respiratory tract, infections of hand
Gastroenteritis	Uncertain	Probably intestinal tract
Streptococcal infections		
Scarlet fever	*Streptococcus pyogenes* (many types of Lancefield Group A)	Respiratory tract, infected wounds
Septic sore throat		
Typhoid and paratyphoid fevers	*Salmonella typhosa,* various *Salmonella*	Intestinal tract
Diseases of Bovine Origin		
Brucellosis (undulant fever)	*Brucella abortus*	Milk, blood, urine, and feces
Q fever	*Coxiella burnetii*	Milk, mammary gland, placenta, meat, hides
Streptococcal infections	*Streptococcus pyogenes* (Group B)	Udder of infected cow
Tuberculosis—bovine	*Mycobacterium tuberculosis bovis*	Respiratory tract; sometimes also in intestinal tract and udder

human beings. When contaminated milk is pooled with milk from other sources, the entire supply, if used raw, may be the cause of a large-scale epidemic. Outbreaks of disease due to contaminated milk still occur, but they are becoming less common as methods of milk handling improve. The following diseases have been repeatedly transmitted by milk and milk products such as cheese or ice cream: streptococcal infections, brucellosis, Q fever, tuberculosis, dysentery, typhoid fever, paratyphoid fever, diphtheria, and gastroenteritis. (See Table 25.)

Because milk permits the multiplication of organisms, drinking contaminated milk often results in the introduction of overwhelming doses of bacteria and bacterial products. As a result, outbreaks of milk-borne disease are characterized by acute illness with sudden onset occurring chiefly among the consumers of milk obtained from a common source. Multiple cases of illness may occur in the same household at the same time.

Methods of Protection against Contamination Inasmuch as milk is subject to contamination at any point on its long route to the consumer, it must be guarded at every step. The following measures are designed to protect the consumer against pathogens transmitted by milk:

1. Healthy cows which are free from mastitis, tuberculosis, contagious abortion (Bang's disease, caused by *Brucella abortus*), and Q fever.
2. Clean barns and clean cows (udders washed before milking).
3. Healthy workers who wear clean clothes and keep their hands clean.
4. Effective sterilization of pails, cans, milking machines, tank cars, pipes, pasteurizing machines.
5. Proper cooling of milk before and after pasteurization.
6. Pasteurization of milk.
7. Adequate protection of milk after pasteurization.

MUNICIPAL CONTROL Since milk is a potential source of disease most cities regulate its quality and sale by defining standards. The term "standard" refers to the minimum legal requirements (sanitary, physical, chemical, and bacteriological) which must be met by those who produce milk for sale. Sanitary standards are requirements relating to the cleanliness of equipment used in milk production and also to the health of milk cows and dairy workers. Physical standards include a description of the taste, odor, specific gravity, and temperature of milk. Chemical standards set the content of butter fat (3.5 per cent) and total solids (12 per cent).

Bacteriological standards set the maximum bacterial content. The number of bacteria present in milk can be used as an index of its history. A relatively low count will be found only in milk which has had very careful handling. A high count indicates either that the milk was collected under unsanitary conditions or that it was not properly cooled. The bacteriological requirements for certified and grade A milk are as follows:

Certified Milk—raw .... Raw milk of good quality and uniform composition produced under sanitary conditions, containing not more than 10,000 bacteria per cc.

Certified Milk—pasteurized ... Contains not more than 500 bacteria per cc.

Grade A—raw .... Raw milk stored continuously at a temperature below 10° C. (50° F.), containing not more than 30,000 bacteria per cc.

Grade A—pasteurized .... Grade A raw milk, after pasteurization, containing not more than 30,000 bacteria per cc. at the time of delivery and at no time more than 200,000 per cc.

PASTEURIZATION   This process was first introduced by Pasteur to prevent spoilage of the fluids used for making beer and wines. Today, its most important use is in the milk industry and is accomplished either by the "flash" or "holding method." In flash pasteurization, milk previously cooled is held at 72° C. (161° F.) for fifteen seconds and then cooled quickly. In the holding process, the milk, after an initial cooling, is quickly heated to 61° to 62° C. (142° to 144° F.), held for thirty minutes, and quickly cooled again. This process kills all the pathogenic bacteria and roughly 90 per cent of all bacteria present in milk. Pasteurization markedly decreases but does not destroy all *Coxiella burnetii*, the rickettsias that cause Q fever. It is a most useful means of preventing disease transmission by milk, but it is not a substitute for the proper protection of milk before and after pasteurization.

Laboratory Examination of Milk   The sanitary quality of milk may be determined by making one or more of the following tests: (1) direct count, (2) standard plate count,

(3) methylene blue reduction test, (4) phosphatase test, and (5) coliform test.

The relative numbers of bacteria present in milk can be estimated by either a *direct count* or by a *standard plate* count. A direct count is made by placing 0.01 cc. of milk on a glass slide and spreading it over an area of 1 square centimeter. The smear is stained and then examined with the aid of a standardized microscope. The number of bacteria in 10, 20, or 50 fields is counted and from that the number in 1 cc. is estimated. For instance, if the average number of bacteria per field is 1 and the number of microscopic fields in the square centimeter is 3000 (diameter of field 0.206 mm.), there would be approximately 3000 bacteria in 0.01 cc. or 300,000 in 1 cc. This technique is speedy and permits one to observe the kinds of microorganisms present. For instance, in milk from an infected cow, it often is possible to see leukocytes and long-chain streptococci.

The standard plate count is made by placing 1 cc. of milk (diluted $\frac{1}{1000}$, $\frac{1}{10,000}$, etc.) in a petri dish and covering it with melted agar. After incubation for forty-eight hours at 37° C. (98.6° F.), the colonies are counted and the total count is estimated. The plate count is an *estimate,* based upon only those bacteria which will grow on nutrient agar medium at 37° C. The plate count is a useful device for checking the day-by-day sanitation of the individual farms, but obviously is too slow to prevent any one sample of milk from entering the general supply.

The *methylene blue reduction* test is made by adding 1 cc. of methylene blue to 10 cc. of milk. If the liquid contains millions of organisms per cubic centimeter the dye will be reduced (changed from blue to colorless) in less than two hours, whereas milk containing relatively few bacteria will show no loss of color in eight hours. This is a rough test but has the advantage of being fast and inexpensive.

The *test for coliform organisms* is made by inoculating lactose broth with measured quantities of milk. Lactose fermentation with gas formation is characteristic of the coliform organisms (*Escherichia coli* and *Aerobacter aerogenes*). Since coliform organisms are killed by pasteurization, their presence in pasteurized milk indicates contamination of the sample after pasteurization.

The *phosphatase test* is used to check on the adequacy of pasteurization. Phosphatase, an enzyme always present in milk, is inactivated by subjection to a temperature of 143° to 145° F. (61° to 63° C.) for thirty minutes. If the test reveals little or no phosphatase one may assume that the milk was adequately heated. If the enzyme is present it means that pasteurization was incomplete or that raw milk has been added to that which was pasteurized.

The examination of milk for the presence of pathogenic organisms is a time-consuming procedure. It is therefore not used in the routine examination of milk.

FOOD

Foods may contribute to ill health by being inadequate in quality or quantity or by carrying chemical poisons or disease-producing organisms. Food-borne diseases of bacterial origin fall into three groups: (1) the infections caused by various organisms including the trichina, salmonella, and shigella, (2) poisoning caused by the anaerobe *Clostridium botulinum* (botulism), and (3) poisoning caused by certain strains of staphylococci and possibly by other organisms. Food poisoning or food infections may be expected to occur whenever the housekeeper or restaurant owner permits conditions that favor the survival or introduction and multiplication of pathogens in food. Food infections and food poisoning are discussed in full in Chapter 22.

WATER

Many natural waters harbor organisms capable of producing disease in man. Contact with such waters in swimming, wading, or working may result in infection by a variety of organisms such as schistosomes and leptospira. Drinking water likewise may transmit numerous intestinal parasites and thus cause disease.

Kinds   It is well to realize that "pure" water does not exist and that the character of any water depends upon its history. Water is commonly described as *clean, polluted,* or *contaminated.* A clean water is one that is characterized by an attractive appearance and the absence of pathogenic organisms and of any substance which contributes an unpleasant odor, taste, or appearance. Polluted water contains foreign substances that change its odor, taste, or appearance. These substances may or may not be harmful. Contaminated water contains human or animal wastes and is therefore potentially harmful. When rain water reaches the earth, it has already collected some dust and bacteria. As it strikes the street or soil, it gathers more living and nonliving materials, and, as its descent continues, it becomes a part of surface or ground waters which may be used to supply drinking water.

SOURCE OF WATER	CHAR-ACTER	IMPURITIES	REMARKS
Surface water from lakes, rivers, and streams	Soft	Organic matter in suspension and solution, may have color, odor, and many bacteria	Definitely polluted—suitable for drinking only after treatment
Ground water, shallow "dug" wells	Hard	Inorganic salts: calcium, ferrous, and magnesium salts, organic matter, bacteria	May be polluted by surface drainage—potentially dangerous
Deep-drilled wells—well-sealed	Hard	Inorganic salts, usually few bacteria	Usually safe but the source is uncertain and the character may change without warning

Surface waters are always polluted because streams constitute the natural drainage system for carrying off debris. The degree of pollution will vary from the minute traces of dissolved or suspended matter present in a remote mountain stream to that of sewage-laden rivers like the Hudson or the Ohio. Surface water contains organic matter which makes it a suitable medium for microscopic life—algae, protozoa, bacteria. The presence of decaying plant life often contributes color and sometimes odor (frequently called "taste") to water. Rivers, streams, or lakes which are large enough to serve as public water supplies are always polluted and therefore require treatment.

Ground water from springs, or from shallow or deep wells,

contains impurities in the form of inorganic salts which it has dissolved as it filters through the soil. These salts make the water hard, and the lack of organic material makes it a relatively unfavorable medium for microscopic life. Ground water contains few bacteria except when it is in contact with a polluted surface supply. The characteristics of surface and ground water are summarized on page 293.

In general, surface water is polluted and therefore requires treatment before use. Although ground water is often of good quality, this character may change without warning as underground streams shift.

Treatment   Satisfactory natural water supplies are seldom available in the large quantities needed for towns and cities. Therefore, some treatment is necessary; the kind of treatment will depend upon the quality of the raw water. In general, water contains a variety of impurities that can be

PURIFICATION OF WATER

(Based on Moore, E. W.: The Purification of Water. In: Rosenau's Preventive Medicine and Hygiene.)

PROCESS	RESULTS
Adsorption with activated carbon	Odors and tastes removed
Aeration	Odors and tastes removed; iron rendered insoluble
Coagulation	Turbidity and bacteria decreased
Chlorination	Bacteria decreased; odors and tastes increased or decreased
Filtration	Particulate matter decreased; color, odors, tastes reduced
Screening	Large bodies removed
Sedimentation	Particulate matter removed

removed by appropriate treatment. The purification of water is accomplished by processes designed to remove odors, tastes, and insoluble matter. When necessary, water may be treated to render it less hard and less corrosive. The treatment of water commonly begins by *screening*—a process of passing water through a coarse sieve which removes floating particles such as leaves, sticks, or fish. Smaller particles are removed by sedimentation with or without coagulation. Plain sedimentation refers to the collection of water in large reservoirs where it is stored until the suspended solids settle. This process can be observed when a bottle of muddy water is allowed to stand until the surface water becomes relatively clear and a layer of mud appears at the bottom. When this natural settling process is not adequate, it can be hastened and improved by adding a coagulant—a chemical which forms fluffy gelatinous flakes. As particles of the coagulant, usually aluminum hydroxide, settle, they carry with them suspended matter such as sand and bacteria. This process is comparable to the old-fashioned way of clearing coffee by the addition of a raw egg. By sedimentation, water often loses as much as 90 per cent of the suspended solids and bacteria. If the water requires further clarification, it is next run through a sand filter.

The word *filter* is misleading because it suggests the mechanical removal of bacteria—a process similar to the straining of tea to free it of leaves. Actually the spaces between the grains of sand are too large to prevent the passage of bacteria. The process of filtration is primarily biological, not mechanical. The filter consists of a deep layer of fine sand over layers of coarse sand and gravel. As water passes through the filter, organic matter, including protozoa, algae, and diatoms, is deposited on the top layer of sand. This film of living matter adsorbs or takes to itself the organic matter that is suspended or dissolved in the water. This adsorption is essentially a feeding process in which living cells remove the available food materials, including bacteria, and hence leave a clear fluid. The structure and operation of filters are essentially engineering problems and will, therefore, not be considered in this text. Filters are useful devices, since they transform dirty river water to a clear fluid by removing a high proportion of the suspended solids. Substances causing tastes and odors can be removed by treatment with activated carbon or by forcing the water through a fine spray (*aeration*). This process permits intimate contact with the oxygen of the air and results in the oxidizing of the substances which cause the unpleasant tastes and odors. Aeration also removes iron and manganese from solution by forming insoluble oxides. Water can be further purified by the addition of chlorine. This disinfectant when present in 0.1 part per million will kill intestinal bacteria, but may not destroy the cysts that cause amebic dysentery.

Providing a pure water supply for a city is a technical problem which is best handled in a central plant under expert supervision. Most cities with more than ten thousand inhabitants provide some means of purifying their water supplies. If these safeguards fail, then protection depends upon detection of the danger involved and upon emergency treatment of the water. Just how serious a polluted water supply can be is well illustrated by an accident which occurred in the city of Rochester, New York, in 1940. A workman opened a valve that allowed polluted river water to run into the city's drinking water for twenty-four hours before the mistake was discovered. As a result of this one exposure to infection, approximately 34,000 persons developed various gastrointestinal infections, including six who contracted typhoid fever.

Boiling from five to ten minutes is one of the most satisfactory methods of treating water from an unknown or suspected source. This method will kill the organisms that cause intestinal disease. When heat is not available, water can be disinfected by adding suitable quantities of sodium hypochlorite, calcium hypochloride, or tincture of iodine.* Water treated with chem-

---

* The New York State Health Department recommends the following emergency disinfection of water:

DISINFECTANT	CONCENTRATION	DISINFECTION TIME
Chloride of lime (bleaching powder) *Stock solution:* Make a paste of 1 teaspoonful of chloride of lime and water, add to 1 quart of water	1 teaspoonful of stock solution in 1 gallon of water	30 minutes
Liquid bleach 5% (Chlorox, Dazzle, White Sail, Rainbow, Rose-X)	2 drops of liquid bleach 5 per cent in 1 gallon of water	30 minutes
Liquid bleach 2½% (S. K., 101)	4 drops of liquid bleach 2½ per cent in 1 gallon of water	30 minutes
Tincture of iodine	4 drops of tincture of iodine in 1 gallon of water	30 minutes
Zonite	10 drops Zonite in 1 gallon of water	30 minutes

icals should be allowed to stand for at least thirty minutes before it is used. In proper concentrations, these chemical agents destroy intestinal bacteria but may not kill the cysts of protozoa.

Laboratory Examination   It is possible to determine the character of water by means of appropriate laboratory tests. A sample of water carefully collected in a sterile bottle may be examined (1) physically, to detect color, odor, and turbidity, and (2) chemically, to reveal the kind and amounts of dissolved matter including nitrates. (In recent years there have been reports of cyanosis in babies [methemoglobinemia] due to the drinking of water containing a high concentration of nitrates.) The biological examination consists of two parts: the microscopic examination, a search for protozoa and odor-producing algae, and the bacteriological examination.

The development of municipal water treatment plants has contributed to the decrease of typhoid and other intestinal infections. Most of these plants are equipped with bacteriological laboratories to make frequent tests at all stages of purification using the methods to be described. The standard procedures for making these tests are outlined by the American Public Health Association and are published in a book called "Standard Methods for the Examination of Water and Sewage."

Laboratory tests used in the examination of water are designed to estimate the number of bacteria in the sample and to detect the presence of coliform bacteria.

NUMBER OF BACTERIA   The number of bacteria is estimated by means of the standard plate count.

PLATE COUNT   A sample is collected in a sterile bottle and sent to the laboratory immediately or stored at a low temperature until it can be sent to the laboratory. Two series of measured samples (1 cc., 0.1 cc., 0.01 cc.) are placed in sterile petri dishes and covered with melted agar.* One set of plates is incubated at 25° C. (77° F.) and the other at 37° C. (98.6° F.). After forty-eight hours the colonies are counted and the number of organisms per cubic centimeter estimated. This is not really a total count; it is a count of the bacteria which could grow under the conditions provided. Waters vary

---

* Gelatin may be used for the plates incubated at 25° C.

considerably in their bacterial count. A single count of an unknown water is of little value, while a cumulative week-by-week record can be quite useful. Suppose that the average counts per cubic centimeter for a municipal water supply for the last six weeks are as follows: 10, 40, 20, 30, 20, 300. The sudden appearance of a high bacterial count should send the sanitary engineer on a search for the cause, which might be a broken water main, a defective chlorinater, or flood conditions. The same count in raw surface water might be an everyday occurrence.

COLIFORM BACTERIA—AN INDEX OF POLLUTION   Although intestinal bacteria are the important pathogens carried by water, it is impractical to search water for a specific organism like the typhoid bacterium. Instead, the examination is directed toward finding coliform bacteria. The presence of these organisms in water indicates fecal pollution. Coliform bacteria are gram-negative nonspore-forming rods which ferment lactose with the formation of acid and gas. These include the colon bacterium (*Escherichia coli*), an inhabitant of the intestines of mammals and birds, and *Aerobacter aerogenes* which is found in soil, vegetable matter, and feces. The test is based on the fact that the coliform organisms belong to a small group of organisms which ferment lactose with the formation of acid and gas. This examination is done in three steps. The first is an elimination procedure called the *presumptive test* for coliform organisms.

PRESUMPTIVE TEST   Measured samples of water are put into fermentation tubes containing lactose broth and dyes that encourage the growth of coliform bacteria but inhibit the growth of cocci and spore-forming rods. After incubation for forty-eight hours at 37° C. (98.6° F.), the tubes will show growth with or without the presence of gas. The interpretation is as follows:

LACTOSE BROTH	INTERPRETATION
No gas—negative reaction	Contains no coliform organisms
Gas—positive reaction	Contains lactose-fermenting organisms which may be coliform bacteria

THE PARTIALLY CONFIRMED TEST   Broth from any tube which contains gas is next streaked on special lactose agar, such as eosin-methylene blue agar. On this differential medium, the acid-forming colon organisms form shiny colonies with a metallic luster. The plates showing typical metallic colonies are reserved for further study, while the others are regarded as negative.

THE CONFIRMED TEST   Transfers are then made from plates with typical metallic colonies to agar slants and to latcose broth, and smears are made for study following treatment with Gram's stain. If cultural characteristics identify the organisms as colon bacilli, the results of the test are reported as positive and all other samples are considered as negative or doubtful. The entire examination may be summarized as shown in Table 26. As noted in the table, samples A and B are free from coliform organisms, while samples C and D show evidence of heavy fecal pollution and are, therefore, unfit for human use.

SOIL

Ordinary black earth is teeming with microscopic life—both plants (fungi) and animals; these bring fertility to the soil. Most of these saprophytes are highly useful organisms which present no threat to human beings. Others are capable of producing disease; these include bacterial saprophytes and parasites, molds, yeasts, and animal parasites.

Bacterial Saprophytes   The organisms which cause tetanus (lockjaw) and gas gangrene are found in the intestinal tract of man and animals, in fertilized soil, and in street dust. Though they can be handled and ingested without harm, they produce disease when they are introduced into puncture wounds or crushed tissues. The dead cells present in association with such injuries supply the food and anaerobic conditions necessary for the growth of these organisms. The organisms present a problem in war wounds and in injuries caused by highway or railway accidents and in firecracker injuries (see page 448).

Bacterial Parasites   Most bacterial parasites that enter the soil with excreta or dead bodies are unable to compete with the hardy natives in the cold soil and promptly die. Others are potentially harmful to man. The intestinal organ-

Table 26   RESULTS OF THE EXAMINATION OF WATER FOR COLIFORM BACTERIA—INCUBATION 48 HOURS— 37° C.

Sample	PRESUMPTIVE TEST LACTOSE BROTH				PARTIAL CONFIRMATION		
	10 cc.	1 cc.	0.1 cc.	0.01 cc.	Special lactose agar plate	Microscopic	Interpretation
A	0	0	0	0	Not per- formed	Not per- formed	No coliform bacteria
	0	0	0	0			
	0	0	0	0			
	0	0	0	0			
	0	0	0	0			
B	+	+	0	0	No metallic colonies		No coliform bacteria
	0	0	0	0			
	+	0	0	0			
	0	0	0	0			
	0	0	0	0			
C	+	+	0	0	Metallic colonies present	Gram-nega- tive non- spore-form- ing rods	Coliform bacteria present
	+	+	0	0			
	+	+	+	0			
	+	0	0	0			
	+	+	0	0			
D	+	+	+	+	Metallic colonies present	Gram-nega- tive non- spore-form- ing rods	Coliform bacteria present
	+	+	+	+			
	+	+	+	0			
	+	+	+	+			
	+	+	+	+			

0 = no gas   + = gas

isms which cause typhoid fever do not multiply in the soil, but sometimes can survive for months. The transfer of these bacteria to raw fruits and vegetables or to drinking water may lead to disease in the persons who ingest them.

Molds and Yeasts   Molds and yeasts are very numerous in the soil and perform valuable service in decomposing complex organic matter. There is growing recognition that certain mold diseases are acquired from contact with the soil or dust. Characteristically these are not transferred from person to person. Infections with two molds (*Coccidioides immitis* and *Histoplasma capsulatum*) are acquired by contact with dust or soil. Both fungi are apparently limited by environmental conditions. The former is found in the hot dry areas of the Southwest while the latter is found in the moist soil of a number of midwestern and eastern states. Dust suppression appears to be useful in the control of coccidiodes infections. As yet the life cycle of the *Histoplasma capsulatum* and other molds is not sufficiently well understood for the planning of control measures. (See pages 474 and 475.)

Animal Parasites   Animal parasites which enter the soil in the resistant cyst or egg form may not find it an uncongenial place. In fact, a well-aerated (sandy) soil which is moist and warm may serve as an excellent incubator for hookworm eggs. Contact with soil polluted with human feces may provide the means of transferring cysts, eggs, or larvae (depending on the species) of intestinal parasites to a new host. (See Chapter 24.)

The transfer of bacteria and animal parasites by soil can be limited by disposing of body wastes in such a manner that the soil and drinking water do not become polluted. Human excreta is therefore an undesirable form of fertilizer for fields used to grow fruits and vegetables since disease-producing organisms may survive for weeks in the soil. In oriental countries, where soil pollution is common, raw foods should be disinfected before eating—preferably by cooking. Washing vegetables in water or detergent solutions is not a reliable way of removing microorganisms. Although the soil is not usually an important source of infection for man, it promotes the transfer of the intestinal parasites of animals which deposit parasite-laden excreta on the grazing areas.

SEWAGE

Sewage is an important source of pollution for drinking water, especially when a city disposes of its sewage by emptying it into a lake or stream that is also used as a source for its water supply. Crude sewage always contains many microorganisms—often from one to ten million per cubic centimeter. These organisms include coliform bacilli, various organisms of the proteus group, streptococci, anaerobic spore-bearing bacteria, denitrifying bacteria, and natural water bacteria. Microorganisms, both protozoa and bacteria, purify sewage by digesting and fermenting complex organic matter. The process is long and complex and is similar to those changes produced by the soil bacteria which were described in Chapter 8.

ANIMALS AS SOURCES OF DISEASE

Disease-producing parasites may be transferred to man by contacts with a variety of living animals. (See Chapter 31.) Mammals are an important source of infections such as bovine tuberculosis, anthrax, and rabies. Control of diseases transmitted by domestic animals is usually accomplished by killing the animal that is infected. For example, by slaughtering infected cattle, hoof and mouth disease has been eliminated in the United States and tuberculosis in cattle has been markedly decreased. Twice England has eliminated rabies by killing all rabid dogs and by instituting a six-month quarantine for all dogs which are imported. Control of diseases transmitted by wild animals may depend upon systematic thinning of the animal population thereby decreasing the number of susceptible hosts in the area. For example, periodic hunting of ground squirrels and foxes may be necessary in some areas to prevent outbreaks of plague in man and rabies in cattle and man.

Various arthropods (mosquitoes, lice, fleas, ticks, mites, flies) transmit infectious agents directly or indirectly to man. The discovery of DDT provided a valuable tool for the control of fly-, mosquito-, and louse-borne diseases. However, this compound may be less effective in the future since certain strains of arthropods are becoming resistant to it. (See Chapters 32 and 33.)

Table 27 shows some typical examples of diseases which are transferred by living agents, together with control measures.

SUMMARY

1. Many pathogenic bacteria are sufficiently hardy to live in man's environment and to be transferred to him by contact with air, milk, food, water, and animals.

2. Although bacteria do not grow in air, both saprophytes and parasites may be present suspended in it. The number of organisms varies with the amount of dust, the number of persons present, and the presence of air currents. Ultraviolet light

Table 27   ANIMAL SOURCES OF DISEASE

ANIMAL	DISEASE	CONTROL MEASURE
Mammals		
Swine	Anthrax	Adequate cooking of
	Brucellosis	pork
	Salmonella infections	
	Tapeworm	Avoid contact with sick
	Trichinosis	animals, their tissues, or excretions
Dog	Rabies	Vaccination of dogs; leash laws to prevent contact
Fox, skunk	Rabies	Periodic thinning to reduce the number of susceptibles
Horse	Glanders	⎫
Cow, goat	Brucellosis	⎪
Cow	Tuberculosis, Q fever	⎬ Destroy the infected animal
Rodents	Salmonella infections	⎪
Birds		⎪
Parrots and others	Psittacosis	⎭
Chickens, ducks, turkeys	Salmonella, psittacosis	
Arthropods		
Cockroaches	Salmonella ?	Destroy cockroaches; avoid feeding them
Flies	Typhoid fever, dysentery	Prevent fly-breeding, kill flies, use screens, protect food
Mosquito	Malaria, yellow fever, dengue fever, equine encephalitis	Kill mosquitoes, prevent mosquito-breeding, protect humans from mosquitoes
Body louse	Typhus	Destroy body louse
Rat flea	Murine typhus	⎱ Destroy rats and rat
Rat louse	Plague	⎰ parasites

and chemical sprays have been successfully used to decrease the number of parasites present in the air.

3. Milk is an important vehicle for transferring parasitic bacteria unless it is safeguarded at every step in its production and is pasteurized.

4. Foods when carelessly handled may be a source of infection or food poisoning.

5. Water contaminated with intestinal organisms is an important source of infection. The protection and purification of the

water supply is essential in preventing typhoid-like diseases. The bacteriological character of water should be determined by suitable laboratory tests.

6. Soil, though not a favorable medium for disease-producing bacteria, may sometimes transfer the more hardy of the intestinal bacteria, mold spores, and still more frequently the cysts or eggs of parasitic protozoa or worms.

7. Sewage provides food for huge populations of protozoa and bacteria that act upon it and in time will change its physical character and its chemical nature. Sewage should be disposed of in such a manner that it will not pollute drinking water and soil.

8. A variety of animals, mammals, birds, and arthropods can transfer disease-producing parasites to man. These parasites can be controlled most effectively by destroying the animal host.

REFERENCES

1. Buchbinder, L., and Phelps, E. B.: Studies of Microorganisms in Simulated Room Environments. J. Bact., *42:* 345–351, 1941.
2. Buchbinder, L.: The Transmission of Certain Infections of Respiratory Origin. J.A.M.A., *118:* 718–730, 1942.

SUPPLEMENTARY READINGS

BOOKS:

Burrows, W.: Jordan-Burrows Textbook of Bacteriology. 15th ed. Philadelphia, W. B. Saunders Co., 1949.
Frobisher, M.: Fundamentals of Bacteriology. 5th ed. Philadelphia, W. B. Saunders Co., 1953.
Maxcy, K. F.: Rosenau Preventive Medicine and Hygiene. 7th ed. New York, Appleton-Century-Crofts, Inc., 1951.
Smillie, W. G.: Preventive Medicine and Public Health, 2d ed. New York, The Macmillan Co., 1952.
Standard Methods for the Examination of Dairy Products. 9th ed. New York, American Public Health Association, 1948.
Standard Methods for the Examination of Water and Sewage. 9th ed. New York, American Public Health Association, 1946.
Zinsser, H.: Rats, Lice and History. Boston, Atlantic Monthly Press, 1935, p. 153.

PERIODICALS:

Aftermath of the Rochester Water Supply Pollution. Health News, *18:* 1, 1941.
Dauer, C. C.: 1952 Summary of Foodborne, Waterborne and Other Disease Outbreaks. Pub. Health Rep., *68:* 696–702, 1953.

Editorial: House Fly Resistance to Chemicals. J.A.M.A. *149:* 1653, 1952.

Emmons, C. W.: The Isolation from Soil of Fungi Which Cause Disease in Man. Tr. New York Acad. Sci., *14:* 51–54, 1951.

Farquhar, J. D., and others: Epidemic of Viral Hepatitis Apparently Spread by Drinking Water. J.A.M.A., *149:* 991–993, 1952.

Feemster, R. F.: Milk-borne Disease in Massachusetts 1946–1950. Am. J. Pub. Health, *41:* 1275–1278, 1951.

Kaufman, G. G.: Outbreak of Infectious Hepatitis—Presumably Food-borne. J.A.M.A., *149:* 993–995, 1952.

Metcalf, R. L.: Insects v. Insecticides. Scient. Am., *187:* 21–25, 1952.

Olson, T. A., and Rueger, M. E.: Experimental Transmission of *Salmonella oranienburg* through Cockroaches. Pub. Health Rep., *65:* 531–540, 1950.

Public Health Service: Milk Ordinance and Code. 1953 Recommendations of the Public Health Service. Public Health Service Bulletin No. 229.

Walton, G.: Survey of Literature Relating to Methemoglobinemia Due to Nitrate Contaminated Water. Am. J. Pub. Health, *41:* 986–996, 1951.

WHEREVER man may be, there one will also find his parasites, because they depend so directly upon him for their livelihood that they accompany him wherever he goes. In fact, the assembling of large numbers of persons in close quarters facilitates the transfer of parasites to new hosts. Hospitals frequently house persons who have either latent or active infections. As a rule, the patient has considerable resistance to his own parasites but he may have little or none against those of his neighbor. Therefore, the ease with which infections can be spread in an active hospital ward is a serious problem and one which requires the most intelligent insight and vigilance on the part of the nurse and hospital attendants.

Each patient brings with him a good many microorganisms. During the course of an active infection, vast numbers of disease-producing bacteria may be present in body excretions. Studies indicate that these organisms are widely distributed in the hospital ward. Buchbinder[1] writes:

If we could actually see the streptococci in a scarlet fever ward the following is what we [might] observe: Entering about 9 o'clock in the morning we examine one of the patients. Many streptococci are seen in his nose and throat. Smaller numbers are also seen on his hands; a few noted on his face in the region of the nose and mouth, and an occasional one appears on more distant surfaces. Likewise the nasopharynx of the attendant is seen to harbor the same type of organism but not in such large numbers; some of the streptococci are noted on her hands and several on her clothes as well. Examination of the bed reveals a fair number of organisms resting on the top sheet. When this is lifted off others are seen on the under sheets, the pillows and the bedclothes of the patient. At a glance the air of the room reveals a fairly uniform distribution of streptococci, except for a temporary concentration within the radius of a few yards of a patient who has just sneezed and around a bed the linen of which is being changed. It is also noted that the streptococci are settling to the floor in a regular manner. Further study of the floor reveals many organisms which tend to gather near the beds and diminish in number around the windows, particularly at the southern end of the room. At this point an attendant walks through the room with his long coat fluttering in the breeze, and it is noted that many streptococci are stirred up from the floor and become resuspended in the air. Finally, if we return to the ward in the middle of the night we might observe few organisms in the air but many on the floor.

This picture suggests the ease with which these organisms may be transferred to other persons. In fact, there is abundant evidence of cross-infections (reinfections) by different strains of the specific organisms as well as by other species of bacteria. Other studies[2] indicate that the nasal carrier of hemolytic streptococcus may expel from 10,000 to 10,000,000 organisms each time he blows his nose, and thus grossly contaminates his handkerchief, his hands, and in turn, everything he touches. More organisms are expelled by blowing the nose than by either sneezing or coughing. These parasites could be transferred by direct contact with the patient, with a carrier, or by indirect contact—by the air, fomites, food, or the hands of an attendant.

ENVIRONMENTAL SOURCES OF INFECTION

Air   During the course of acute respiratory infections, some pollution of the air is inevitable. Bacteria are sprayed into the air by sneezing and, to a lesser degree, by coughing and talking. Infected droplets may be projected to the skin or mucous membrane of a second person, as when a person coughs or sneezes into the face of another. Covering the mouth and nose will tend to limit the contamination to the immediate environment of the infected person. However, some infected droplets will reach the air. The very fine droplets will evaporate, forming *droplet nuclei* which remain suspended in the air for long periods of time. The larger droplets settle and become a part of the dust.

The following methods have proved useful in avoiding the transfer of pathogens by dust or droplet nuclei, and in decreasing the number of microorganisms present in the air of a room: (1) limiting the number of persons in the room; (2) treating floors and blankets with oils, in order to cause dust particles to adhere to them; (3) removing dust and bacteria from floors and furniture by damp-dusting or washing; (4) handling linens in a manner that will prevent raising dust; (5) introducing fresh air and sunlight; (6) using individual closed cubicles or rooms with outside ventilation; (7) removing microorganisms from the air by (a) filtration, (b) ultraviolet light, or (c) germicidal vapors. Mechanical devices for washing and filtering air are common in theaters, office buildings, and industrial plants, but are only occasionally used in schools and hospitals.

Fomites   A fomite is any article or substance, other than food, that may harbor and transmit bacteria. Dishes, handkerchiefs, masks, blankets, clothing, equipment, and personal articles are examples of fomites. Little is known about the extent and the degree of contamination which they cause. In one study,[3] it was found that contamination of blankets with hemolytic streptococci varied with the season. In the spring, 75 per cent of the blankets carried streptococci; in winter, 23 per cent; and in summer, 18 per cent. In one instance, six blankets which had been heavily contaminated by contact with streptococcus carriers were left on unused beds for a period and then stored in a dark closet. At the end of three and one-half months, living streptococci were recovered from all six blankets. These findings suggest that under certain conditions, bacteria may survive for long periods of time and the fomites may be a relatively important source of infection. The major responsibility for preventing the transfer of infection by fomites must rest with the nurse. It is she who must be constantly aware of this problem, who must recognize it at its source, and who must maintain environmental conditions that are relatively free from this danger. The patients' environment may be greatly safeguarded by limiting the number of articles that are used in common by all patients; many problems involving fomites may be prevented by providing individual equipment, such as thermometers, wash basins, mouth wash cups, and bed pans. By properly disinfecting and sterilizing dishes and utensils used by many persons, the nurse can protect patients from the ever-present danger of fomites.

Needles and syringes are especially dangerous since they may transmit the virus of infectious hepatitis (infectious jaundice). To prevent this all syringes and needles should be sterilized by steam under pressure. Each needle and syringe should, of course, be used for one patient only.

Food   In hospitals, as in restaurants, the preparation and serving of food are often assigned to untrained persons who may not be naturally fastidious in their habits. By careless handling they may introduce parasitic bacteria into foods. This problem requires a constant vigilance on the part of the dietary and nursing staffs. For obvious reasons, persons suffering from infections of the skin or of the upper respiratory tract, or from any form of diarrhea, should not prepare or handle food for others.

HUMAN SOURCES OF INFECTION

The Healthy Carrier   The infected human being is an important source of disease-producing organisms. The person with a mild infection and the *healthy carrier* (one who harbors disease-producing organisms) may be even more important sources of infection than individuals having severe infections because their activities are less restricted. Many of the parasites which cause infections, such as streptococci (Group A), pneumococci, and diphtheria organisms, are found periodically in the throats of healthy persons—hospital visitors, doctors, and nurses. The role of the carrier in the transfer of hemolytic streptococci is being clarified. Recent studies indicate that some carriers (called *active dispersers* or *dangerous carriers*) cause heavy contamination of their environment. A recent study made by the Army reports the activities of such a carrier.[3] During a routine survey, the throat culture of one man revealed many streptococci (Group A, Type 46). During the next four weeks, nine persons from the same barracks were admitted to the hospital with respiratory infections caused by streptococcus (Group A, Type 46). Two and a half weeks after discovery, the carrier was transferred to a second barracks. Within two weeks, twenty-seven men became carriers and four had active infections with streptococcus (Group A, Type 46). Although the carrier was not ill, he was brought to the hospital for study and for treatment with sulfonamides. During his stay, he lost the Type 46 organisms, but acquired Types 17 and 30 which had previously not been found in his barracks. The morning after his return to the barracks, streptococcus (Group A, Types 17 and 30) were recovered from the air. During the next four weeks, thirty men acquired either active or latent infection with streptococcus (Types 17 or 30).

Unless a special investigation is in progress, a carrier is likely to go unrecognized. Yet he is a prolific source of infection to others. Contact with the sick person and his environment increases the chance of the attendant acquiring latent infections. Transfer of organisms by members of the hospital staff constitutes a danger to be reckoned with. Rountree found that 50 per cent of the nurses in one hospital became persistent (nasal) carriers of resistant strains of *Micrococcus pyogenes* (*Staphylococcus aureus*). These apparently harmless organisms are often quite capable of causing disease when they are transferred to a susceptible person. The following are especially susceptible to infections by the throat streptococci: (1) premature infants; (2) sick infants and sick children; (3) persons with open wounds; (4) women after childbirth; (5) malnourished people of all ages; (6) persons weakened by illness. The protection of these susceptible persons depends in large part on a realistic appraisal of the danger and on the use of techniques which *minimize the transfer of organisms from patient to patient and from nurse or doctor to patient.*

Hands   The hands are a most important agent in the transfer of disease-producing organisms because they touch so many things—and every contact fosters an exchange of bacteria. The hands have a permanent and a transient flora of bacteria. The normal bacterial flora of the skin varies in different parts of the body. Few organisms are present on smooth surfaces while many will be found in moist areas. The permanent residents, chiefly the micrococci, are saprophytes living in hair follicles and glands; they can be decreased by thorough washing but can never be entirely eliminated from living skin. The character of the temporary flora depends on what has been touched recently. These organisms may be harmless saprophytes or they may be parasites from the intestines, the respiratory tract, or from boils, eruptions, or wounds. Any contact with the patient or his environment will transfer some of his bacteria to the hands of the attendant. Likewise any

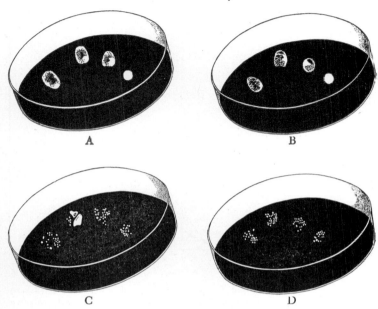

Figure 54   The effectiveness of different methods of handwashing. The fingers, contaminated with a culture of harmless bacteria (*Serratia marcescens*), were washed as indicated below, and then touched to the agar plate. After incubation, the results were as follows:

  A, Touched with unwashed fingers—shows a heavy growth of red colonies (indicated by the heavy white areas) of the contaminant.

  B, Touched by fingers after casual washing—also shows a heavy growth of red colonies.

  C, Touched by fingers after careful washing with soap and water—shows very few red colonies but many small yellow and white colonies. These bacteria, the normal inhabitants of the skin, are not removed by washing or scrubbing.

  D, Touched by fingers after thorough scrubbing with a sterile brush, soap, and water—shows many small yellow and white colonies but no red ones. In this instance, thorough scrubbing removed all of the contaminants but not the normal flora of the skin.

contact with the individual's own handkerchief, nasal secretions or saliva will contaminate the hands. For that reason, frequent and thorough handwashing is mandatory. Whenever possible, the hands should be protected from gross contamination, e.g., body secretions or articles soiled by them, by the use of gloves or forceps. If such contamination cannot be avoided, the contact should be made with clean hands which are then promptly

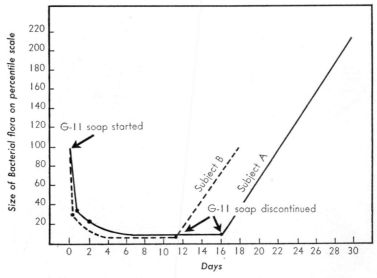

Figure 55   Effects of *frequent daily* use of 2 per cent G-11 soap upon the flora of the hands and arms. Note that the bacteria increase rapidly after the G-11 is discontinued. (Redrawn from Price, P.: The Meaning of Bacteriostasis.)

and thoroughly washed with soap and water.* It is important that pathogens be removed as promptly and completely as possible to prevent their transfer to others and to prevent them from establishing themselves as a part of the skin flora. Price reported that while dressing several gunshot wounds without gloves, the bacterial flora of his hands changed so that 50 per cent of the organisms were pathogens (hemolytic streptococci, hemolytic micrococci, *Escherichia coli,* and *Pseudomonas aeruginosa*). He reported that scrubbing did not reduce the percentage of pathogens and that weeks elapsed before the last disease-producing organism disappeared from his hands.

* Philip B. Price recommends drying the hands after washing, then wetting them with a few cubic centimeters of 70 per cent alcohol by *weight* (not volume) and then allowing them to dry by evaporation. Badly contaminated hands, after washing and drying, may be submersed in alcohol (70 per cent by weight) for from two to three minutes.

BARRIERS AGAINST INFECTION

Masks   Masks are of two varieties: those which are impervious and which deflect droplets, and those which absorb the spray expelled by the wearer. According to McKahn, the ordinary mask made of ten to twelve layers of gauze is inadequate to prevent droplet transmission of bacteria. (See Figure 56.) Experiments show that absorbent masks made of paper or of pressed cotton covered by gauze are more effective than plain gauze alone. Both types of masks must be discarded before they become wet. To be of value, a mask must be large enough to cover both the nose and the mouth. It is difficult to assess the value of a mask in preventing the spread of bacteria and viruses. A dry mask of porous, densely packed filters of absorbent material filters out many of the bacteria and possibly some of the viruses which are expelled while breathing or talking. It is important to remember that a used mask is as contaminated as a used handkerchief and should therefore be handled and disposed of like any other contaminated article.

Masks are essential for those performing or helping with surgical operations. The wearing of masks by persons working in medical and surgical wards is being questioned by many. They contend that since masks are uncomfortable they are likely to be handled and that wet masks and handled masks are of greater danger to the wearer and others than none at all. Furthermore, a mask may give the wearer a false sense of security.

PROTECTION AGAINST INFECTION

The safety of the patient in the hospital depends upon these measures which prevent or minimize contacts with pathogenic organisms. The principles are well illustrated by the problems of the hospital nursery. Infants are highly susceptible to many infections. Housing a large number of susceptible infants in close proximity provides conditions which favor the transfer of disease from the sick to the well infant. Outbreaks of epidemic diarrhea (page 361), a fatal disease of newborn infants, have occurred in nurseries where the hospital sanitation was inadequate. Although nursery infections appear to be associated

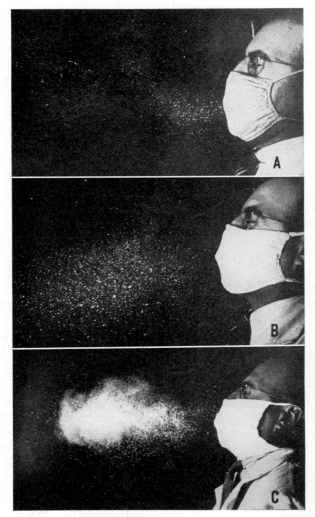

Figure 56   Masks vary in the protection they afford. A sneeze through a mask constructed of *A*, four layers of muslin 50 by 56 mesh, *B,* four layers of muslin 48 by 52 mesh, *C,* four layers of gauze 28 by 34 mesh. (Committee on Materials for Visual Instruction in Microbiology, Society of American Bacteriologists, University of Penna.)

with a variety of agents, the organisms causing them come from one of the following sources: (1) environment, (2) food, (3) other infants, or (4) adults (mother, doctors, nurses, visitors). Obviously then, protection must depend on preventing the transfer of bacteria from these sources.

The following measures recommended by Korns have proved useful in preventing infections in the newborn nurseries:

1. Proper preparation and terminal heating of formulas (250° F. for five minutes or 230° F. ten minutes).
2. Adequate isolation of normal newborn and premature infants.
3. Immediate removal from the nurseries of any infant suspected of having an infection.
4. Individual equipment for the care and transportation of each infant. Nursing care to be given to each infant in his own crib.
5. Provision of adequate floor space to prevent crowding (to average not less than 24 square feet per infant unless individual cubicles are used).
6. Limiting size of the nursery—not more than twelve infants to one nursery.
7. Limiting the contacts of a single nurse; no nurse to give care to more than twelve infants and their equipment.
8. Provision of adequate handwashing facilities in each nursery—hot and cold running water controlled by knee, elbow, or foot valves.

Handwashing   The washing of hands before meals and whenever they become soiled is an important health measure for all persons. It is doubly important for persons who work in environments that are contaminated (bacteriology laboratory, doctor's or dentist's offices, clinic, or hospital). Casual washing is likely to be ineffective especially if the hands are dirty or grossly contaminated.

The difficulty of removing gross contamination can be demonstrated by touching a sterile agar plate with a hand which has been dipped into a suspension of harmless bacteria (serratia), dried, and then washed. (See Figure 54.) Observe that casual washing is ineffective and that thorough washing with soap and water is more effective. The small colonies of bacteria which appear on the plates touched by the well-washed hands indicate that other bacteria are still present. This resident flora which is not removed by washing usually consists of relatively harmless organisms. The scrubbing of the hands with soap and water is an important part of aseptic technique used to prevent the transfer of disease-producing organisms. Price, in well-controlled experiments, demonstrated that thorough scrubbing with brush, soap, and water for one minute removes dirt and that scrubbing for two or three minutes removes almost all transient bacteria.

Handscrubbing in preparation for surgery aims to remove dirt, oil, and transient bacteria. Thorough mechanical scrubbing for six to eight minutes will remove dirt, transient bacteria, and about half of the resident flora. The scrubbing time and the total number of bacteria left on the hands can be further reduced by the use of an appropriate chemical. Hexachlorophene (G-11) when used daily will markedly reduce the bacterial flora of the hands. *p*-Hisoderm (a mixture of sodium octylphenoxyethoxyethyl ether sulfonate, lanolin, cholesterols, and petrolatum) likewise has been reported to be more effective than ordinary soap. When these substances, alone or in combination, are used *daily* in place of soap, the scrubbing time can safely be reduced. Walter* recommends the following:

SCRUB-UP PROCEDURE

1. Make certain that nails are trimmed so that the free edge is only 1 mm. wide.
2. Turn on water faucets and regulate the temperature and rate of flow.
3. Take brush from container.
4. Wet the hands and arms.
5. Add 1 cc. of *p*-Hisoderm.
6. Holding the brush "lengthwise," scrub thoroughly, using the following anatomic scrub so that every area of the skin receives the correct number of strokes:
    a. For those who scrub at intervals of more than 3 days—30 brush strokes to the skin; 50 to the nails.
    b. For those who scrub daily—15 brush strokes to the skin, 25 to the nails.
    c. For those who routinely use *p*-Hisoderm with 3 per cent hexachlorophene when washing their hands—9 strokes to the skin; 15 to the nails.
7. Apply 3 brush strokes to every area of the skin.
8. Rinse thoroughly under running water.

* Walter, C. W.: Scrubbing for Surgery. Am. J. Nursing, 52: 189, 1952.

9. Apply detergent and water to the nails.
10. Scrape any subungual spaces with the sharp edged tip of a stainless steel nail file.
11. Rinse.
12. Apply detergent and scrub 3 strokes to each area of the skin.
13. Rinse thoroughly under running water.
14. Immerse hands and arms for one minute in either 1:1000 aqueous benzyl-trialkonium chloride (Zephiran) or in 0.1 per cent hexachlorophene and 0.5 per cent cetyl alcohol in 70 per cent isopropyl alcohol.

SUMMARY

1. The hospital situation presents many opportunities for the transfer of parasites to new hosts.

2. The good records of many modern hospitals show that the danger of infection can be minimized by conscious effort on the part of medical and hospital personnel.

3. To date, air-borne transmission has been one of the most difficult to control. Recent experiments point to the possibility of air sanitation by such means as ultraviolet rays and germicidal vapors.

4. The transfer of microorganisms by contaminated articles can be controlled by the use of individual equipment and by adequate disinfection and sterilization processes.

5. Foods require very careful handling to prevent them from becoming sources of infection.

6. Because hands are important agents for transferring infections the necessity for frequent and thorough handwashing cannot be overemphasized.

7. Good masks when properly used have some value in preventing the transfer of bacteria.

8. The safety of the hospital patient depends, in large part, upon intelligent control of the environment to prevent or minimize the transfer of microorganisms from person to person.

9. Special care must be taken to protect infants against the various possible sources of infection.

REFERENCES

1. Buchbinder, L.: The Transmission of Certain Infections of Respiratory Origin. J.A.M.A., *118:* 718–730, 1942.
2. Hamburger, M., Jr., and Green, M. J.: The Problem of the Dangerous Carrier of Hemolytic Streptococci. J. Infec. Dis., *79:* 33–44, 1946.

3. Loosli, C. C.: Studies on the Transmission of Control of Respiratory Disease within Army Barracks. *Ibid.*, 82: 59–85, 1948.

SUPPLEMENTARY READINGS

BOOKS:

Greenberg, M., and Matz, A. V.: Modern Concepts of Communicable Disease. New York, G. P. Putnam's Sons, 1953.
Walter, C. W.: Aseptic Treatment of Wounds. New York, The Macmillan Co., 1948.

PERIODICALS:

Korns, R. F., and others: The Control of Communicable Disease in Hospital Nurseries for the Newborn: Progress Report. New York State Plan. New York State J. of Med., 52: 39–41, 1952.
Loosli, C. G., and others: Transmission of Hemolytic Streptococcal Infection in Infant Wards with Special Reference to Skin "Dispersers." J. Lab. & Clin. Med., 36: 342–359, 1950.
Price, P. B.: The Bacteriology of the Normal Skin. J. Infect. Dis., 63: 301–318, 1938.
Rountree, P., and Barbour, R. G. H.: Nasal Carrier Rates of Staphylococcus pyogenes in Hospital Nurses. J. Path. & Bact., 63: 313–324, 1951.
Rubenstein, A. D., and Foley, G. E.: Epidemic Diarrhea of the Newborn in Massachusetts. New England J. Med., 236: 87–94, 1947.
Walker, P. E.: Mechanical Air Drying of Hands Following Preoperative Scrubbing. Pub. Health Rep., 68: 317–319, 1953.
Walter, C. W.: Scrubbing for Surgery. Am. J. Nursing, 52: 188–189, 1952.
Watt, J.: Practical Implications of the Epidemiology of Diarrheal Diseases of the Newborn. Am. J. Pub. Health, 35: 1205–1209, 1945.

Suggested Laboratory Experience for Unit III

Introduction

THE MUCOUS membrane of the digestive and the respiratory tract and the layers of skin cells supply favorable conditions for bacterial growth. One may therefore expect to find parasitic bacteria which have adapted themselves to living on the various body surfaces. These usually harmless organisms which are constantly present are often spoken of as the normal bacterial *flora*. There is no hard and fast line between the harmless parasite and the disease-producing organism because healthy people often carry organisms which are potentially dangerous to others.

Suggested Laboratory Exercises

1. THE BACTERIAL FLORA OF THE SKIN

The skin has a transient flora of any bacteria that adhere to it. In addition, there are the bacteria which are always present on the skin. The transients can usually be removed by thorough washing, while the permanent residents remain. To determine the normal flora of the skin, it is therefore desirable to culture a clean skin area.

EXPERIMENT

Materials: Sterile cotton swabs
           Tube of broth

Method:
1. Moisten the cotton swab with broth.
2. Rub the moist swab (rolling movement) over a clean skin surface.
3. Place the swab in a tube of broth.
4. Incubate the broth culture at 37°, or at 20° C. for 24 hours.
5. Observe culture. Prepare stained smears. Record results. Did you anticipate these results?

319

2. The Removal of Bacterial Contamination

It is difficult to test the effectiveness of handwashing when the relative numbers and kinds of contaminating organisms are unknown. This obstacle can be avoided by using a harmless saprophyte which is easily recognized and which is usually not present on the skin. The serratia, which form bright red colonies when grown *at room temperature,* are satisfactory contaminants for this experiment.

EXPERIMENT

Materials: Culture of *Serratia marcescens,* diluted 1:100 or 1:200, in a bowl
2 agar plates
1 sterile brush

Method:

1. Divide plates into two equal parts by marking the *bottom* of the petri dishes; label areas 1 a, 1 b, 2 a, 2 b.
2. Dip fingers of one hand into the suspension of *serratia;* partially dry the fingers in air to remove excess moisture; gently touch agar plate 1 a.
3. Contaminate the fingers with *serratia* and dry in air as before, then wash the hand casually in running water. Partially dry the hand again; when the fingers are slightly moist (*not wet*), touch agar plate 1 b.
4. Contaminate the fingers and dry in air as before, then wash the hands carefully with soap under running water. *Rinse well* to remove all soap. Partially dry in air; when the fingers are slightly moist, touch agar plate 2 a.
5. Repeat (4) except use a sterile brush and scrub with soap under running water for at least two minutes. When fingers are slightly moist, touch agar plate 2 b.
6. Invert plates and incubate at room temperature for 48 to 72 hours.
7. Note and record results. Were all methods equally effective? Might the results have been different if the contaminating organisms had been more numerous? less numerous? Were there other organisms on the hands? How do you account for them? Of what significance are they?

It is desirable to have a slight film of moisture on the hand because dry skin often fails to transfer to the plate those organisms that are present in the grooves and creases. Too much moisture, however, interferes with discrete colony formation.

This experiment illustrates the difficulty of removing gross contamination. It may be modified by diluting the suspension of serratia to 1:500 or 1:1000.

3. BACTERIAL FLORA OF THE RESPIRATORY TRACT

The organisms in the pharynx are sufficiently numerous to examine without culturing them. A direct smear will often show epithelial (lining) cells as well as bacteria. Secretions from persons with acute or chronic infections of the mouth or respiratory tract always contain large numbers of phagocytes as well as bacteria.

EXPERIMENT—A THROAT SMEAR

Materials: Small square of newspaper
　　　　Sterile cotton swabs
　　　　Clean glass slide
　　　　Tongue blades

Method:
1. Rub the swab moistened with tap water over the tonsillar area taking care to avoid the tongue.
2. Roll the swab over the glass slide. Wrap swab in newspaper.
3. Stain with methylene blue or Gram's stain.
4. Look for body cells and note different types of bacteria.
5. What types of bacteria are present? Name some of the common organisms that may be found in the throat of a well person.

Sometimes epithelial cells from normal persons, when stained with methylene blue (not Gram's stain), show *inclusion bodies.* This fact suggests that, like bacteria, some viruses may be present without causing disease. The use of a moist swab facilitates the removal of epithelial cells to the slide.

EXPERIMENT—A THROAT CULTURE

Materials: Sterile cotton swabs
　　　　Blood agar plate*
　　　　Tongue blade
　　　　Newspaper

* Preparation of blood agar plate: Place from 1 to 2 cc. sterile blood in a sterile petri dish. Pour over the blood 10 cc. nutrient agar which contains 0.85 per cent sodium chloride melted and cooled to 45° C. (113° F.). Mix by gentle movement of the dish and allow to stand for at least four hours before streaking.

Method:
1. Rub swab (with rolling motion) over the tonsillar area.
2. Rotating the swab, make two strokes over one surface of the plate. Using a sterile inoculating needle, streak repeatedly at right angles to the original strokes.
3. Incubate at 37° C. for 24 hours.
4. Observe plates for the presence of pinpoint colonies with green or transparent (hemolytic) zones around them.
5. Pick several colonies, prepare smears, and stain with methylene blue or Gram's stain.
6. What types of bacteria are present? What is their significance?

4. The Bacterial Flora of the Mouth

The mouth of the average person contains a large variety of bacterial parasites. Spirochetes are often present between the teeth and around dentures, and are more numerous in persons with inflamed or receding gums. Squamous cells and phagocytes may also be present in scrapings from the teeth.

EXPERIMENT

Materials: Toothpick, dental floss, or sterile (*cold*) inoculating needle
Glass slides
Method:
1. Transfer a small amount of saliva and scrapings from the teeth to a glass slide.
2. Stain with methylene blue or Gram's stain.
3. Observe many fields. Record types of bacteria seen.
4. Of what significance are these organisms?

5. The Bacterial Flora of the Intestine

Feces consists chiefly of shreds of cellulose, dead and living bacteria, and water. As bacteria are very numerous in the intestine, a direct examination is a quick and easy method of observing the various types of microorganisms present.

EXPERIMENT

Materials: Emulsion of feces (prepared by mixing a small amount with saline solution or broth)
Glass slide
Method:
1. Prepare a smear of diluted feces.

2. Stain by Gram's method.
3. Observe and record types of bacteria found.
4. Of what significance are these organisms?

PART II. ANTIGENS AND ANTIBODIES

6. THE PREPARATION OF A BACTERIAL VACCINE

Antigens are substances that stimulate the host to form antibodies. They may consist of living (attenuated) viruses, killed bacteria, or the products from bacterial cells. Some of the steps in the preparation of a bacterial vaccine are simple enough to be carried out in the student's laboratory. The main purpose of the exercise is to help the student to distinguish between bacterial vaccines and other biological products.

EXPERIMENT A

Materials: 24-hour culture of *Micrococcus pyogenes*
        Agar slant
        Saline solution
        Pipettes

Method: *Purpose:*
1. Inoculate agar slant with a culture; incubate for 24   1.
   hours at 37° C. (98.6° F.).
2. Examine culture: (1) macroscopically and (2)   2.
   microscopically.
3. Suspend organisms in saline solution and transfer to   3.
   sterile test tube.
4. Hold in waterbath at 60° C. (140° F.) for 1 hour.   4.
5. Transfer a loopful of the heated vaccine to (1)   5.
   nutrient broth, (2) anaerobic media (optional).

(Steps 1 to 5 may be carried out in class. The following steps are necessary to complete the preparation of a vaccine but present some difficulties as a class exercise.)

Optional:
6. Estimate the number of organisms per cc.   6.
   (a) By mixing equal quantities fresh blood and
       vaccine. Count red cells and micrococci in
       several areas of counting chamber. De-
       termine proportion of cocci to red cells.
   (b) By comparing with turbidity standards.
7. Inject a laboratory animal.   7.
8. Transfer a measured quantity into a small test tube.   8.
   Prepare a sealed ampule. Label.

Materials: Commercial vaccines in their original packages

Method:

1. Observe commercial antigens.
2. What information is given on the label? What is the content of each?
3. For what purpose are they used?
4. What precautions must be taken to protect them from deterioration? from contamination?

7. ANTITOXINS, ANTIBACTERIAL SERUMS, AND IMMUNE SERUMS

Antiserums containing specific antibodies may be obtained from an animal that has been inoculated with bacterial cells or with toxins, or from a human being who has recovered from the disease. They confer passive immunity of short duration and may be used to prevent or to modify the disease.

The potency of these products is measured in terms of units, according to standards set by The National Institute of Health (U. S. Public Health Service).

Demonstration: Examine the display of commercial preparations of antitoxins, antibacterial serums, and gamma globulin.

1. Outline briefly the method by which each type of immune serum was prepared. What is the essential constituent of each?
2. How do antiserums differ from vaccines?

PART III. BACTERIA IN ENVIRONMENT

8. BACTERIA IN THE AIR

Some microorganisms are always present in the air. To make a thorough study of the organisms in the air requires special equipment such as an air centrifuge—a machine which pulls in a measured quantity of air while the organisms are caught in a suitable medium. A sample of the bacteria in the air can be obtained by exposing agar plates because some of the microorganisms that settle on the plates will form colonies.

Materials: Agar plates or blood agar plates
Method:
  (a) 1. Expose agar plates for 15 to 30 minutes in selected places.
      2. Label. Invert. Incubate as directed.
  (b) 1. Expose one plate for 15 minutes in a busy ward or work-room. Expose a second plate for the same period during the middle of the night or during a quiet period.
      2. Invert and incubate as directed.

Most air plates show a variety of saprophytes—molds, yeasts, and bacteria. Molds sometimes tend to overgrow the plates. This can often be prevented by incubating the plates at 37° C. (98.6° F.) for twenty-four hours and then placing them at room temperature for from four to seven days.

The colonies which appear on air plates are often both varied and interesting. A tentative identification can sometimes be made on the basis of colony structure and microscopic appearance.

9. Bacteria in Water

Water always contains some bacteria. The bacteriological examination of water is designed to reveal its sanitary quality. The tests described below will answer two questions: "Are coliform organisms present? How many bacteria (which will grow on plain nutrient agar) are present in 1 cc.?" The first question is answered by testing for lactose-fermenting organisms. If present, these organisms are presumed to belong to the coliform group until further tests prove their identity. When no lactose-fermenting organisms are found, the water is considered free from *evidence* of fecal pollution.

EXPERIMENT—THE PRESUMPTIVE TEST FOR COLIFORM ORGANISMS
Materials: Sample of tap water
         Sample of water containing *Escherichia coli*
         5 large tubes of lactose broth containing inverted vial and indicator
         10 small tubes of lactose broth containing vial and indicator
         Sterile water for dilutions
         10-cc. and 1-cc. pipettes

Eosin-methylene blue or other lactose agar plates (page 297)

Method:

1. Transfer 10 cc. of tap water to each of 5 tubes of lactose broth (large).
2. Transfer 1 cc. of tap water to each of 5 tubes of lactose broth.
3. Transfer 1 cc. of 1:10 dilution of tap water to each of 5 tubes of lactose.
4. Repeat 1, 2, 3, using second sample of water.
5. Incubate at 37° C. (98.6° F.) for 48 hours.
6. Observe tubes for the presence of gas.
7. Transfer a loopful of broth from tubes showing gas to eosin-methylene blue agar plates. Incubate at 37° C. (98.6° F.) for 24 hours.
8. Observe plates for characteristic metallic colonies. Compare with a plate streaked with a known culture of *Escherichia coli.*
9. Prepare Gram's stain. Observe. Are small gram-negative rods present? If so, what is their significance?

EXPERIMENT—THE PLATE COUNT

Materials: Sample of tap water
Sample of water containing *Escherichia coli*
10 petri dishes
10 tubes of melted agar
Sterile pipettes
Tubes containing 9 cc. sterile water

Method:

1. Place 1 cc. of tap water in each of 5 petri dishes. Cover with melted agar. Incubate at 37° C. (98.6° F.) for 48 hours.
2. Place 1 cc. of 1:10 or 1:100 dilution of second sample of water in each of 5 petri dishes. Cover with melted agar. Incubate at 37° C. (98.6° F.) for 48 hours.
3. Count colonies. Estimate the number per cc. Compare the counts obtained from the two samples. Interpret results.

The standard methods for the examination of water are described in full in *Standard Methods for the Examination of Water and Sewage*—published by the American Public Health Association. The use of methods that have been standardized is essential whenever comparable results are desired because the results obtained will depend upon the methods used. Different laboratories and different investigators can agree on the sanitary quality of a particular sample of water only if they use an accepted method for the examination.

10. BACTERIA IN MILK

Milk always contains large numbers of bacteria. Pathogenic organisms can sometimes be isolated from raw milk. However, the routine examination is usually limited to estimating the relative number of organisms present at various stages during production and distribution. This can be done by the direct method or by plating. Plate counts made by the inexperienced are seldom consistent or accurate. There are two factors which may contribute large errors. First, cream contains a higher proportion of bacteria than milk. Therefore, if the sample plated contains more than an average amount of cream, the count is likely to be too high. Second, the bacteria to be counted are those in the 1 cc. column *within* the pipette. If the outside of the pipette touches the diluting solution, additional bacteria enter from this source.

EXPERIMENT—THE PLATE COUNT

Materials: Sterile water
Petri dishes
Melted agar
Pipettes
Raw milk

Method:
1. Keep milk in the refrigerator until ready to use. Mix thoroughly.
2. Prepare dilutions 1:100, 1:1000, 1:10,000.
3. Place 1 cc. of the 1:1000 and 1:10,000 dilutions in sterile petri dishes and cover with melted agar.
4. Incubate for 48 hours at 37° C. (98.6° F.).
5. Count a section of the plate; estimate the number of bacteria per cc.
6. In the hands of a trained technician, what would a high count indicate? a low count? What are the limitations of this method of examination?

The details of the procedure are included in *Standard Methods or the Examination of Dairy Products* which is published by the American Public Health Association.

SUPPLEMENTARY READINGS

Salle, A. J.: Laboratory Manual on Fundamental Principles of Bacteriology. 3d ed. New York, McGraw-Hill Book Co., 1948.

Standard Methods for the Examination of Water and Sewage. 9th ed. New York, American Public Health Association, 1946.

Standard Methods for the Examination of Dairy Products. 9th ed. New York, American Public Health Association, 1948.

Unit IV   THE PATHOGENS

CHAPTER 21   *The Detection and Recognition of Pathogens*

IMPORTANCE OF THE BACTERIOLOGICAL LABORATORY

THERE are thousands of bacteriology laboratories in the United States contributing to the advancement of medical science. Research laboratories discover new facts about microorganisms and their influence upon the environment and upon laboratory animals. Some of the discoveries lead to a better understanding of disease processes and to the development of improved methods of controlling and preventing disease. Certain laboratories specialize in the preparation of vaccines and antiserums in accordance with standards set by the National Institute of Health of the United States Public Health Service. These institutions are required by law to obtain a license from the National Institute, to test each product prepared, and to submit samples of each lot to the National Institute for examination in order to determine the potency, sterility, and toxicity of the product. Other laboratories are chiefly concerned with tests which assist the physician in making accurate diagnoses.

This service is so essential to proper treatment of the patient and adequate protection for the public that all states and many cities maintain laboratories to provide diagnostic service as well as to check the sanitary quality of water and milk supplies. In addition, many private laboratories also perform diagnostic tests for the physician. Inasmuch as nurses and other hospital personnel must of necessity cooperate with the diagnostic laboratory, the work of that organization will be considered in some detail.

LABORATORY METHODS

The bacteriologist who offers diagnostic service is a detective in every sense of the word. His duty is to discover evidence that will enable him to identify the parasite that is the cause of the disease. This problem can be approached either by searching for the disease-producing organism (the *pathogen*) or by searching for antibodies formed in response to the pathogen. The laboratory does not make a diagnosis; it simply reports the presence or absence of certain bacteria or of specific antibodies in the specimens examined. The laboratory report together with the history and clinical signs of disease provides the evidence which enables the physician to make a diagnosis. For example, the finding of typhoid organisms (*Salmonella typhosa*) in a culture made from feces may indicate that the person has typhoid fever or that he is a carrier. Likewise, the presence of typhoid antibodies in the blood may mean (1) that the person has typhoid fever now, (2) that he has had typhoid fever, or (3) that he has been inoculated with typhoid vaccine. Obviously, only the physician has sufficient information to interpret such findings and the interpretation of negative results is even more difficult. Consider the report of a throat culture which reads: "No diphtheria bacilli found." That report may mean that the organisms were absent, or were present in very small numbers, or perhaps that the specimen was collected in such a manner that the organisms were not obtained. Furthermore, the failure to find antibodies may mean that the person does not have the infection and therefore is not forming antibodies, or that the test was made early in the disease when the antibody content was too small to be significant.

The Search for the Microorganism   MATERIALS   A thorough knowledge of the life cycle of the parasite is essential to good laboratory work. Before a real search for the organism can be made, one must know where it lives and how it escapes from the body. The following materials may contain disease-producing organisms and therefore are suitable for laboratory examination:

1. Tissue, pus, or fluid from wounds.
2. Whole blood or blood serum.
3. Sputum and mucus from nose and throat.
4. Feces and gastric or duodenal contents.
5. Urine.
6. Spinal fluid.

COLLECTION OF SPECIMENS   The collection of material for bacteriological examination is an important task because the success or failure of the laboratory procedure is often determined by what happens to the specimen before it reaches the laboratory. Blood, spinal fluid, and urine for bacteriological examination should be collected in sterile containers, care being taken to prevent the introduction of bacteria from body surfaces or from the air. Sterile containers are also desirable for the collection of pus, sputum, and feces because they are free from contaminants which might multiply in the material and increase until they are so numerous that they obscure the pathogens. Disinfectants should not be added to specimens because they will kill the organisms which the laboratory is expected to grow. Preserving fluids, such as glycerin, are sometimes required to prevent drying and to inhibit the growth of nonpathogens when a long time must elapse before the specimen reaches the laboratory. Such preservatives should be used only when the laboratory specifically requests their use, since it is desirable to have specimens arrive at the laboratory unchanged in character. When time must elapse, an optimal temperature should be used for storage. Feces, urine, and sputum should be put in a cold place to prevent hardy bacteria from overgrowing the pathogens; in contrast, spinal fluid and diphtheria cultures should be kept warm. When special directions have been given concerning the collection of specimens, they should be followed to facilitate the work of the laboratory.

REQUESTS FOR LABORATORY EXAMINATIONS   All materials sent to the laboratory should be accompanied by written requests for the examinations required. The information provided should be as complete as possible and should indicate the kind of examination ordered by the physician. This is especially important when requests are made for examination of fecal specimens because the number and variety of organisms present distinct problems requiring different techniques. For example, methods that are useful for revealing tubercle bacilli will fail to demonstrate typhoid organisms and vice versa. Therefore, in addition to identifying data such as date, name of patient, room number, and name of physician, the request should state the tentative diagnosis, the type of material to be studied, and the type of examination required. When no tentative diagnosis has been made, a list of the outstanding symptoms of the disease may be given to provide a clue for the bacteriologist.

METHODS OF DETECTING PARASITES   WORMS   Parasitic worms from the intestine can usually be detected by direct macroscopic or microscopic examination of feces for the presence of ova or the adult worms. In the case of tapeworms, segments of the worm may be passed in the feces, especially after a cathartic has been given. When worms are sought, the laboratory workers may request that the entire stool be sent to the laboratory.

Worms which inhabit striated muscles, such as *Trichinella spiralis*, can be demonstrated by biopsy (surgical removal and microscopic examination of a piece of living tissue).

PROTOZOA   The cysts of intestinal protozoa can be demonstrated by direct microscopic examination of feces. A fresh, *warm* specimen is required for detection of the motile form of the *Endamoeba histolytica* (see page 374).

Blood parasites, as, for example, the malarial parasite (*Plasmodium vivax, P. falciparum*), can be identified by microscopic examination of thin or thick blood smears. In acute

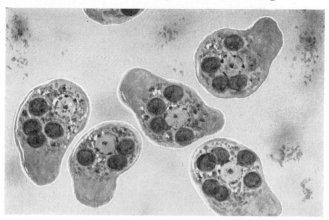

Figure 57   *Endamoeba histolytica* containing red blood cells. This is the pathogenic stage found in semiliquid and liquid stools. (Courtesy of Harold W. Brown in "Seminar," 1953, Sharp & Dohme.)

malaria it is often desirable that the blood be collected at the time the patient is having a chill.

YEASTS AND MOLDS   Yeasts and molds may be recognized by direct examination of sputum or infected structures (hair, skin, nails). In addition, most can be cultured in suitable medium on coverslips or in petri dishes. Both direct examination and culture methods are commonly employed because the fungi often assume one form in the body and another when growing on an artificial medium.

BACTERIA WHICH DO NOT GROW READILY ON ARTIFICIAL MEDIA Pathogenic spirochetes are usually demonstrated by viewing fresh exudate (for detection of such microorganisms as *Treponema pallidum* and *Borrelia vincentii*) or blood (for *Leptospira icterohaemorrhagiae*, *Borrelia recurrentis*, and *Spirillum minus*) through a microscope equipped with a darkfield apparatus. Darkfield illumination enables one to see living, unstained, moving organisms against a black background (see page 454). *Treponema pallidum* is difficult to stain. The other spirochetes can be stained with basic dyes. Spirochetes in blood may be inoculated into suitable laboratory animals—usually mice, rats, or guinea pigs.

BACTERIA WHICH WILL GROW ON ARTIFICIAL MEDIA   Direct

microscopic examination of bacteria usually provides too little information for identification. It is necessary, therefore, to grow the organism in pure culture and to determine the chemical changes it produces in differential media. It is usually not difficult to obtain pure cultures of bacteria present in blood or spinal fluid. However, in the case of the bacteria-laden excretions, sputum, and feces the isolation of the pathogen requires both time and skill. Success in this task often depends upon the use of special media which will either encourage the growth of the pathogen or inhibit competing microorganisms. The process includes the following steps:

1. Inoculating a solid medium to secure isolated colonies.
2. Transferring selected colonies to a liquid or solid medium to obtain pure cultures.
3. Identification of the pure cultures by
   a. microscopic examination,
   b. biochemical reactions in special media,
   c. serological tests.

Some organisms may be cultured by the inoculation of a suitable laboratory animal. The use of experimental animals is definitely limited by the ability of the microorganism to grow and to produce disease in a certain species. For example, neither the bacteria which cause typhoid fever nor those which cause gonorrhea produce these diseases in animals; the influenza virus causes an infection in ferrets but not in guinea pigs or rabbits. On the other hand, tuberculosis organisms grow well in guinea pigs, and pneumococci are highly fatal to white mice. Animal inoculation, therefore, may be useful in the identification of some microorganisms but not of others. Obviously the selection of the method of examination will depend upon the nature of the pathogen and the material to be examined.

TYPICAL LABORATORY PROBLEMS   The diagnostic procedures used in the bacteriology laboratory are too complex to be discussed in detail in this text. However, three common procedures will be presented in brief to suggest some of the problems of the laboratory and to illustrate certain important working principles.

PROBLEM I. The Identification of Enteric Bacteria. *Situation:* Patient ill with typhoid (?) fever. Materials to be examined: Blood, urine, feces. Laboratory procedures: Blood culture, stool culture, urine culture.

The blood culture, a useful test in the early stages of the disease, is made by adding samples of the patient's blood to melted agar and to broth. After an incubation period of twenty-four hours, the bacteria if in pure culture are ready for identification. In contrast to the simplicity of the blood culture, the isolation of pathogens from feces is complicated by the presence of tremendous numbers of organisms that are very much alike. Fortunately, these organisms present striking differences in their behavior on sugar media. The fact that the harmless parasites (*Escherichia coli*) ferment lactose, forming acid and gas, serves to separate them from the pathogens which do not change the sugar. Many media used for isolating the intestinal organisms contain lactose and a dye. A loopful of feces or urine is streaked on lactose agar plates and then the plates are incubated for twenty-four hours. As the bacteria grow, those which ferment the sugar, forming acids, change the color of the medium or of the colonies. This reaction will distinguish between (1) the lactose-fermenters (*Escherichia coli* and others that change the medium) and (2) the non-lactose fermenters (the pathogens). The next step is to transfer several of the colorless colonies to a fresh medium to obtain pure cultures. When this has been done, the organisms can be grown in various media to determine their distinguishing charasteristics. Table 28 shows the significant cultural reactions which are useful in identifying a group of intestinal organisms.

The methods just discussed will be summarized together with those suitable for the isolation and identification of the organisms causing diphtheria and tuberculosis. Observe that the procedures differ one from another and also that the time required for the completion of the tests varies greatly.

PROCEDURE	PURPOSE
1st day .... Streak feces on differential plates (lactose); incubate at 37° C. (98.6° F.) for 24 hours	To isolate pathogens
2nd day ... Transfer nonlactose fermenting organisms to special sugar medium	To secure pure culture
3rd day ... Transfer pure culture to gelatin, litmus milk, and sugar media Motility tests Agglutination tests	} To collect identifying data
4th to 6th day ... Complete identification by comparing characteristics of unknown with those of known organisms	

PROBLEM II. The Identification of Diphtheria Organisms

PROCEDURE	PURPOSE
1st day .... Streak throat swab over special blood serum medium and incubate at 37° C.; smear over glass slide—stain with methylene blue and examine microscopically	To isolate pathogens
8 to 18 hours later ...... Microscopic examination of organisms from colonies grown on blood serum agar; isolation of typical organisms in broth	To secure pure culture
3rd day ... Transfer pure culture to various sugar broths 4th to 10th day .. Inject culture into the skin of a susceptible animal to determine virulence, i.e., its ability to destroy cells	To complete identification on the basis of (1) appearance, (2) cultural characteristics, and (3) virulence test

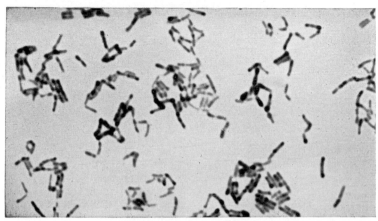

Figure 58   Diphtheria organisms (*Corynebacterium diphtheriae*). Observe that many of the slender club-shaped rods lie parallel and that they tend to form the letters L or V. Also observe the irregular staining, indicating the presence of granules or bars. (Burrows, W.: Jordan-Burrows Textbook of Bacteriology.)

Table 28   IDENTIFYING CHARACTERISTICS OF SOME GRAM-NEGATIVE BACTERIA FOUND IN FECES

SPECIES	MOTIL- ITY	REACTIONS IN MEDIA CONTAINING							SEROLOGICAL REACTION
		DEXTROSE	MANNITOL	LACTOSE	SACCHAROSE	XYLOSE	RHAMNOSE	DULCITOL	
Salmonella typhosa	Yes	A	A	—	—	V	—	—	Agglutination with *Salmonella typhosa* serum
Salmonella enteritides (paratyphoid)	Yes	AG	AG	—	—	AG	AG	AG	Agglutination with Salmonella antiserum (multivalent or univalent)
Shigella dysenteriae	No	A	—	—	—	—	—	—	Agglutination with Shigella antiserum (multivalent or univalent)
Shigella sonnei	No	A	A	A	A	—	A	—	
Shigella paradysenteriae	No	A	A	—	V	V	V		
Coliform group	V	AG	AG	AG	V	V	V	V	Seldom used—of questionable value

Key: A = acid   AG = acid and gas   V = variable   — = no acid

PROBLEM III. The Identification of Tuberculosis Organisms

PROCEDURE	PURPOSE
1st day . . . . Direct examination of sputum stained by Ziehl-Neelsen method Inoculation of special selective medium Inoculation of rabbit or guinea pig	To identify the organisms on the basis of acid-fast stain Tentative report the same day
From 3 to 6 weeks later . . . . . . Complete tests	To identify organisms by examination of tissues and cultures

METHODS FOR DETECTING VIRUSES AND RICKETTSIAS   The methods commonly used for isolating and identifying bacteria are not suitable for viruses and rickettsias. The latter require living cells to enable them to multiply. Body fluids containing rickettsias or viruses may be treated to destroy bacteria and then may be cultured by introducing them into a developing chick embryo or into the tissues of a suitable laboratory animal. The characteristic signs of disease which follow constitute an important clue to the identity of the parasite.

Serological Tests   Antibodies are formed in response to stimulation of the host by antigens from microorganisms. These specific protective substances, present in the globulin of cells and blood serum, can be demonstrated by the following laboratory tests:

1. Animal-protection tests (see page 243, Chapter 15).
2. Agglutination tests.
3. Precipitation tests.
4. Complement-fixation tests.

In all of these tests, the patient's serum, drawn during the acute or the convalescent period or both, is used with a suitable antigen. A positive reaction indicates the presence of antibodies.

ANIMAL-PROTECTION TESTS (NEUTRALIZATION TESTS)   Animal-protection tests give information that is valuable in the diagnosis of certain virus, rickettsial, and bacterial diseases. Blood samples are collected early in the disease and again two and four weeks after the onset of illness. Varying dilutions of each sample are mixed with the organism, or, in some instances, its toxin, and injected into groups of mice. In this way, the smallest effective dose is determined. For example, mice given 0.1 cc. of blood may survive, while those that receive less die. Should the blood taken late in the disease or during convalescence show increased protective power, it is an indication that the patient had formed antibodies against the test organism.

AGGLUTINATION TESTS   These tests are made by placing appropriate amounts of the antigen (bacterial cells) with varying dilutions of patient's serum. The specific antibody globulin, if present, will unite with and change the outer surface of the bacteria, causing the formation of visible clumps. When the agglutination takes place in tubes, these clumped organisms slowly settle out, leaving the liquid clear. When no antibody is present, the bacteria remain in suspension so that the fluid remains uniformly cloudy. This test may be outlined as follows:

TEST MATERIAL COMBINED	POSSIBLE RESULTS	INTERPRETATION
Antigen Suspension of known bacterial cells (Ex., typhoid, salmonella, brucella, etc.)	1. Agglutination (clumping of cells)	Serum contains specific antibodies which react with this antigen
Antibody Patient's serum	2. No agglutination	Serum contains no antibodies which react with this antigen

Agglutination tests are usually specific; i.e., typhoid bacteria are used to test for typhoid antibodies. Closely related organisms containing one or more common antigens may, however, be clumped by the same serum; these cross agglutinations can be eliminated by diluting the antiserum.

In rare instances, the antibodies formed against one organism will also react with organisms of a different species or class. This circumstance is useful when the specific antigen is difficult to obtain. For instance, the blood serum of a patient with typhus, containing antibodies against the rickettsias, will also clump bacteria of the Proteus (OX19, OX2, OXK) group. This nonspecific agglutination reaction (Weil-Felix test) is sometimes used to aid in the diagnosis of rickettsial diseases.

PRECIPITATION TESTS   When serum containing specific antibodies is mixed with suitable amounts of antigen (carbohydrate or protein in solution), a white precipitate appears. The chief difference between the agglutination and the precipitation reactions lies in the fact that antigen in the agglutination test is in the form of organized cells, while the antigen in the precipitation test is in solution. The precipitation reaction can be outlined as follows:

TEST MATERIALS COMBINED	POSSIBLE RESULTS	INTERPRETATION
Antigen Extract of bacterial cells or other protein or carbohydrate solution *Antibody* Patient's serum	1. Precipitation	Serum contains specific antibodies that react with the test antigen
	2. No precipitation	Serum contains no antibodies that react with the test antigen

Precipitation reactions are usually determined by the use of the specific antigen. For example, an extract of *Pneumococcus Type I* would be used to test for antibodies formed against *Pneumococcus Type I*. Sometimes specific antibodies will react with a chemically similar substance that is entirely unrelated to the disease process which caused the formation of the antibodies. Such nonspecific reactions are useful when the true antigen is not available. In the case of syphilis, the spirochetes cannot be cultivated to serve as the antigen in the test. However, precipitation tests in which fatty extracts of beef heart are used are valuable diagnostic aids because a precipitate forms when suitable quantities of the extract and syphilitic serum are mixed. The Kline, Kahn, and Hinton tests are diagnostic precipitation tests for syphilis which employ an extract of beef heart as the substitute antigen. These tests are so sensitive that a small percentage of false positive reactions will occur; i.e., precipitation will occasionally take place in the presence of serum from a person who does not have syphilis. Furthermore, false positive reactions may occur following smallpox vaccination and during the course of certain infections such as malaria and yaws.

To facilitate the work of the laboratory, a preliminary (screen, or exclusion) test may be made with a very sensitive antigen for the purpose of detecting those sera which are definitely negative. Then careful test procedures are used to study only those sera which give positive or doubtful reactions.

SEROLOGICAL TESTS USED FOR IDENTIFICATION   Precipitation tests, using a known specific antiserum and solutions of carbohydrate or proteins, can be used to identify microorganisms or specific antigenic substances. Agglutination tests are likewise useful in the identification of some organisms. If a pure culture of an unknown bacterium, isolated from the feces of a person suffering from enteric disease, is mixed with specific antiserum for typhoid, paratyphoid, dysentery, and brucella organisms, the results might be as follows:

CULTURE 122 IN	REACTION	INTERPRETATION
Typhoid (*Salmonella typhosa*)		
antiserum 1:500 . . . . Agglutination		Culture 122 is *Salmonella typhosa* if the cultural characteristics are typical
Salmonella antiserum 1:850 . . No agglutination		
Shigella antiserum 1:100 . . . . . No agglutination		
Brucella antiserum 1:100 . . . . . No agglutination		

GROUPING OR TYPING OF MICROORGANISMS   Organisms of the same species that are similar in appearance and in cultural reactions may differ with regard to their chemical or antigen structure as determined by agglutination or precipitation tests. On this basis, the pneumococci can be divided into more than seventy types (Types I, II, III, IV, etc.) and the *Streptococcus hemolyticus* classified into groups A, B, C–to K, with Group A alone subdivided into more than thirty types. The organisms which comprise these species contain some common (*group* or *species*) antigens and some which are characteristic of a single type. For example, repeated injections of a culture of streptococcus Group A, Type I, will stimulate a rabbit to form antibodies that react with all group A streptococci as well as some that are specific for Type I antigens. For purposes of discussion, consider that streptococci (Group A, Types I, II, III) contain the following antigens:

Group A, Type	I antigens:	X, T 1
Type	II "	X, T 2
Type	III "	X, T 3

The antiserum formed against Type I organisms would contain antibodies specific for X and for T 1, and is, therefore, group specific—that is, it will react with the X antigens of all group A strains. The common antibody can be removed or *adsorbed* by mixing Type I antiserum with an extract of Type II or Type III organisms, leaving a serum that is type specific since it will then react only with Type I organisms. Microorganisms are grouped or typed by means of agglutination or precipitation tests using group or type specific serums. Pneumococci and streptococci may be typed by mixing an extract of the bacterial cells with different type specific serums.

In the case of the pneumococcus, the swelling of the capsule, in response to the type specific serum, provides a simpler method (Neufeld test) of typing these organisms. The test is performed by mixing a suspension of pneumococci from culture or sputum with the serum on a glass slide which is then observed under the microscope. When Type I pneumococci are mixed with Type I serum, the antibody unites with the capsule, causing it to swell markedly and to take on a glassy appearance, while serums for the other types cause no swelling. The change in the size and appearance of the capsule occurs only when organisms and the antiserum of the same type are combined. (See Figure 64, page 399.)

IMMOBILIZING ANTIBODIES   Immobilizing antibodies are those which inhibit the movement of a motile bacterium. Let us consider as an example the *Treponema pallidum*. A few weeks after the initial infection with this organism the blood serum contains an antibody which in the presence of complement immobilizes and kills living active treponema organisms. This reaction can be observed with the darkfield microscope. It is of interest that this is the first specific test for syphilis.

(Precipitation and complement-fixation tests are nonspecific since they use alcoholic extracts of beef heart instead of materials derived from the spirochete.)

HEMAGGLUTINATION AND HEMAGGLUTINATION INHIBITION Some viruses, the influenza virus, for example, have the ability to agglutinate human and fowl red blood cells (*hemagglutination*). It is therefore possible to test for the presence of influenza virus by adding red blood cells to a suspension of material thought to contain the virus. Fluid from a chick embryo infected with influenza virus will agglutinate or clump the red blood cells. Antibodies against the specific strain of the virus will prevent the agglutination of red blood cells. Antibodies formed against influenza virus A will inhibit clumping by virus A but not by virus B or C. These tests make it possible to identify either the virus or the antibody.

Hemagglutination will also occur when an antigen such as tuberculin (tuberculosis protein) is adsorbed on the surface of the red cells and then is mixed with serum containing specific antibody. This method is useful when the amounts of antibody present in serum are very small.

COMPLEMENT-FIXATION TEST   THE NATURE OF COMPLEMENT   The complement-fixation test is one which involves the interaction of three substances, namely, antigen, antibody, and *complement*. Complement, a substance present in all normal fresh blood serum, is destroyed by heat and disappears upon standing. Complement reacts with neither antigen nor antibody alone, but after the union of any antigen with its specific antibody the combination, called the "sensitized" antigen, is capable of uniting with and "fixing" or removing definite quantities of complement. This reaction produces visible results when suitable amounts of the following substances are combined as indicated:

MATERIALS: *Antigen*—red blood cells of the sheep (washed to remove complement)

Antibody—hemolysin—serum of a rabbit immunized against the red blood cells of the sheep (inactivated by heat to destroy complement present)

Complement—fresh blood serum from a guinea pig

COMBINATION	RESULTS
Red blood cells Hemolysin—fresh serum containing *complement* and antibodies	Hemolysis (laking, or separation of hemoglobin from red blood cells)
Red blood cells Hemolysin—inactivated by heat to destroy complement	No hemolysis
Red blood cells Hemolysin—inactivated by heat Complement	Hemolysis

It will be observed that the lysis, or destruction of the blood cells, after their union with the hemolysin, is dependent upon the presence of complement. In this reaction, the antigen and antibody unite without complement, but the latter must be present before hemolysis occurs. This hemolysin reaction is a useful part of the complement-fixation test described below since it serves as an indicator of complement; that is, when complement is present, hemolysis occurs, when absent, it does not.

THE SPECIFIC COMPLEMENT-FIXATION TEST   The following materials are needed for a complement-fixation test:

TEST MATERIAL	SOURCE
Antigen	Specific organism, e.g., *Hemophilus pertussis* or *Gonococcus*
Antibody(?)	Patient's serum
Complement	Fresh guinea pig serum
Indicator system: Red blood cells	Sheep
Hemolysin	Serum from rabbit inoculated with red cells from sheep

The quantities of each of the test materials are carefully adjusted so that if the antibody is present all of the complement will be fixed. Then the antigen, patient's serum, and complement are combined and allowed to incubate. After that, the indicator system (hemolysin and red blood cells) is added and the mixture incubated again. The results may be outlined as follows:

TEST MATERIALS COMBINED	RESULTS	INTERPRETATION
Antigen; e.g., extract of gonococcus (or pertussis) Patient's serum Complement	None visible (antigen combines with antibody if present, and fixes complement)	
Indicator system (hemolysin and red cells) added	1. Hemolysis	Negative reaction: * no complement-fixing antibodies in serum
	2. No hemolysis	Positive reaction: complement-fixing antibodies present

A NONSPECIFIC COMPLEMENT-FIXATION REACTION (WASSERMANN TEST)   The Wassermann test for syphilis is similar to the specific complement-fixation test, except that reagent, a fatty extract of beef heart, is used as a substitute for the antigen. The results are commonly reported in terms of the highest dilution of the patient's serum which will fix complement in the presence of beef heart antigen. The concentration of complement-fixing antibodies decreases as treatment progresses. A patient's serum may fix complement in dilutions 1:40, 1:80, 1:160, and 1:320 before treatment, whereas after treatment, a positive reaction may occur only in dilutions of 1:20 and 1:40.

This test has certain definite limitations. The serum of most persons with late infections of syphilis and yaws fixes complement. The reaction to the test is often negative in the early

* A positive reaction to the complement-fixation test does not always indicate disease—nor does a negative reaction always mean absence of disease. For instance, a serum which fixes complement when tested with the gonococcus (or pertussis) antigen suggests:
1. Past or present gonococcal (or pertussis) infection;
2. The use of gonococcal (or pertussis) vaccine; or
3. Cross fixation with the complement-fixing antibodies for meningococci (or para-pertussis).
A negative reaction may mean:
1. Patient is free from gonococcal (or pertussis) infection;
2. Serum taken at an early stage of the disease before antibodies appear;
3. Infection local and well drained—not enough antigen absorbed to stimulate antibody formation. (This reaction is unlikely in pertussis but may occur in gonorrhea.)
(Modified from "Diagnostic Procedures and Reagents." 2d ed. New York, American Public Health Association, 1945, p. 122.)

stages of the disease and also after the patient has been treated. In rare instances, complement may be fixed by the serum of a nonsyphilitic person. Obviously, the interpretation of the Wassermann and of other serological tests is a problem for the physician. (See page 455.)

SUMMARY

1. The functions of a bacteriology laboratory include: (a) research, (b) the preparation of vaccines or antiserums, (c) the performance of diagnostic tests and tests for determining the sanitary character of milk and water.

2. Laboratory examinations often include a search for the causative organism by means of direct microscopic examination, cultures on artificial media, or the inoculation of experimental animals.

3. Laboratory investigations may also include serological tests for the presence of antibodies. These tests are usually specific, but in a few instances nonspecific antigens are used. Serological tests may also be used for the identification or the typing of microorganisms.

4. Laboratory tests, though not conclusive in themselves, furnish valuable evidence which the physician uses, together with the clinical signs to complete and to confirm a diagnosis.

SUPPLEMENTARY READINGS

BOOKS:

   Boyd, W. C.: Fundamentals of Immunology. 2d ed. New York, Interscience Publishers, Inc., 1947.
   Burrows, W.: Jordan-Burrows Textbook of Bacteriology. 15th ed. Philadelphia, W. B. Saunders Co., 1949.
   Diagnostic Procedures and Reagents. New York, American Public Health Association, 1945.
   Diagnostic Procedures for Virus and Rickettsial Diseases. New York, American Public Health Association, 1948.
   Frobisher, M.: Fundamentals of Microbiology. 5th ed. Philadelphia, W. B. Saunders Co., 1953.
   Simmons, J. S., and Gentzkow, C. J.: Laboratory Methods of the United States Army. 5th ed. Philadelphia, Lea & Febiger, 1944.
   Smith, D. T., and Conant, C. F.: Zinsser's Textbook of Bacteriology. 10th ed. New York, Appleton-Century-Crofts, Inc., 1952.

PERIODICAL:

   Miller, J. L.: Reliability of Treponemal Immobilization Test for Diagnosis of Syphilis. J.A.M.A., *149:* 987–990, 1952.

CHAPTER 22

**Bacteria Transmitted by
Food and Water**

BACTERIA CAUSING FOOD POISONING:
*Micrococcus pyogenes; Clostridium
botulinum*

BACTERIA CAUSING DIARRHEAL DISEASES:
*Salmonella; Shigella; Vibrio comma;
Coliform Bacteria; Paracolon Bacteria*

THE INTESTINES of man and animal supply food and shelter for
many parasites. Most of these organisms are a constant part of
the internal environment and do no harm. In fact, some contribute to the welfare of the host by synthesizing certain enzymes and vitamins and by antagonizing or inhibiting the
growth of harmful organisms. Other parasites, like the enteric
pathogens, possess definite power to invade and to injure.

Some organisms grow and produce toxins in food before it is
ingested, thereby causing food poisoning. Other organisms,
including a variety of bacteria, enter by the mouth and invade
the intestinal mucous membrane, causing local or systemic infections during which the organisms are excreted in the feces
and sometimes in the urine.

The association of man and the intestinal pathogens has
undoubtedly been long and close. For centuries these organisms have been the scourge of armies and of cities. In every
war before 1900, more men were killed by disease than by
bullets. That was true of the Civil War when there were
186,184 deaths due to disease, compared with 118,123 deaths
from all other causes.[1] During the Spanish-American War,
86 per cent of the deaths were due to typhoid fever. During
the same period, sanitary conditions in army camps located in
the continental United States were so bad that typhoid occurred in 90 per cent[2] of the volunteer regiments of soldiers
within eight weeks after coming to camp. However, as sanitary conditions improved and the army and navy made vac-

cination against typhoid compulsory, the prevalence of this disease decreased. The great decline in deaths from typhoid and paratyphoid fevers has been due in large part to the improvement of water supplies and to the pasteurization of milk. At present typhoid and paratyphoid fevers are rare in the army and in cities, but they still occur in communities where sanitation is primitive. In fact, the death rates from typhoid fever and the illness rates from dysentery may be used as an index of sanitation because the rates are always high where hygiene is poor.

During and following World War II, enteric diseases occurred in epidemic form in the countries of Central Europe and also in Italy and Greece. For example, in the period from October 22 to December 1, 1945, the incidence of typhoid fever in Austria was 28 times that of the pre-war period; paratyphoid fever and dysentery too were very prevalent. In the United States Army, diarrheal disease rates have continued high, although typhoid and paratyphoid have progressively decreased. The future of these diseases will depend upon the ability of community housekeeping to prevent the transfer of living parasites to susceptible persons.

FOOD-POISONING BACTERIA

Bacterial food poisoning is a disease due to toxins formed by bacteria growing in food. As a rule the organisms that cause food poisoning do not invade the gastrointestinal tract. The disease is due to injury produced by toxins. The organisms commonly associated with food poisoning are *Micrococcus pyogenes* and *Clostridium botulinum.*

Micrococcus pyogenes (Staphylococcus aureus)   This common body parasite is constantly present on the human skin and mucous membranes. Pathogenic strains of the organism may be carried by healthy persons as well as by those with obvious infections of the skin or respiratory tract (see Chapter 28). Although micrococci are usually unable to invade the digestive tract,* certain strains when growing in food

---

* Prolonged antibotic therapy apparently fosters conditions that enable *Micrococcus pyogenes* to grow in the intestine causing a staphylococcus dysentery.

produce enterotoxins (*enteron*—intestine) which give rise to acute gastrointestinal distress.

Toxin-producing micrococci are introduced into the food by a worker who has a boil, infected burn, or sinus infection. The bacteria grow in the food and form a toxin which acts through the nervous system, causing severe nausea and vomiting. The toxin is heat stable, and may resist boiling or refrigeration. Since the disease is due to the *bacterial products* and not to the organisms, only a short incubation period (from two to four hours) precedes the symptoms of food poisoning. In the past, this type of illness has followed the eating of protein foods such as ham, cream-filled pastries, chocolate eclairs, chicken salad, and Hollandaise sauce.

Micrococcus food poisoning can be prevented by (1) excluding from the kitchen all persons who have skin infections or other purulent lesions; (2) cooking thoroughly those foods that can be cooked; (3) refrigerating foods that may serve as media for bacteria, and (4) avoiding the conditions that favor the growth of bacteria. In general, much-handled foods should be refrigerated before and after preparation and should be eaten without delay. All foods should be prepared in sanitary kitchens by persons who are both healthy and clean, and they should be protected from contamination during storage and delivery.

Clostridium botulinum* and *Cl. parabotulinum The botulinus organisms are large, anaerobic, spore-forming rods that are commonly found in soil and in decaying material. There are many strains of these organisms. Some produce potent toxins when growing in partially processed foods or in decaying animal or vegetable matter. These toxins when ingested cause botulism in man and "limber neck" in chickens and ducks. Like other spore-formers, they are difficult to kill unless high temperatures are used. Therefore, coldpack canning methods are unsafe for processing nonacid foods, since temperatures above 100° C. can be obtained only by the use of a pressure cooker. These organisms, obligate anaerobes, will grow and form toxin only when oxygen is absent and when the medium is slightly alkaline. These conditions are found in canned meats and vegetables which have not been heated sufficiently to kill the spores of the botulinus organism. Acid foods, such as tomatoes, cherries, jams, and jellies, do not provide satisfactory growth conditions for the organism and therefore seldom cause botulism. *Clostridium botulinum* may or may not change the appearance and odor of the food in which it is growing. To date, there have been no cases of botulism associated with frozen foods. Furthermore, experiments indicate that the organisms do not produce toxins at refrigerator temperatures. This evidence suggests that there is little or no danger of botulism from frozen foods.

Botulinus toxins (Types A, B, C, D, E) are so potent that minute amounts may produce illness or death. These toxins are very stable; they can withstand boiling for several minutes and are not changed by the digestive juices. Though the organism seldom if ever invades tissues, the toxin is absorbed, from the stomach, intestines, and possibly from the mouth, into the blood stream. Botulinus toxin causes paralysis of the peripheral nerves (parasympathetic and skeletal motor) by inhibiting the production of an enzyme (acetylcholine) required for the transmission of nerve impulses. From one to three days after taking the poisonous food, the person complains of weakness, gastrointestinal pain, and diarrhea or constipation. Paralysis of the muscles of the tongue, eye, pharynx, diaphragm, and intestine are also common symptoms. Fatality rates are very high. Fortunately, this disease is rare; in recent years there have been no cases due to commercial canned goods. Home-canned foods, usually meats and vegetables, still account for some deaths.

A specific antitoxin can be formed for each of the botulinus toxins. A polyvalent antitoxin (Types A and B) is used in treatment of botulism, but it is frequently administered too late to be of real value. This delay is usually unavoidable because the disease is seldom recognized until nerve damage has occurred. A botulinus toxoid is available but is used primarily for animals.

Botulism can be prevented by taking the following precautions:

1. Use only sound foods for canning. They should be fresh from the garden, well washed, and clean.

2. Sterilize nonacid foods with steam under pressure for sixty to ninety minutes at 15 pounds pressure or about 120° C. (248° F.). Sterilize acid fruits and vegetables for ten to fifteen minutes at 15 pounds pressure or about 120° C.

3. Store cans at room temperature for ten days; observe for signs of spoilage such as bulging of can, fermentation, souring, or discoloration. If any signs of spoiling occur, discard cans of spoiled food and repeat the heating process for all the others in the same lot.

4. *Never taste* any canned food which shows signs of spoilage!

5. Boil home-canned meats and vegetables (nonacid foods) for fifteen mintues before using or tasting.

Other Food-Poisoning Organisms At times, investigations of food-poisoning outbreaks reveal large numbers of bacteria (usually *Clostridium perfringens, Proteus, Pseudomonas, Bacillus subtilis*), but no toxin-forming micrococci. Though these organisms have been recovered from food which caused illness, their ability to produce an enterotoxin has not been demonstrated. Various streptococci have been associated with food-borne illness. They are thought to produce illness by actual invasion of the intestinal or respiratory tract and therefore may be considered to produce streptococcus food infection rather than food poisoning. Occasionally in the same outbreak some who ate the contaminated food will develop scarlet fever or septic sore throat while in others the disease is characterized by nausea, vomiting, and diarrhea.

ENTERIC BACTERIA

A variety of bacteria may invade the walls of the large or small intestine or the intestinal and mesenteric lymph nodes. Such invasion is frequently accompanied by illness which may vary from mild to severe. The organisms commonly responsible for enteric disease include the salmonella, shigella, cholera vibrio, and possibly some strains of the coliform and paracolon bacteria. Conditions which disturb the normal flora of the intestines, as, for example, prolonged administration of antibiotics, may permit yeasts or gram-positive cocci to flourish in the intestines. Their presence may be associated with diarrhea.

Common and Distinguishing Characteristics   The enteric bacteria differ from one another in motility, in antigen composition, and in enzyme production. They can therefore be distinguished on the basis of motility and agglutination tests and by the use of suitable culture media. (See page 335.)

The enteric bacteria closely resemble one another in appearance, in life history, and in resistance and adaptability. All are gram-negative nonspore-forming straight rods, except the cholera vibrio which is a curved rod. All grow readily at room temperature in ordinary nutrient media, milk, and other common foods. (For this reason, contaminated food which has been standing at room temperature for several hours may contain millions or billions of pathogens.) All enter the body by way of the mouth and leave in feces or urine. All produce endotoxins which apparently injure lymphoid or epithelial cells.

As they form no spores, they are readily killed by boiling and by chemical disinfection. They may remain alive and virulent in cold, moist, or frozen materials for months. During warm weather these organisms die quickly in sewage or soil but may remain alive for considerable periods during cold weather.

The intestinal bacteria readily adapt themselves to the increasing resistance of the host. As a result they are often able to remain in the body after the acute infection has terminated. In fact, in some instances they establish themselves without causing the typical symptoms of disease. The carrier state is common and carriers of intestinal organisms are an important factor in the spread of enteric disease.

Coliform and Paracolon Bacteria   The term "coliform organisms" refers to *Escherichia coli* (*Bacterium coli*), *Aerobacter aerogenes*, and *Klebsiella pneumoniae*. Variants of the three organisms are often so similar that they are difficult to differentiate. The *Klebsiella* are pathogenic for man. *Escherichia coli* is a normal inhabitant of the intestine of man and of animals. *Aerobacter aerogenes* is commonly found on grain and vegetable matter but may also be found in feces. *Escherichia coli* and *Aerobacter aerogenes*, sometimes called the coliaerogenes group, are usually considered nonpathogenic. Under favorable conditions these organisms may invade the urinary tract or wounds. From time to time certain strains of *Escherichia coli* and *Aerobacter aerogenes* are present in large numbers in the feces of infants and others suffering from diarrhea and are therefore thought to be pathogenic. (See page 313.)

The paracolon bacteria, a group intermediate to the coliforms and the salmonella, are common inhabitants of the intestine. At times they too appear to be associated with diarrheal disease. The three groups—paracolon bacteria, salmonella, and coliforms—can be differentiated on the basis of lactose fermentation. *Escherichia coli* ferments lactose rapidly, the paracolon organisms ferment lactose slowly, and the salmonella do not change the sugar.

ENTERIC INFECTIONS

Some bacterial pathogens characteristically produce local disease of the intestines while others produce general infections. The salmonella organisms may cause either type of infection while the cholera vibrio and the shigella produce local lesions associated with diarrhea. The loss of fluids, nutrients, and electrolytes associated with diarrhea constitute additional stress for the body that is combating intestinal or other infection.

Salmonella and Salmonella Infections   The genus *Salmonella* consists of more than two hundred and fifty strains of closely related organisms. All are parasites, and many cause typhoid-like diseases in man or animals. Some of these have been given names that suggest their animal origin—as *Salmonella typhimurium* (rats, mice) and *Salmonella pullorum* (fowls); others have been named for countries or cities— *Salmonella panama* and *Salmonella newport*. On the basis of serological tests, they can be placed in six groups (A, B, C, D, E, F). *Salmonella typhosa* causes typhoid fever, while *Salmonella paratyphi* and *Salmonella schottmuelleri* cause paratyphoid fever. These three species are parasites of man and are seldom if ever found in lower animals. Many of the other salmonella are primarily animal pathogens, but may cause disease in man.

SALMONELLA FOOD INFECTION (SALMONELLOSIS)   Salmonella food infection was formerly considered a type of food poisoning similar to that caused by staphylococci. Since extensive studies failed to reveal any toxin in the cultures or food in which the salmonella have grown, the disease is now considered to be a true infection due to the *invasion of the bacteria.* The bacteria multiply in and may be transmitted by a variety of foods which have been contaminated by contacts with infected persons or various animals including insects, dogs,* and rodents. Salmonella food infection is an acute illness which occurs from eight to forty-eight hours after taking food containing salmonella organisms. The symptoms, nausea, vomiting, and diarrhea, are thought to be due to infection by the bacteria. The disease is usually of short duration, and is seldom fatal. Salmonella have been ingested with meats, fish, duck eggs, milk, dairy products, salad dressing, and drinking water. The following organisms are commonly associated with food infection:

ORGANISM	ANIMAL DISEASE
Salmonella typhimurium	Septicemia in rats and mice (rat typhoid)
Salmonella enteritidis	Septicemia in calves
Salmonella (various species)	Septicemia in hogs
Salmonella pullorum	White diarrhea in fowls (fowl typhoid)
Salmonella (various species)	Enteritis and septicemia in dogs

Food-borne outbreaks, in general, are associated with foods that have been stored at room temperature. Some outbreaks have been traced to baked foods, such as macaroni or turkey dressing, prepared in such large quantities that the inside of the food mass was not thoroughly heated. It is important to realize that many foods such as dried eggs, sausage, and chopped meats may at times be infected with a few salmonella organisms. If these foods are allowed to stand at room temperature the salmonella population may quickly increase to the point where the individual eating the food will ingest an overwhelming dose of the organisms.

Salmonella food infections can be avoided by observing the following precautions:

* In a recent study 12 to 43 per cent of dogs studied were infected with fifty-three different types of salmonella.

1. Use only healthy animals as a source of food; cook meats well.
2. Prepare and store foods in a way that will prevent contamination of the foods by human carriers, insects, rodents, or dogs.
3. Refrigerate foods before and after preparing.
4. Serve much-handled foods immediately.

SALMONELLA ENTERITIS   Salmonella enteritis or diarrhea may be caused by any of the numerous strains of *Salmonella*. It is characterized by fever, pain, and diarrhea. It is more prevalent and dangerous among children and old persons. It differs from salmonella food infection in that it has a longer incubation period and although it tends to be less acute it persists for a longer time. After recovery, many persons may become carriers for weeks or months. Many cases of diarrhea and so-called "intestinal flu" are in reality salmonella or shigella infections.

SALMONELLA SEPTICEMIA—TYPHOID FEVER   A generalized infection may be caused by any one of the *Salmonella* though it is commonly associated with *Salmonella typhosa*. The organisms are swallowed with food and water and enter the intestinal lymph nodes. Then follows an incubation period of three to thirty-eight days, which is undoubtedly influenced by such factors as the number and virulence of the organisms and the resistance of the host. In food-borne epidemics, the incubation period is usually short. By successive stages, the bacteria continue to multiply and invade the intestinal and mesenteric lymph nodes, the lymph, and the blood stream. These organisms (characteristically intracellular) grow within the phagocytic cells of lymph nodes. They produce endotoxins which cause widespread damage to lymphoid tissue and to capillary walls. Any or all of the tissues of the body may be invaded and the infection may be mild or very severe. Commonly, invasion is followed by inflammation and ulceration of the lymph nodes of the intestinal wall and mesentery, and destructive changes in the bone marrow, liver, spleen, and heart muscle. Colonization of bacteria in the skin may give rise to rose spots. The gallbladder becomes heavily infected and empties organisms into the intestine beginning in the second or third week.

As would be expected, this infection gives a picture of a body reacting to stress as indicated by (1) destruction of lymphoid tissue (nodes and phagocytes), (2) impaired circulation, (3) increased capillary permeability, (4) disturbed electrolyte balance and kidney function. These are usually associated with the following symptoms: fever, headache, backache, loss of appetite, weakness, abdominal pain, and stupor.

During the first week of illness, the organisms are present in the blood and can usually be demonstrated by blood culture. It is thought that the destruction of bacterial cells in the blood liberates endotoxins which are responsible for the characteristic symptoms of the disease. As the infection progresses, the inflamed lymph nodes (Peyer's patches) often suppurate and rupture. This process may destroy the wall of the intestine or the wall of a blood vessel with consequent perforation or hemorrhage. During the second or third week of the disease, the presence of specific antibodies can be demonstrated by agglutination (Widal) or animal protection tests. By the second or third week of the disease, the typhoid organisms are excreted in the feces or urine in sufficient numbers to be recovered by cultural methods. Diagnosis is confirmed by finding *Salmonella* in the blood, feces, or urine and by the presence of antibodies against O and Vi antigens.* The outcome of the infection will depend upon the ability of the host to check and to destroy the invaders and, in any case, recovery is a long, slow process, accompanied by a gradual decrease in the severity of the symptoms. In some persons, the body defenses appear to free the host of the parasites, but the bacteria often adjust themselves to the increased resistance of the convalescent and continue to live and multiply in the kidney, gallbladder, or the intestine long after the person is apparently well. This person is a carrier and actually promotes the survival of these organisms. It has been estimated that from 2 to 5 per cent of those who recover from typhoid fever become carriers.

* Vi antigens occur on the surface of virulent typhoid organisms. O antigens are derived from the interior of the cell. When testing the serum of a patient suspected of having typhoid fever the O antigen or both O and Vi antigens may be used. A third antigen, the H antigen, is derived from protein of the flagella. H, O, and Vi antibodies increase during typhoid fever.

(Lansing) will also grow in the cotton rat. They can also be grown in cultures of nerve or other tissue. In the monkey and in the human being it is thought that the viruses grow in the cells of the alimentary tract and of the blood-forming organs. In some individuals they also invade the central nervous system causing paralysis. Infected individuals excrete these viruses in their saliva and feces.

The viruses apparently enter the body of the new host by way of the mouth. As would be expected they can be recovered from sewage and from flies that have fed on sewage. Water-borne outbreaks of infection have been reported, but these are exceedingly rare. Although most epidemics occur in warm months, some occur during cold weather. This means that flies are not essential to the transfer to the viruses. In all probability poliomyelitis viruses are transmitted by symptomless carriers, both young and old. It has been suggested that young children with viruses in their saliva may be an important source of infection. (See Figure 59.)

Infection   Recent investigations indicate that the viruses of poliomyelitis are able to multiply in nerve cells and also in other tissues. After ingestion they invade and multiply in cells of the gastrointestinal tract and probably also in the blood-forming organs. In many individuals this encounter results in antibody formation with no invasion of the nervous system. In some, perhaps those who have some antibody against the infecting strain of virus derived from the mother or as the result of a previous attack, the infection occurs without symptoms. Others may have a day or two of mild illness characterized by fever, headache, sore throat, and vomiting. Usually the viruses fail to enter the nervous system and the affected individual recovers from what seems to have been a mild infection of the gastrointestinal or respiratory tract. These persons may carry the viruses in the throat for several days before and after showing symptoms and may excrete them from the intestine for weeks or months. These mild infections are often termed *abortive infections* in contrast to those that result in temporary damage to the motor nerves—the *nonparalytic*—and those which cause permanent loss of muscular function—the so-called *paralytic infections*.

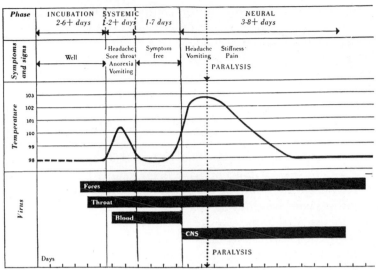

Phase	INCUBATION 2-6+ days	SYSTEMIC 1-2+ days	1-7 days	NEURAL 3-8+ days

Figure 59   Time chart showing phases of the natural course of paralytic poliomyelitis. Based on studies of human and experimental infections. (J.A.M.A., *149*.)

As indicated above, some individuals develop more widespread and serious infections. These infections also usually begin with a mild illness of one or two days' duration during which the individual suffers fever, headache, and vomiting. Then follows several days of seeming well-being during which the virus invades the nervous system causing damage to motor nerve cells. When the damage is severe it results in degeneration of the invaded nerve cells, inflammation, and increased pressure on the cord and brain. Invasion of the anterior horn cells of the cord is followed by pain and stiffness of the spine and back, and tenderness of the affected muscles with or without flaccid paralysis of the extremities. When the virus attacks the brain stem the result is paralysis of the muscles controlling speech, swallowing, and respiration. There is considerable evidence indicating that the paralytic form of the disease is relatively rare and that the mild form of the disease is common though frequently unrecognized.

Disease Pattern   Poliomyelitis is an old disease which

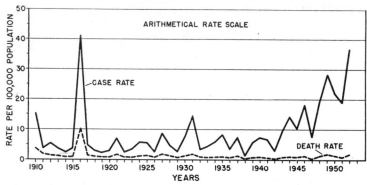

Figure 60   Annual poliomyelitis cases and death rates in States
reporting both cases and deaths, United States, 1910–1952.

has been known for hundreds of years and still occurs sporadically in many parts of the world. About fifty years ago, the
disease began to appear in epidemic form in certain countries
including the United States. (See Figure 60.)

It may occur in all parts of the world, including the Arctic
region, and at any time of the year. In the United States it is
more prevalent during the hot months when humidity is high.
It has been suggested that conditions of high humidity may
be associated with changes in the mucous membranes which
favor virus invasion (Armstrong). Paradoxically, epidemics are
more common in countries with high standards of sanitation
and hygiene. The reason for this is unknown. One might sus-
pect that modern sanitation, so valuable in preventing typhoid-
like diseases, may interfere with some well-established relationship between the virus and host population. In countries
where sanitation is primitive, the disease is a mild one, occurring in young individuals (one to four years of age) and
seldom causing paralysis. In the United States, children in
lower income groups tend to develop antibodies (evidence of
subclinical infection) at an earlier age than do children in
higher income groups. The living conditions of the poor probably provide for earlier and more continuous contact with the
virus. There seems to be less risk of paralysis when the infection occurs in a young child. Sabin has said that "the best way

to avoid paralysis is to be born of a mother immune to poliomyelitis and then to be exposed early and often."*

The available evidence suggests that the virus is essentially
a parasite of man, since no natural animal host has been found.

Susceptibility   Poliomyelitis without paralysis is a common disease in many parts of the world. In Guam, for example,
more than 75 per cent of the children tested had formed antibodies against one strain (Lansing) of the virus before they
reached the age of four. One investigation revealed that in
San Francisco 18 per cent of children under four and 64 per
cent of those thirteen to fifteen years of age had developed
antibodies. Second and third attacks may occur because there
are at least three different strains of the virus. The risk of
paralysis is higher in regions where exposure is delayed until
after the individual is five years of age. It is now evident that
when the average person experiences the disease, his natural
barriers prevent invasion of the nervous system. In certain
individuals the body defenses are apparently unequal to the
task of limiting the progress of the virus.

The conditions which favor or permit the entry of the virus
into the brain and cord are not fully understood. A number
of factors appear to increase the risk of nerve involvement.
These include: (1) age, (2) inheritance, and (3) stresses such
as pregnancy, exposure to cold, strenuous exercise, and trauma
(tonsillectomy, inoculations). The relation of age to susceptibility has already been presented. Some authorities consider
genetic factors of importance in susceptibility to nerve injury.
This view is supported by the observation of very high rates
of paralysis among certain inbred groups in the Arctic region.
Pregnant women are more likely to develop paralysis than
other women of the same age group. It has been suggested
that increased production of hormones of the adrenal cortex
in pregnancy may favor virus invasion. Exposure to cold water,
strenuous exercise during the early period of infection, and
trauma appear to predispose to nerve injury. Removal of tonsils
within one month before infection seems to increase the risk of

* Sabin, A. B.: Paralytic Consequences of Poliomyelitis in Different
Parts of the World and in Different Population Groups. Am. J. Pub.
Health, *41:* 1215–1230, 1951.

acquiring the bulbar type of the infection. Inoculation with diphtheria toxoid or pertussis vaccine within one month of infection appears to increase the likelihood of paralysis in the arm or leg that was used for the inoculation. These observations have led to the practice of delaying throat operations and prophylactic inoculations until after the poliomyelitis season.

Prevention and Control   In a disease as widespread as poliomyelitis, complete prevention is likely to be both impossible and probably also undesirable. The aim then must be to prevent paralysis. Although at present we do not know how to accomplish this, recent discoveries suggest that someday it may be possible. The fact that infants and most adults are immune to poliomyelitis suggests that antibodies may provide protection. Preliminary investigations have proved that gamma globulin (Red Cross gamma globulin*) is of some value in preventing or modifying the infection.† Further investigation, now in progress, is needed to determine dosage, time of administration, and duration of immunity. It is especially important to determine who should receive gamma globulin as it is obviously impractical to administer globulin to every child every year. For this reason renewed efforts are being made to prepare a vaccine of poliomyelitis virus grown in nonnervous tissue. To date an experimental vaccine capable of stimulating antibody formation in monkeys and human beings has been developed. This investigation is still in progress.

During epidemics citizens who are naturally concerned for the safety of their children often demand that health authorities set up quarantines, close schools and camps, or restrict travel. Such restrictions are likely to be of little or no value. If one remembers that the virus is widespread in the population before a single case is recognized, it is obvious that person-to-

* Red Cross gamma globulin, prepared from pooled samples of blood collected from approximately 50,000 persons, contains antibodies against the three strains of the virus. Commercial gamma globulins prepared from blood contributed by a small number of individuals have not been tested. It seems likely that they will be less reliable sources of antibodies against poliomyelitis.

† In persons who acquired the infection within a week after receiving the gamma globulin, the risk of infection was essentially the same as in the control group. These children were probably already infected at the time of administration.

person transfer will usually not be prevented by the means suggested. By the time a case of recognized poliomyelitis appears in a school or camp many of the children are already carrying the virus. Closing the camp or school may actually spread the virus and probably will be of little value to the individual child. Securing prompt medical care for minor illnesses and the avoidance of strenuous competitive exercises may be of value and certainly will do no harm. Allowing children to play with their usual contacts will probably not increase the hazard. Travel and increasing the circle of contacts may well be limited by individual families during the outbreak. Operations for the removal of tonsils and prophylactic inoculations should, of course, be delayed until the outbreak has subsided.

In caring for individuals with acute infections, it should be remembered that the virus is excreted in saliva and feces. It is equally important to remember that, during epidemic periods, many other patients and members of hospital staffs will also be excreting the virus.

COXSACKIE VIRUSES

Infection due to a Coxsackie virus, commonly called "devil's grip" or "epidemic myositis," has been reported from time to time. The Coxsackie viruses are similar to the poliomyelitis viruses and may sometimes be present in an individual who is infected with poliomyelitis. The relation of these viruses to poliomyelitis viruses in regard to disease production is not known. Coxsackie viruses have been isolated from the blood, serum, stools, and throat washings of well carriers and infected persons and from flies and sewage. The infection is most common in young individuals and has been reported in seventeen states and several foreign countries. It appears to spread from person to person. After an incubation period of about four days (the period varies from one to nine days) the individual may develop some of the following symptoms: headache, backache, abdominal pain, nasal obstruction, pain in the chest, cough, abdominal tenderness, stomatitis, pain in the eyes, vomiting. Little is known regarding immunity or prevention and control.

INFECTIOUS HEPATITIS AND SERUM JAUNDICE VIRUSES

Infectious Hepatitis Virus   This virus causes an acute infection of the liver known as infectious hepatitis or acute catarrhal jaundice. It commonly attacks children and young adults. Symptoms develop after an incubation period of from twenty to forty days. The disease is characterized by fever and jaundice which may be severe or mild. The early symptoms include headache, abdominal pain, weakness, nausea, and vomiting. The virus is present in the blood and feces and possibly in any discharge emitted by the infected person. The disease has been common in combat troops in World Wars I and II. Family and institutional outbreaks may occur and are more common where sanitation is poor. Transmission is thought to be primarily by person-to-person contact or contact with and ingesion of infected excretions. The infection is also transferred by infected blood or plasma and by inoculations with syringes and needles contaminated by the virus. Prevention therefore probably depends upon protecting food and water from fecal contamination and avoiding contact with infected blood or needles.

Experimental infections have been caused by the feeding of infected filtrates to human volunteers, but as yet no animals have been infected by the feeding of infected materials. Like poliomyelitis viruses, this virus is apparently widespread in the population. The reservoir of infection may be in children and adults who are apparently well or have an early or mild illness without jaundice. In one nursery caring for young children who had apparently been well over a long period of time, infection was transmitted to attendants who cared for these children.

Gamma globulin appears to have real value in preventing and treating this infection.

Serum Hepatitis Virus   The serum hepatitis (serum jaundice) virus is similar to the virus of infectious hepatitis. Serum hepatitis also is similar to infectious hepatitis but differs in that it has a very long incubation period (one to six months) and is not easily transmitted by natural means. It is definitely a man-sponsored infection transmitted by (1) injecting infected blood, plasma, or serum or (2) by the use of contaminated needles in collecting blood or in giving vaccines or medications. Since the serum hepatitis virus is highly resistant, great care must be taken to prevent infection. Blood products should be irradiated even though this precaution sometimes fails to kill the virus. Separate syringes should be used for each individual. Syringes and needles should be thoroughly cleaned and sterilized, preferably by autoclave or dry oven, if available, otherwise by boiling for twenty minutes.

OTHER VIRUSES CAUSING INFECTIONS

Dysentery Viruses   Observations made in the United States and England suggest that some dysentery infections may be due to viruses. Filtrates containing a virus obtained from persons suffering from diarrhea in an epidemic caused disease in human volunteers who inhaled spray containing virus. At present little is known about these diseases.

Viruses Causing Infectious Diarrhea of the Newborn Certain outbreaks of epidemic diarrhea in the newborn have been attributed to filtrable viruses. At present little is known about the virus or viruses associated with such infections. It is known that a large variety of bacteria seem to be able to produce this illness (see page 361).

SUPPLEMENTARY READINGS

BOOKS:

Maxcy, K. F.: Rosenau Preventive Medicine and Hygiene. New York, Appleton-Century-Crofts, Inc., 1951.

Rivers, T. M.: Viral and Rickettsial Infections of Man. 2d ed. Philadelphia, J. B. Lippincott Co., 1952.

PERIODICALS:

Allen, J. G., and others: Homologous Serum Jaundice and Its Relation to Methods of Plasma Storage. J.A.M.A., *144:* 1069–1074, 1950.

Ames, W.: Variation in the Age Selection of Poliomyelitis Associated with Differences in Economic Status in Buffalo, New York, 1929, 1939, 1944 and 1949. Am. J. Pub. Health, *41:* 388–395, 1951.

Armstrong, C.: Atmospheric Conditions and the Spread of Poliomyelitis. Am. J. Pub. Health, *41:* 1231–1237, 1951.

Cole, R. M., and others: Studies on Coxsackie Viruses: Observations on Epidemiological Aspects of Group A Viruses. Am. J. Pub. Health, *41:* 1342–1358, 1951.

Editorial: Immunization against Poliomyelitis. J.A.M.A., *149:* 278–279, 1951.

Fales, T. W., and Taback, M.: Observations on Epidemiology of Poliomyelitis. Pub. Health Rep., *67:* 47–52, 1952.

Farquhar, J. D.: Epidemic of Viral Hepatitis Apparently Spread by Drinking Water and Contact. J.A.M.A., *149:* 991–993, 1952.

Galloway, T. C.: Relationship of Tonsillectomy to Poliomyelitis. J.A.M.A., *151:* 1180–1182, 1953.

Greenberg, M., and others: The Relation between Recent Injections and Paralytic Poliomyelitis in Children. Am. J. Pub. Health, *42:* 142–152, 1952.

Hammon, W. McD.: Evaluation of Red Cross Gamma Globulin as a Prophylactic Agent for Poliomyelitis. J.A.M.A., *151:* 1272–1285, 1953.

Havens, W. P., Jr.: Epidemiological Studies on Infectious Hepatitis. Am. J. Pub. Health, *36:* 27–44, 1946.

Howe, H. A.: Epidemiology of Poliomyelitis in the Light of Modern Research. Am. J. Med., *6:* 537–550, 1949.

Kaufman, G. G., and Havens, W. P., Jr.: Outbreak of Infectious Hepatitis—Presumably Food-Borne. J.A.M.A., *149:* 993–995, 1952.

Korns, R. F., and others: The Association of Parenteral Injections with Poliomyelitis. Am. J. Pub. Health, *42:* 153–169, 1952.

Lazarus, A. S., and others: An Outbreak of Pleurodynia with Special Reference to Laboratory Diagnosis of Coxsackie Virus Infections. Am. J. Pub. Health, *42:* 20–26, 1952.

Lesses, M. F., and Hamolsky, M. W.: Epidemic of Homologous Serum Hepatitis Apparently Caused by Human Thrombin. J.A.M.A., *147:* 727–730, 1951.

Light, J. S., and Hades, H. L.: Studies of Epidemic Diarrhea of the Newborn: Isolation of a Filtrable Agent Causing Diarrhea in Calves. Am. J. Health, *33:* 1451–1454, 1943.

Sabin, A. B.: Antipoliomyelitic Substance in the Milk of Human Beings and Certain Cows. (Abstract.) Am. J. Dis. Child., *80:* 866, 1950.

Sabin, A. B.: Paralytic Consequences in Different Parts of the World and in Different Population Groups. Am. J. Pub. Health, *41:* 1215–1230, 1951.

Salk, J. E.: Studies in Human Subjects on Active Immunization against Poliomyelitis. J.A.M.A., *151:* 1081–1098, 1953.

Serfling, R. E., and Sherman, I. L.: Poliomyelitis Distribution in the United States. Pub. Health Rep., *68:* 453–466, 1953.

Sigel, M. M.: Coxsackie Viruses and Poliomyelitis. Nursing Outlook, *1:* 438–440, 1953.

Stokes, J., Jr.: Epidemiology of Viral Hepatitis. Am. J. Pub. Health, *43:* 1097–1100, 1953.

Trumbull, M. L., and Greiner, D. J.: Homologous Serum Jaundice—An Occupational Hazard to Medical Personnel. J.A.M.A., *145:* 965–967, 1951.

CHAPTER 24

Animal Parasites Transmitted by Food and Water or Contact

PROTOZOA: *Endamoeba histolytica; Giardia lamblia; Balantidium coli*

METAZOA: ROUNDWORMS: *Pinworms; Whipworms; Ascarides; Hookworms; Trichinae*

METAZOA: FLATWORMS: *Flukes (Schistosomes); Tapeworms*

MANY ANIMAL parasites both large and small find the intestine of man a suitable place in which to live. Other parasites enter by way of the intestine then migrate to other tissues. Intestinal parasites fall into two groups: the *protozoa* which are unicellular, and the *metazoa* which are relatively large multicellular worms. Many of the parasitic worms have complex life cycles, requiring two or more hosts. Their survival and transmission to man are influenced by a variety of environmental factors such as temperature, humidity, and the presence of specific vertebrate or invertebrate hosts. The food habits of the population and the methods used for disposing of body wastes also influence parasite transfer.

PROTOZOA

Most intestinal protozoa pass through two stages: the active, motile form (*trophozoite*) and the resting, nonmotile form (*cyst*). The active form moves, feeds, and multiplies, but it is usually too fragile to survive outside of the body. The cyst is able to survive transfer to a second host since it is relatively resistant to chemicals and to temperatures below 70° C. (158° F.). The important protozoa of man are *Endamoeba histolytica, Giardia lamblia,* and *Balantidium coli.*

Endamoeba histolytica Amebic dysentery (amebiasis)

is caused by a large, motile cell—the *Endamoeba histolytica*. This organism is a typical ameba, with nucleus, granuoles, and vacuoles. A parasite of man, it is found in the lower bowel where it lives by absorbing food and ingesting red blood cells and other tissue structures. As the name *histolytica* (*histo*-cell + *lytica* dissolve) suggests this organism produces an enzyme which destroys cells thereby enabling it to burrow into the deeper layers of the intestinal wall.

The cyst form of the parasite enters the body by ingestion. After an incubation period which varies from three days to four months, the organism forms deep ulcers. As the parasites multiply they extend the infection to other areas of the intestine. Although these parasites may be present without producing symptoms, they often disturb bowel function producing (1) an acute amebic dysentery (characterized by pain and bloody stools), (2) a chronic amebic dysentery (intermittent diarrhea), or (3) an amebic colitis (alternating diarrhea and constipation).

The organisms often migrate to other parts of the body (liver, lungs, brain) where they destroy tissues. For instance, liver abscesses are found in association with 20 to 25 per cent of the acute infections. The amebas are readily destroyed by chloroquine, carbarsone, diiodo-hydroxyquinoline (Diodoquin), chiniofon, and emetine. Aureomycin, chloramphenicol, and Terramycin have been reported as effective in the treatment of amebiasis. It is not certain whether these drugs act directly on the ameba or whether their action is on the bacteria which act as secondary invaders and also serve as food for the ameba. Prolonged treatment with these antibiotics may decrease the synthesis of vitamins of the B complex group and thereby cause vitamin deficiency. Fumagillin, a new antibiotic, is said to destroy amebas without disturbing the normal flora of the intestines.

The parasite may be present in either the motile form or as a dormant cyst with four nuclei. (See Figure 15, page 73.) Persons with the active infection excrete the motile form, which seldom survives transfer to another host, since it is fragile and easily killed. The carrier maintains the infection by excreting the resistant cysts. (It has been estimated that

5 per cent of the population are carriers. Where the sanitary conditions are poor, the carrier rate among apparently well people may be as high as 50 per cent.) These inactive forms can be killed by boiling, but are not susceptible to the concentration of chlorine used in drinking water. When the cysts transmitted by raw foods or water reach the intestine, they develop into motile forms which are capable of multiplying and invading. Since the carrier really has a subclinical infection, he should be treated until the parasites are eliminated.

The infection is diagnosed by observing motile amebas or cysts in a direct microscopic examination. The active motile form can be seen in a warm, fresh specimen of the excreta. It is imperative that the specimen be kept warm because the organisms stop moving and die when the temperature drops. For experimental purposes, the organisms can be grown in kittens or in cultures where bacteria grown on a rice flour, serum, or egg mixture serve as food for the amebas.

Experimental evidence suggests that relatively large doses of organisms are required to infect healthy, well-nourished individuals. Amebic dysentery is endemic in certain institutions (children's homes, psychiatric hospitals) and in rural areas where there is gross fecal contamination of the environment. In one children's home, cysts were recovered from dust, furniture, sandboxes, swimming pool, laundry chute, laundry tubs, and clothing.[1] Epidemics are infrequent but may occur. Of special interest is the epidemic which caused more than 1400 cases with fifty deaths among the visitors to the World's Fair in Chicago in 1933. This outbreak was traced to defective plumbing, which permitted sewage pollution of drinking water in two hotels. Food handlers who were carriers were also found among the employees and may have contaminated raw foods. Since there were no cases of typhoid or dysentery following this exposure, it seems likely that the chlorine in the water killed the bacterial pathogens but did not kill the cysts. Obviously, like the other intestinal diseases, amebic dysentery can be prevented by protecting food, water, and environment from fecal contamination.

Giardia lamblia   *Giardia lamblia* is a relatively large (6 to 12 μ) pear-shaped cell with eight flagella. The cell contains two nuclei connected by a bridge—a feature which gives

on the anus, ther
scopic examinati
female worm.

Repeated trea
cate the infectior
tive in the treatn
require simultan
fitting shorts sho
be changed dail
frequently with s
nails is of course

Whipworm (
a whiplike appea
worm (female 35
attach themselve
lay eggs which a
that the female
per day. When d
a period of twen
They are readily

Whipworm inf
infective eggs. T
may be the caus
bility, and sleepl
in the feces. Th
amebic and bac:
organism by pr
hands.

Ascaris (Asc
(female 200 to 3
tine. The ova are
in soil. After ing
immature parasi
intestinal wall ir
where they unde
up the respirato
In this way, the
mate, and lay eg;
to temperatures

the parasite the appearance of wearing spectacles. Although both the cyst and the active form may be present without apparent symptoms, they may be associated with a chronic disease (giardiasis) characterized by recurrent diarrhea and chronic inflammation of the gallbladder. The parasite is susceptible to treatment with quinacrine hydrochloride (atabrine).

Balantidium coli   *Balantidium coli* is a large (50 to 65 μ) oval cell which is covered with cilia. It invades the intestinal mucosa of man, hogs, and monkeys, causing destruction and ulceration of tissue. The disease (balantidiasis) is variable in that it may cause no symptoms or it may cause severe diarrhea.

Diagnosis is made by finding the active cells in liquid stools, or cysts in formed stools. Carbarsone is used in treatment and sulfonamides may be used to control secondary infection by bacteria.

METAZOA

The multicellular parasites of man are usually macroscopic and vary markedly in size. Some are barely visible while others may be several feet in length. Their structures are complex and variable. Usually they do not multiply in the body of the host; instead they produce large numbers of eggs which are excreted in the feces. Worms show numerous modifications of structure and function which are related to their parasitic life. For example, they secrete a protective layer which protects their cells against the actions of the digestive enzymes of the host. As a rule, they possess no organs of locomotion and their digestive systems may be rudimentary or absent. In contrast, the reproductive organs are usually both prominent and active. Suckers or other structures which attach the worm to the intestinal wall are commonly present. Many parasitic worms possess hooks, cutting plates, or spines which injure the cells of the host; some secrete enzymes which prevent clotting or which dissolve cell walls of the host. These injuries enable the parasite either to feed upon the injured cells or blood or to invade the deeper tissues. They also encourage secondary infection by intestinal bacteria.

The various worm parasites take nourishment from the host,

injuring a
ble to b
mechanic
toxins. T
by inflam
infected
test if ar
antibody
from the
dence th:
place in
delay its
assimilat

The n
worms (1

Pinw
small, s
5 mm.)
colon. T
testine.
but mig
eggs on
one fem
tain we
They ar
tive for
contami
tating a
Unless
is likely
fect hin
into a m

Pinw
itching,
tite, res
made b
by plac

Ascaris infections (ascariasis) have two phases, one caused by the adult worms, and the other by the larvae. The invasion of the lungs by larvae may be associated with fever, coughing, and an atypical pneumonia which may be fatal if complicated by bacterial invasion. Severe infection with the adult worms may produce toxemia and gastrointestinal symptoms. Treatment is similar to that for pinworms. Prevention depends upon protecting food, water, and hands from contamination and also the sanitary disposal of human excreta.

Hookworm (Necator americanus and Ancylostoma duodenale)

The hookworm is a small roundworm (female 9 to 11 mm., male 5 to 9 mm.) which is equipped with cutting plates or teeth. The eggs pass out in feces and if deposited on warm sandy soil they develop into active larvae in twenty-four to twenty-six hours. The larvae feed on bacteria, increase in size, and after a short time become infective. Then they migrate to the top of the soil. Then they enter the skin of the human foot, causing a local irritation called "ground itch."* Later they penetrate into the lymph and blood stream and are transferred to the lungs. Here they migrate through the capillary walls into the alveoli, through the bronchi and trachea and down the esophagus to the intestine where they develop into mature worms. Eggs may be found in the feces four to six weeks after the larvae have entered the body. Because the eggs are easily killed by drying and freezing, hookworm disease is found only in tropical and subtropical countries where there is abundant rainfall. In the United States, hookworm disease is found chiefly among rural white children living on the sandy coastal plain of the southern states. Negroes are relatively resistant.

The worms attach themselves to the wall of the small intestine and suck blood. They destroy tissue at the point of attachment, and secrete an anticoagulant which causes continued loss of blood. Symptoms depend upon the severity of the infection. Anemia is always present and may be accompanied by weakness and fatigue. Children with hookworm infection are often

* Larvae of the dog and cat hookworm may enter the skin causing "creeping eruption." These organisms are unable to complete their life cycle in man and eventually die.

on the anus, then transferring the tape to a glass slide. Microscopic examination will reveal the eggs, and sometimes the female worm.

Repeated treatment with gentian violet is needed to eradicate the infection. Terramycin has also been reported as effective in the treatment of pinworms. Often the entire family will require simultaneous treatment. To avoid reinfection, tight-fitting shorts should be worn day and night and linen should be changed daily and boiled. Toilet seats should be washed frequently with soap and water. Careful washing of hands and nails is of course very important.

Whipworm (Trichuris trichiura)   This parasite has a whiplike appearance and is considerably larger than the pinworm (female 35 to 50 mm., male 30 to 45 mm.). The parasites attach themselves to the wall of the cecum and appendix, and lay eggs which are passed in the stool. It has been estimated that the female whipworm produces from 1000 to 5000 eggs per day. When deposited on warm moist soil, the eggs require a period of twenty-one days to develop and become infective. They are readily killed by drying and direct sunlight.

Whipworm infection (trichuriasis) follows the ingestion of infective eggs. The disease often occurs without symptoms but may be the cause of anemia, nausea, abdominal pain, irritability, and sleeplessness. Diagnosis is made by finding the eggs in the feces. The methods of prevention are the same as for amebic and bacillary dysentery; namely, avoid ingesting the organism by preventing contamination of water, food, and hands.

Ascaris (Ascaris lumbricoides)   Ascaris is a large (female 200 to 350 mm.) roundworm found in the small intestine. The ova are excreted in feces and develop for three weeks in soil. After ingestion, the infective eggs develop into minute immature parasites called larvae. These migrate through the intestinal wall into the lymph and blood stream to the lungs where they undergo further development. Later they migrate up the respiratory tract to the epiglottis and are swallowed. In this way, the worms reach the intestine where they mature, mate, and lay eggs. These eggs are very resistant to drying and to temperatures below 70° C. (158° F.).

Ascaris infections (ascariasis) have two phases, one caused by the adult worms, and the other by the larvae. The invasion of the lungs by larvae may be associated with fever, coughing, and an atypical pneumonia which may be fatal if complicated by bacterial invasion. Severe infection with the adult worms may produce toxemia and gastrointestinal symptoms. Treatment is similar to that for pinworms. Prevention depends upon protecting food, water, and hands from contamination and also the sanitary disposal of human excreta.

Hookworm (*Necator americanus* and *Ancylostoma duodenale*)   The hookworm is a small roundworm (female 9 to 11 mm., male 5 to 9 mm.) which is equipped with cutting plates or teeth. The eggs pass out in feces and if deposited on warm sandy soil they develop into active larvae in twenty-four to twenty-six hours. The larvae feed on bacteria, increase in size, and after a short time become infective. Then they migrate to the top of the soil. Then they enter the skin of the human foot, causing a local irritation called "ground itch."* Later they penetrate into the lymph and blood stream and are transferred to the lungs. Here they migrate through the capillary walls into the alveoli, through the bronchi and trachea and down the esophagus to the intestine where they develop into mature worms. Eggs may be found in the feces four to six weeks after the larvae have entered the body. Because the eggs are easily killed by drying and freezing, hookworm disease is found only in tropical and subtropical countries where there is abundant rainfall. In the United States, hookworm disease is found chiefly among rural white children living on the sandy coastal plain of the southern states. Negroes are relatively resistant.

The worms attach themselves to the wall of the small intestine and suck blood. They destroy tissue at the point of attachment, and secrete an anticoagulant which causes continued loss of blood. Symptoms depend upon the severity of the infection. Anemia is always present and may be accompanied by weakness and fatigue. Children with hookworm infection are often

---

* Larvae of the dog and cat hookworm may enter the skin causing "creeping eruption." These organisms are unable to complete their life cycle in man and eventually die.

potbellied and may have an appetite for abnormal substances such as clay or ashes. Diagnosis depends upon finding the hookworm eggs in the stool. Tetrachlorethylene is commonly used in treatment. Sanitary disposal of human excreta and wearing shoes are important factors in preventing hookworm infections. Adequate nutrition is important to enable the individual to develop an active immunity against hookworms. This resistance is readily lost if the diet is deficient in protein and vitamins A and B.

Trichinella spiralis The trichina worm is a small white worm (female 3 to 4 mm., male 1.4 to 1.6 mm.). The adult worms live in the intestine of hogs and produce larvae which migrate to the skeletal muscles. Man acquires the parasites by eating undercooked pork which contains encysted larvae. The parasites after being freed from the cysts by the action of the digestive juices enter the duodenal epithelium. Within a few days the worms mature and the females are fertilized and begin to discharge larvae into the blood stream. It has been estimated that one female may produce from 1000 to 1500 larvae which enter the muscles and form cysts. In man, these cysts remain indefinitely and may be deposited with calcium. No effective way of killing worms or larvae has been reported.

The severity of the disease (trichinosis) depends upon the number of cysts that are ingested. Within twenty-four hours the penetration of the intestinal wall by the parasites may cause nausea, vomiting, and diarrhea. A week or two later when the larvae enter the blood stream, the host may develop fever, edema of the eyelids, muscle soreness, and rheumatic pains. In severe infections, the symptoms may include rash, toxemia, secondary pneumonia, and cardiac failure. Diagnosis may be confirmed by a skin test for hypersensitivity and by biopsy of muscle to detect cysts.

Trichinosis in man can be prevented by thorough cooking of pork. The larvae are easily killed by cooking and also by freezing at —15° C. (5° F.) for twenty days. Cooking the garbage used to feed hogs will prevent the infection in hogs. It is well to remember that trichina cysts occur *within* the muscle and can only be detected by careful microscopic examination. Governmental inspection of pork is, therefore, no protection against trichinosis. Thorough cooking of pork and pork products is the only sure way of avoiding trichinosis.

FLATWORMS (PLATYHELMINTHES)

In contrast to the roundworms already described, certain other parasites are classified as flatworms. Two groups infect man: the leaflike flukes, and the ribbonlike tapeworms.

Flukes (Trematoda) Schistosomes, or blood flukes, are small, flattened worms ranging in length from 6.5 to 26 mm. They live in the blood vessels of the mesenteric or pelvic region. The female is longer and more slender than the male. Both have suckers that enable them to attach themselves to the blood vessel walls. The body of the male forms a groove in which the female rests. When the eggs are ready for discharge, the adult worms swim downstream into the portal venules where the female deposits spined ova which occlude the blood vessels. The eggs pass through the capillary walls into the intestine (*Schistosoma mansoni*), or into the urinary bladder (*Schistosoma haematobium*). When the ova present in urine or feces are deposited in water they develop into free-swimming forms (miracidia). The miracidia enter snails and continue their development for several weeks. In four to seven weeks, forked-tailed parasites (cercariae) emerge in the water and attach themselves to the skin of persons who wash, bathe, or wade in the water. The parasites penetrate the skin and enter peripheral blood vessels and are carried to the capillaries of the lungs and then to the capillaries of the mesentery or bladder. Here the parasites mature and the female begins to produce eggs.

Schistosomiasis occurs in three stages. The early symptoms are caused by the migration of the parasites and usually include a dry cough, fever, chills, and muscle pains. Later, as ova are deposited, they injure vessel walls by their sharp spines and also by producing tissue-dissolving enzymes. They cause acute inflammation, often accompanied by enlargement of the liver and spleen, fever, pain, and diarrhea. These symptoms may last for two or three months and may recur at intervals. Since the parasites lay eggs daily for years, there is progressive damage to the liver and intestinal walls. Scar tissue formation eventually prevents the passage of eggs into the intestine. Then they float up the portal system through the heart and are deposited in various parts of the body. Within five years, severe infections cause cirrhosis of the liver, enlargement of the spleen, anemia, and cerebral symptoms such as blindness and paralysis.

Prevention depends upon avoiding contact with the parasite by refraining from bathing or wading in infected water. Sanitary sewage disposal and the use of chemicals to kill the snail host are also important ways of breaking the life cycle of the parasite.

Schistosome Dermatitis (Swimmer's Itch)   Schistosome parasites of lower animals may penetrate the human skin and cause schistosome dermatitis (swimmer's itch). The parasites are destroyed in the skin giving rising to skin irritation with papular lesions. The disease can be prevented by avoiding contact with water which contains schistosomes and by destroying the snail host by treating the water with lime and copper sulfate.

Other Flukes   Various flukes infect the lungs, liver and intestines of man. All are leaflike parasites which attach themselves to the tissues of the host by suckers. All except the schistosomes are hermaphroditic; that is, each parasite contains both male and female sex organs. All first infect a snail, then spend a period of development in an aquatic animal or plant. Man acquires the infection by ingesting the raw or undercooked plant or animal host. Typical flukes are *Fasciolopsis buski, Clonorchis sinensis,* and *Paragonimus westermani.*

Tapeworms (Cestoda)   Tapeworms are flat, ribbonlike parasites ranging in length from 40 mm. to 10 to 12 meters (400 inches). In structure they differ markedly from the other parasites studied. Each has a rounded head (*scolex*) with hooks, suckers, or grooves which attach the worm to the intestinal wall of the host. Below the head is a slender neck which joins directly to a series of segments (*proglottids*). The segments at the neck end are small and undeveloped while those at the distal end of the worm are mature. Tapeworms have no digestive organs and only rudimentary nervous and excretory systems. The most conspicuous structures in the tapeworm are the reproductive organs. Each segment contains a complete set of female and a complete set of male reproductive organs. Usually both do not function at the same time.

The adult parasite develops in the human intestine. The mature segments containing innumerable embryonated eggs are passed with the feces. When the eggs contaminate grass or water which is swallowed by hogs or cattle, the cyst wall is digested away. Then the immature worm (cysticercus) leaves the intestine and migrates to the muscle of the new host. When man eats raw or undercooked pork or beef, the parasite is carried to the intestine where it attaches itself to the intestinal wall. Here it begins to grow, and develops into the mature worm. The presence of the mature tapeworm in the intestine causes few symptoms other than digestive disturbances and hunger pains. When man swallows the eggs instead of the cysts, tapeworm cysts may form in any tissues of the body and cause severe damage especially if they invade the brain, cord, or heart.

Prevention depends upon (1) proper disposal of human feces to prevent infection of the animal hosts, (2) cold storage of beef to permit death of encysted worms, and (3) thorough cooking of meat. The immature worms form visible nodules. The flesh containing them is spoken of as "measly beef" or "measly pork" and can be detected by routine inspection of meat.

The fish tapeworm (*Diphyllobothrium latum*) differs from the pork tapeworm in that the eggs must be in water to hatch. In two weeks, the free-swimming larvae enter a water animal called a *copepod*. After a period of development, the cycle is completed when host and parasite are ingested by a freshwater fish. Later, man and other mammals acquire the infection by eating raw fish.

Hydatid disease (echinocociasis, echinococcosis) is a disease of dogs and sheep caused by the *Echinococcus granulosus*. In sheep-raising countries when man lives in close contact with sheep and dogs, the parasite may reach man. The adult tapeworm occurs in dogs and other carnivores. Human infection follows the swallowing of the eggs which hatch in the duo-

SUMMARY

ORGANISM	DISEASE	SITE OF INFECTION	DIAGNOSTIC PROCEDURES	CHEMOTHERAPY
Protozoa				
Endamoeba histolytica	Amebiasis	Intestinal mucosa, sometimes liver, lungs, brain	Direct examination of stool for presence of motile organisms or cysts	Emetine, carbarsone, chiniofon, diiodohydrooxyquinoline, chloroquine, fumagillin
Giardia lamblia	Giardiasis	Intestine, gallbladder	Same as for amebiasis	Quinacrine hydrochloride
Balantidium coli	Balantidiasis	Intestinal mucosa	Same as for amebiasis	Carbarsone
Metazoa Pinworm	Enterobiasis	Colon	Examination of anal mucosa for presence of eggs	Terramycin, gentian violet
Whipworm	Trichuriasis	Intestines	Examination of feces for presence of eggs	Tetrachlorethylene and oil of chenopodium
Hookworm	Hookworm infection	Small intestine	Examination of stool for the presence of eggs	Tetrachlorethylene
Trichinella spiralis	Trichinosis	Larvae encyst in skeletal muscles	Biopsy of muscle, skin test	None
Schistosomes	Schistosomiasis	Blood vessels of abdomen or pelvis	Examination of feces for presence of eggs	
Tapeworms	Taeniasis	Intestine (adult) Muscle (cyst)	Examination of feces for mature segments or eggs	

denum and then migrate to the liver and lungs. Here they form expanding tumors in which parasites continue to develop and migrate to other tissues. Prevention depends on keeping dogs from contact with sheep carcasses and in protecting man against contamination of food, water, and hands with dog feces.

REFERENCE

1. Ivanhoe, G. L.: Transmission of Amebiasis in a Children's Home in New Orleans. Am. J. Trop. Med., *23:* 401–419, 1943.

SUPPLEMENTARY READINGS

BOOKS:

American Public Health Association: The Control of Communicable Diseases in Man. 7th ed. New York, The American Public Health Association, 1950.

Belding, D. L.: Clinical Parasitology. 2d ed. New York, Appleton-Century-Crofts, Inc., 1952.

Craig, C. F., and Faust, E. C.: Clinical Parasitology. Philadelphia, Lea & Febiger, 1951.

Greenberg, M., and Matz, A. V.: Modern Concepts of Communicable Disease. New York, G. P. Putnam's Sons, 1953.

Mackie, T. T., Hunter, G. W., and Worth, C. B.: A Manual of Tropical Medicine. 2d ed. Philadelphia, W. B. Saunders Co., 1954.

Maxcy, K. F.: Rosenau Preventive Medicine and Hygiene. 7th ed. New York, Appleton-Century-Crofts, Inc., 1951.

Smillie, W. G.: Preventive Medicine and Public Health. 2d ed. New York, The Macmillan Co., 1952.

PERIODICALS:

Anderson, H. H., and others: Fumagillin in Amebiasis. Am. J. Trop. Med., *1:* 522, 1952.

Berberian, D. A., and others: Drug Prophylaxis of Amebiasis. J.A.M.A., *148:* 700–704, 1952.

Chang, T. H., and others: Cerebral Granuloma Due to Schistosomiasis. J.A.M.A., *136:* 230–238, 1948.

Editorial: Trichinosis. J.A.M.A., *152:* 241, 1953.

Felsenfeld, O., and others: *In vitro* and *in vivo* Tests with Newer Antibiotics against *Endamoeba histolytica.* Am. J. Pub. Health, *41:* 1078–1081, 1951.

Ivanhoe, G. L.: Transmission of Amebiasis in a Children's Home in New Orleans. Am. J. Trop. Med., *23:* 401–419, 1943.

Martin, G. A., and others: Comparative Efficacy of Amebacides and Antibiotics in Acute Amebic Dysentery. J.A.M.A., *151:* 1055–1059, 1953.

McCowen, M. C., and others: Fumagillin (H-3) a New Antibiotic with Amebicidal Properties. Science, *113:* 202, 1951.

Sodeman, W. A., and Jung, R. C.: Treatment of Teniasis with Quinacrine Hydrochloride. J.A.M.A., *148:* 285–286, 1952.
Taliferro, W. H.: The Mechanism of Acquired Immunity in Infections with Parasitic Worms. Physiol. Rev., *20:* 468–489, 1947.
Wright, W. H., and others: The Control of Schistosomiasis Japonica. J. Hyg., *47:* 33, 1948.

CHAPTER 25

Bacteria Transmitted by Respiratory Secretions

BACTERIA: *Streptococcus; Meningococcus; Pneumococcus; Hemophilus pertussis; Hemophilus influenzae*

THE MICROORGANISMS which invade the respiratory organs and multiply there leave the host by way of sputum, saliva, and nasal secretions. They may be transferred to food or fomites by contaminated hands, or sprayed into the air by coughing and sneezing. The smaller droplets remain suspended in the air for considerable periods of time, while the larger droplets settle to the floor to be resuspended whenever dust is raised. Streptococci and other bacteria from respiratory secretions may remain viable for several days in floor dust. Whenever and wherever people congregate in closed spaces, therefore, an exchange of nose and throat bacteria is likely to occur. To date, efforts to prevent this transfer have not been wholly successful. Handwashing, especially after using a handkerchief, is important. Ventilation aids by diluting polluted air, thus decreasing the number of bacteria inhaled. Ultraviolet lights and antiseptic sprays appear to have little effect on the occurrence of infections among those who live or work in treated areas.

For the average person, it is impossible to avoid contact with nose and throat organisms. Therefore, protection must depend upon measures which will minimize the concentration of organisms and increase the general or specific resistance of the host. This chapter will consider the streptococcus, meningococcus, pneumococcus, and the hemophilic organisms.

STREPTOCOCCUS

The name *streptococcus* means "chain coccus" and refers to a very large group of organisms composed of saprophytes and parasites. The parasites are often found on the mucous membrane of the human body—especially in the nose and throat. Here they may live without producing injury or they may invade and cause severe illness. One group, the enterococci, commonly found in the intestine of man and animals, may cause disease when introduced into wounds or other parts of the body. Enterococci are more hardy than other streptococci since they can survive pasteurization and are very resistant to most antibiotics. Streptococci grow readily in milk or in laboratory medium containing blood. Like other nonspore-forming organisms, most are easily killed by heat and chemicals although they may remain alive in sputum for several weeks. Furthermore, many strains appear to survive drying and cold for varying periods of time.

There have been many attempts to *classify* this miscellaneous group of organisms. According to one classification, which is based on the action of the bacteria when grown on blood agar, the streptococci are divided into three large groups:

1. Those that produce *no change in the appearance* of the blood, *nonhemolytic* streptococci; this group includes some of the intestinal and some of the saprophytic strains.

2. Those that form a brownish-green zone around the colonies, the *alpha* (viridans) or "green-forming" streptococci; these organisms are often associated with chronic infections.

3. Those that produce a clear, transparent (hemolytic) zone around the colonies, the *beta hemolytic* streptococci.

By means of precipitation tests, Lancefield has divided *hemolytic Streptococcus pyogenes* into the following groups:

Group A ....Pathogenic for man (Groups B, C, D, F, G, O are occasionally pathogenic for man)
Group B ....Pathogenic for cows—causes mastitis
Group C ....Pathogenic for animals
Group D ....Seldom pathogenic, found in human intestine and throat and sometimes in dairy products
Group E ....Saprophytic, in dairy products
Groups F, G, H, K, L, M, N, O — Usually nonpathogenic / Found in upper respiratory tract of man

Griffith, an English worker, has further subdivided Group A

(Lancefield) into some forty different types based on agglutination tests. While this finer classification is sometimes useful in tracing the source of an epidemic, it is not commonly employed in routine work. It is usually sufficient to identify a given organism as a streptococcus Group A or Group B.

Infection   There are literally dozens of different pathogenic streptococci that are able to produce disease in various body structures. Many of these organisms form potent toxins that cause severe illness and even death. The diseases commonly ascribed to beta hemolytic streptococcus (Lancefield Group A) may be grouped as follows:

I. Streptococcal Infection—respiratory
   A. Without rash—*Tonsillitis, septic sore throat*
   B. With rash—*Scarlet fever*
II. Streptococcal Infections—other than respiratory
   A. Of skin—*Erysipelas, impetigo*
   B. Of genital tract—*Puerperal infection*
   C. Of wounds—*Wound infection*

Streptococcal infections of the respiratory tract are frequently caused by various types of Group A and less frequently by members of Groups C and G. Since these infections are not distinct clinical entities, the name *Streptococcicosis* has been suggested as a term to include tonsillitis, septic sore throat, and scarlet fever.

TONSILLITIS AND SEPTIC SORE THROAT   Pharyngitis or tonsillitis may be caused by the invasion of various kinds of bacteria, but severe infections of this type are frequently due to streptococci. Epidemics of *septic sore throat* have often been traced to contaminated raw milk. The pathogens may come from the cow but more frequently are introduced by an infected human being. Since the organisms can grow freely in milk, the ingestion of this fluid culture may introduce an overwhelming dose of the organisms and their toxins.

The organisms' ability to produce disease is related to various products excreted by the growing streptococci. Some of these products are toxic and many but not all stimulate antibody formation. Injurious substances produced by various strains of pathogenic streptococci include capsular material, a skin-reddening toxin, and several enzymes. Their effects on body cells and fluids are shown below:

ACTION OF STREPTOCOCCAL SUBSTANCE	STREPTOCOCCAL EXCRETION	ANTIBODY
Injures capillaries of skin	Erythrogenic (skin-reddening) toxin	Antitoxin
Increases permeability of red blood cells	Streptolysin O (hemolysin)	Antistreptolysin O
	Streptolysin S (hemolysin)	None
Uncertain	Hyaluronic acid (capsular material)	None
Decreases viscosity of fluids and cells	Hyaluronidase (spreading factor)	Antihyaluronidase
Hydrolyzes proteins	Proteinase	Antiproteinase
Activates body enzyme which digests fibrin	Streptokinase (fibrinolysin)	Antistreptokinase
Digests viscous component of nucleus	Streptodornase (spreading factor)	Antistreptodornase

The injurious effects of the various products formed by growing streptococci can readily be surmised. The streptolysins (sometimes called hemolysins) cause hemoglobin to leak from the red blood cells. The enzymes—streptokinase, streptodornase, and hyaluronidase—tend to liquefy viscous substances such as fibrin and exudates from injured tissues. Proteinases are obviously harmful since they destroy cell and body proteins. The production of one or more of these substances accounts for the organisms' ability to injure host cells. The organisms usually invade the tissues of the throat and cervical lymph glands, causing marked inflammation. The infection may spread to other parts of the respiratory tract or to the blood stream. Even when the process remains local streptococcal infections may give rise to nonspecific stress effects resulting in damage to the heart, kidneys, or joints. (Rheumatic fever so commonly follows streptococcal infections that penicillin treatment of sore throat has been advocated as a means of preventing rheumatic fever.)

The character of the illness produced is related to the age of the host. In infants under six months of age, streptococcal infections or streptococcal fever is characterized by a generalized illness with no sore throat and no rash. In infants six months to one year old, streptococcal infections are often prolonged, subacute, and tend to spread to sinuses, lymph glands, and middle ear. Older children and adults respond more vigorously and the infection tends to localize in the tonsils, pharynx, and lymph nodes. It is thought that repeated early infections cause the cells to become sensitive to the organisms and their products and that this sensitivity increases the ability of the host to localize the infection.

If the infection is overcome, various antibodies including antistreptolysin and antifibrinolysin may be found in the blood serum. The immunity developed in response to infection is either very short lived or it is so highly specific that it protects against only one type of organism. At any rate, one streptococcal infection does not protect against a second infection. It is, of course, possible and likely that the second infection may be caused by a different type of streptococcus.

The pathogenic streptococcus is a dangerous invader and often threatens the life of the host. Most hemolytic streptococci are susceptible to sulfonamides and to various antibiotics. (The enterococci and certain anaerobic streptococci are relatively resistant to antibiotics.) They may, however, develop resistance to these inhibiting agents particularly if treatment is intermittent or the dosage inadequate. Therefore, these drugs are of value in treating infections, but as a rule will not decrease the incidence of infection. After recovery, the infected person and the well persons in close contact with him may carry virulent organisms for varying periods of time.

Streptococci are so versatile in their method of attack that the same strain may cause a number of different infections in the same household. For example, a child may have a typical case of scarlet fever, while one adult has a septic sore throat and infection of the middle ear, and another, an infected finger.

SCARLET FEVER   Scarlet fever is an acute disease of childhood which is associated with different types of streptococcus (Group A). During the incubation period (from two to seven days), the organisms invade the throat and produce toxins. These products are responsible for the characteristic symptoms of the disease, e.g., nausea, vomiting, sore throat, and rash. Scarlet fever, like other streptococcal infections, may vary in character from mild to very severe. The scarlet eruption or rash which gives the infection its name is caused by a specific skin-reddening (erythrogenic) toxin which injures the cells of the palate, tongue, and skin. The rash fades after two or three days and is followed by the scaling or desquamation of the dead cells. These scales do not carry the infection unless they have been contaminated with discharges from nose, throat, ear, or wound. One attack usually confers a lasting immunity against scarlet fever, but not against other types of streptococcal infections. This immunity is thought to be developed against the toxin rather than the organism. The experimental injection of the toxin (free from organisms) may cause the typical symptoms of scarlet fever, such as headache, muscular pains, nausea, vomiting, and rash. The severity of the response depends upon the dose and also upon the susceptibility of the person. The introduction of the specific antitoxin causes the rash to fade.

This is the basis for the *Schultz-Charlton reaction* or *blanching test* in which 0.1 cc. to 0.5 cc. of scarlet fever antitoxin (or convalescent serum) is injected into skin showing a well-developed rash. If the skin eruption is due to scarlet fever, the toxin is neutralized and the rash fades in from six to thirty-six hours. This test is of some value in confirming a diagnosis of scarlet fever.

Susceptibility to scarlet fever can be determined by the Dick test which is comparable to the Schick test for diphtheria.* A small amount of rash-producing streptococcus (Group A) toxin is injected into the skin of the forearm. The susceptible person develops a red area of 1 sq. cm. or more at the site of inoculation within twenty-four hours. This constitutes a positive reaction and indicates that the person lacks antitoxin. A negative reaction occurs in the person who possesses circulating antibodies against the specific toxin, but is not as reliable a reaction as is a positive one.

An active immunity against clinically recognizable scarlet fever can be acquired by inoculation with scarlet fever toxin.

* One skin-test dose—the least amount of scarlet fever toxin which will cause a positive reaction in a person susceptible to scarlet fever and a negative reaction in an immune person. In the Dick test, this dose is contained in 0.1 cc.

The series usually consists of five weekly injections containing 500, 2500, 20,000, 40,000, and 80,000 skin test doses. This method is seldom used because it often gives rise to severe reactions and, furthermore, antibiotic therapy is very effective in controlling the infection.

Scarlet fever antitoxin or convalescent serum can be given to prevent or to modify the course of the disease and to hasten recovery. When it is administered early in adequate doses, it usually causes the rash to fade, the temperature to fall, and the risk of complications to decrease. Sulfonamides and penicillin have proved so valuable that they have often replaced serums in the treatment of scarlet fever.

CONTROL   The spread of streptococci from person to person is difficult to control because the organisms are often carried by healthy people. Such carriers are especially dangerous when they are working in a nursery or operating room, or when working with food, milk, or dairy cattle. Since the streptococci grow readily in milk, the pasteurization of dairy products is an important means of preventing outbreaks of septic sore throat. Dust suppression is useful as a means of minimizing the spread of organisms and is especially necessary in theaters, schoolrooms, dormitories, and hospital wards. Persons suffering from streptococcal infections including scarlet fever should be isolated for a week or more until the mucous membranes of the nose and throat appear normal or, in case of sinus or middle ear infections, until abnormal discharges cease. If discharges persist, the patient can be released from isolation when cultures taken on successive days no longer reveal hemolytic streptococci. Healthy contacts are permitted to go to work or to school but are not permitted to sell or work with dairy products or other foods which might transmit streptococci.

MENINGOCOCCUS

The meningococcus (*Neisseria intracellularis*) is a small gram-negative diplococcus that often lives as a harmless parasite in the pharynx but sometimes invades the coverings of the central nervous system, i.e., the meninges. The common names of the organism are significant. "Meningococcus" suggests that it is the coccus causing meningitis. "Neisseria" is the genus

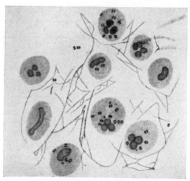

Figure 61   Meningococci in white blood cells—also a few diplococci and delicate threads of fibrin in the exudate surrounding the phagocytes.

name for the gram-negative diplococci and "intracellularis" refers to the fact that these bacteria are readily engulfed by phagocytes and are often found within the leukocytes (see Figure 61).

These bacteria are parasites that may resist drying for several days but are easily killed by heat or chemicals. In appearance, the organisms are like the harmless parasite *Neisseria catarrhalis* that is commonly found on the mucous membranes of the nose and throat. In the laboratory, they can be distinguished by the fact that *Neisseria catarrhalis* will grow on ordinary nutrient medium whereas the meningococcus organisms require a special medium containing blood. Meningococci fall into several types. Type I is commonly associated with epidemics while Types II and IIa are more likely to be found when no epidemics are manifest.

Apparently the parasite has little power to invade except when the host's resistance is low. The carrier rate is high (estimated to be from 1 to 10 per cent and may at times be as high as 70 or 80 per cent), especially where people are living in crowded quarters or barracks which make for easy and rapid transfer of the organisms. It is probable that latent infections develop a certain degree of immunity in urban populations since the disease is uncommon except among infants and among the new recruits in the army. Meningococcal disease tends to be epidemic at intervals of eight to twelve years. The

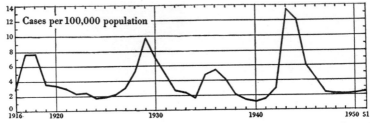

Figure 62A   Meningococcus meningitis. Chart shows peaks of
        incidence at approximately twelve-year intervals.

highest rates occur during periods of high industrial or military
activity when large groups of people move to army camps or
congested areas. (See Figure 62A.)

   Infection   The organisms are usually spread by carriers, and multiply rapidly in susceptible persons. Meningococcal disease occurs in three forms: (1) a local infection of
the mucous membrane of the upper respiratory tract, (2) a
blood stream infection, or (3) an invasion of the meninges.
The local type of the disease though seldom recognized may,
during epidemics, be as frequent as the common cold. After
invasion the organisms injure cells in the capillary networks
throughout the body causing loss of blood proteins and sometimes minute hemorrhages in the skin, meninges, and brain.
Severe infections are characterized by fever, headache, nausea,
rigidity of the neck, and sometimes a rash. The symptoms are
due to toxemia and to mechanical injury caused by increased
pressure upon the brain and spinal cord. Mortality rates often
ranged from 35 to 80 per cent before modern methods of treatment were developed.

   Early diagnosis is important and is confirmed by one or
both of the following: (1) finding the organisms within the
leukocytes in the cloudy spinal fluid, (2) recovering meningococci from skin lesions by injecting saline and asperating the
fluid, or (3) finding the organisms in cultures grown from the
blood or spinal fluid. Since these organisms are not hardy,
there should be no delay in transferring spinal fluid or blood
to the laboratory. The sulfonamides and penicillin have been
used with great success in the treatment of meningococcus

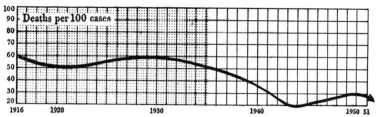

Figure 62B   Meningococcus meningitis. Smooth mortality curve shows drop after the advent of sulfonamides (white area). The dip in 1942–44 represents the effect of low army mortality (3 to 4 per cent). (Pfizer Spectrum.)

meningitis. Death rates from meningococcus meningitis have decreased since sulfonamides and antibiotics became available. (See Figure 62B.)

Meningitis is usually endemic in large cities and may become epidemic, especially in camps or barracks. Persons suffering from the disease should be isolated until nose and throat cultures are negative. Discharges and fomites should be disinfected to prevent the transmission of organisms to other persons. Small doses of sulfonamides given under medical supervision have been successfully used in army groups to decrease carrier rates and to prevent the spread of the disease.

PNEUMOCOCCUS

Pneumococci are spheral cells which frequently appear in pairs or short chains. They are soluble in bile—a characteristic that differentiates them from green-forming (viridans) streptococci. They grow readily on blood medium and retain Gram's stain. Although these organisms are strict parasites, they are fairly hardy. Like other nonspore-forming organisms, they are easily killed by heat and chemicals but may live for days in moist or dried sputum. They are especially susceptible to surface-acting agents such as bile and soap. Surveys show that they are intermittently present in the nose and throat of human beings, and that the carrier rate in well persons is often as high as 60 per cent in winter and somewhat lower in summer.

Pneumococci are surrounded by starchlike capsules which protect them from the body fluids and phagocytes of the host.

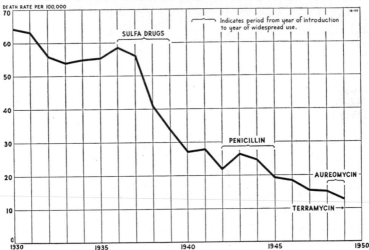

Standardized Death Rates per 100,000 from Pneumonia

Total Persons, Ages 1-74 Years.

Metropolitan Life Insurance Company, Weekly Premium-Paying Business, 1930-1949

Figure 63   Standard death rates per 100,000 from pneumonia. Note the marked decrease in deaths since the advent of sulfonamide and antibiotic therapy. (Statistical Bulletin, Sept., 1950.)

More than seventy-five distinct types of pneumococci have been recognized and designated as Types 1, 2, 3, . . . 75.* The capsules of each type are composed of a specific carbohydrate substance which is sometimes referred to as "SSS" or the *specific soluble substance.* The presence of a characteristic polysaccharide in the capsule makes it possible to identify the type by means of specific serum reactions demonstrated by precipitation or Neufeld capsule swelling tests (see Figure 64 and Chapter 21, page 342).

Pneumococci of different types differ in virulence. Types 1, 3, 2, 5, 8, 7, 4 (in order of frequency) are those commonly encountered in lobar pneumonia.[1] Types 3 and the higher types are commonly carried by well persons and may cause infections in adults and in children. Types 1 and 2 have been commonly associated with disease or they may be carried by

* Arabic numerals have been substituted for the cumbersome Roman numerals usually used to designate types.

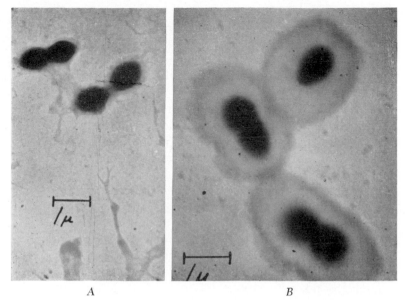

A   B

Figure 64   Electron micrographs of: A, *Diplococcus pneumoniae,*
Type 3 in Type 1 serum, shows a protein deposit on the mount with no
effect on the capsules of the pneumococci. B, *Diplococcus pneumoniae,*
Type 1 in Type 1 serum, shows capsules markedly swollen in response
to the type specific antiserum. (The electron micrographs reproduced in
article by Mudd, Heimets, and Anderson: J. Exper. Med., 78: 327–332.)

persons who have had contacts with other persons infected
with those organisms. Pneumococci as a group are responsible
for 96 per cent of the cases of lobar pneumonia; in the past,
50 per cent have been due to Types 1 and 2. In recent years
there has been a decrease in Type 1 infections with a corresponding increase in those caused by the higher types. Lobar
pneumonia tends to be seasonal (cold months) and to have a
short incubation period. In contrast, bronchopneumonia tends
to occur sporadically throughout the year and to have a longer
incubation period. About one half of the cases of bronchopneumonia are caused by pneumococci, while the remainder
are due to streptococci, staphylococci, influenza bacilli, and
so on. These two types of lung disease are differentiated on
anatomic bases. Lobar pneumonia is an acute respiratory in-

fection which leads to inflammation and consolidation of one or more lobes of one or both lungs. Bronchopneumonia is often secondary to a bronchitis which extends into the terminal bronchioles and lobules of the lungs. The so-called atypical pneumonias may be caused by various viruses, rickettsias, and fungi.

Susceptibility to Infection   The human body possesses considerable ability to resist pneumococcus infections. Infants and aged persons are more susceptible than children and young adults. Various stresses such as infection, malnutrition, fatigue, and exposure to dampness and cold render persons susceptible to pneumonia. Acute and chronic infections such as measles, influenza, the common cold, and sinusitis also predispose to pneumococcus infections, including pneumonia. As a rule, men, especially those performing heavy manual labor, are more susceptible than women. Since contact with infected persons and carriers increases the risk of infection, special care should be taken to protect infants, sick children, and other susceptibles against nose and throat organisms carried by other persons.

Infection   Pneumococci cause a variety of infections, such as sinusitis, bronchitis, pharyngitis, mastoiditis, and pneumococcus pneumonia. Although the prevalence of types causing infection may vary with time and place, the following common types are listed in the order of decreasing prevalence: Types 1, 3, 2, 8, 5, 7, 4, and 14.[1] Type 1 is most common in adults, while Types 14, 1, 6, 5, 7, and 12 are frequently the cause of infections in children.

Normally, when clumps of pneumococci reach the lungs they fall on a moving layer of mucus which conveys them upward or they may be engulfed and destroyed by phagocytes. When these defenses fail the pneumococci invade and grow rapidly. Since they do not produce toxins, they are thought to injure cells by competing for essential nutrients. Hypersensitivity of the host cells may also contribute to cellular damage. (Since all persons from time to time carry pneumococci as a part of the flora of the nasopharynx, all have an opportunity to become sensitive to proteins of the pneumococcus.)

Once established, virulent pneumococci multiply rapidly and

invade scattered or large areas as, for example, an entire lobe
of the lung. The injury to capillary networks and accompany-
ing inflammation produce a complex series of changes including:

1. Leaking of blood proteins into the alveolar spaces.
2. Migration of bacteria and leukocytes into the infected
   tissues and alveolar spaces.
3. Complete filling of alveolar sacs with pneumococci and
   exudate from capillaries and injured cells.
4. Fibrin shrinkage and refilling of capillaries with regener-
   ation of lining of alveolar sacs.
5. Appearance of macrophages which clear away the debris.

Lobar pneumonia constitutes a severe stress by virtue of direct
injury to an extensive area of lung tissue, reinforced by a decreased oxygen supply and pain due to the rubbing of the
inflamed pleura as the individual breathes. Furthermore the
shallow respiration impairs the venous return to the heart by
decreasing the pumping action of the heart. The resulting poor
circulation, in turn, deprives all cells of adequate supplies of
oxygen, food, and hormones and may, therefore, bring about
irreversible changes and death. (See page 226.)

The infection is characterized by a sudden onset of fever,
pain, difficulty in breathing, coughing, and the production of
a rusty sputum. The person with pneumonia looks and feels ill
although the severity of the infection and the degree of invasion varies in different persons and seems to be due in part to
the virulence of the organism. The appearance of bacteria in
the blood stream, as shown by a positive blood culture, indicates that the host has failed to localize the infection and to
prevent multiplication of the invaders. The outcome depends
on the ability of the body to eliminate the bacteria and their
products and at the same time to maintain vital life processes.
In a moderate infection, the patient is very ill for several days
with the characteristic signs of fever, cough, difficulty in
breathing, and general prostration. By the fourth day, agglutinins, precipitins, and protective antibodies usually appear in
the blood and increase until the combined action of antibodies
and leukocytes dispose of the bacteria. At this time, the patient
shows a sudden improvement in condition; the fever drops to

normal by crisis, and cough and pain disappear. Because spontaneous recovery frequently does not take place, many attempts have been made to assist the body defenses. First, serum therapy was developed; then later sulfonamides and penicillin proved even more valuable. Penicillin is especially effective since it kills the pneumococci. Bacteriostatic agents such as the sulfonamides, aureomycin, and Terramycin are also useful. Although these drugs are effective against all pneumococci, type determination may be desirable because it gives a clue to the nature and severity of the infection. The sputum for typing should be collected as early as possible, because a few doses of the drug will decrease the number of organisms to the point at which they are difficult to find.

The antibiotics change the course of the infection. Often within twenty-four hours the fever and pain leave and the patient looks better and feels better. When bacteriostatic drugs are used, treatment should continue until the body forms antibodies which enable the phagocytes to dispose of the invaders. Cortisone which has been used experimentally promptly relieves symptoms of infections but has no effect upon the organisms which continue to multiply and invade.

Modern therapy has been so successful that deaths from pneumonia have markedly decreased. (See Figure 63.) The decline in deaths has been especially rapid since 1938 when sulfonamide therapy was introduced; however, there is little evidence that the incidence of the disease is declining. The lowered death rates reflect the effects of better treatment rather than prevention of infection. Two doses of vaccine prepared from virulent strains of pneumococci will increase the resistance of the person for a year. The use of the vaccine is not advocated for the general population because the incidence of the disease is low. It may be of value in institutional groups where the risk of pneumonia is great.

HEMOPHILUS PERTUSSIS

The hemophilic (blood-loving) bacteria are a group of small, gram-negative rods that require blood or hemoglobin for growth outside of the body. Two of the most important of this

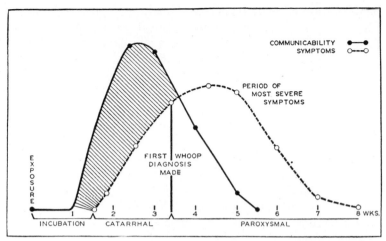

Figure 65   Epidemiology of whooping cough. Note that the disease is communicable during the later part of the incubation period and during the early stages of the infection. (Smillie, W. G.: Preventive Medicine and Public Health. By permission of The Macmillan Co., publishers.)

group, *Hemophilus pertussis* and *Hemophilus parapertussis*,* cause whooping cough. They are fragile organisms that are easily killed by physical and chemical agents. They are present in the respiratory secretions during the early stages of the infection and apparently are seldom carried by well persons.

Infections   When the organisms enter a susceptible person they multiply and invade the mucous membranes of the nasopharynx, larynx, and bronchial tree. After an incubation period of about seven days the infected individual develops the symptoms of a cold which persist for a week or two. Then follows a period characterized by a paroxysmal, whooping cough.

The disease is highly communicable during the catarrhal stage when the organisms are present in large numbers. After the third week the number of organisms gradually decreases although the organisms may persist for several weeks. (See Figure 63.) *Hemophilus pertussis* and *H. parapertussis* can

* There have been reports of whooping cough due to infection with *Hemophilus influenzae* and *Bacillus bronchoseptica*.

be demonstrated by nasopharyngeal culture or by cough plate. The latter is made by holding a blood agar plate open in front of the victim's mouth during a paroxysm of coughing.

Pertussis organisms invade the walls of the air sacs (*alveoli*) and also multiply freely on the ciliated epithelium of the bronchial tree. The injured cells pour forth a thick, heavy secretion which stimulates the cough reflex. The bacteria apparently prevent the cilia from carrying on their normal function of removing secretion and particles. The bacteria and accumulating secretions cause irritation which results in bouts of severe coughing. The paroxysmal coughing and frequent vomiting which accompany the disease constitute severe stress for the infected child. In young children, the disease is often complicated by a bronchopneumonia caused by *H. pertussis* or other bacteria.

Susceptibility and Immunity   Susceptibility is general and one attack usually results in an immunity which lasts for years. The disease pattern of pertussis differs from that of other common childhood diseases (measles, mumps, rubella, chickenpox) in that it is more prevalent in the South than in the North and attacks more children in the younger age groups. Furthermore the risk of infection and death is higher for girls than for boys. In children over five, whooping cough is a mild infection attended by little danger. Virtually all deaths from this disease occur in infants under two years of age. Sick children, and infants who have been exposed, may be protected for a short time by the administration of antipertussis serum. Like all gram-negative organisms, *H. pertussis* is relatively resistant to antibiotics. Recent reports suggest that Terramycin, aureomycin, and chloramphenicol are of value in treating severe infections. Pertussis antiserum and hyperimmune gamma globulin also appear to be useful. Vaccination of the mother during the last three months of pregnancy can be used to provide the infant with a passive immunity against whooping cough.

Pertussis vaccine, made of killed bacteria (alum-precipitated), may be given to infants one month of age. Three or four doses of pertussis vaccine (total 40 to 60 million organisms) are given at one-month intervals. This may be supplemented by a single booster dose when the child reaches school age. A small number of cases of encephalitis have occurred following inoculation with pertussis vaccine. In view of this, vaccines should not be given when a child is febrile and severe reactions should be reported to the physician. Vaccination induces antibody formation and also sensitivity to pertussis protein. Therefore, a complement-fixation test (page 343) can be used to demonstrate the presence of antibodies and a skin test similar to the tuberculin test will show sensitivity.

Few people escape an attack of whooping cough. In persons over five who are well nourished, the disease rarely, if ever, causes death. In infants under one year, the mortality is often as high as 10 per cent while that in the one- to two-year group is 5 per cent. Lives can be saved by preventing the infection until after the person is five years of age.

Children under five, and especially those under two, should be protected from contact with an infected person. Children with whooping cough should be excluded from school for five weeks after the initial symptoms. As a rule, there is no quarantine, and isolation is limited to protecting susceptible infants. In contrast to other infections, the child is not confined to bed but encouraged to play in the sunshine and fresh air. The aim in community efforts to control the disease is to postpone it until the child has reached the age of minimum risk. The value of measures for control is attested by the steady decline in pertussis death rates in the last twenty years.

HEMOPHILUS INFLUENZAE

This organism resembles *Hemophilus pertussis* in character and appearance. It is frequently present in the respiratory tract of well persons and is often important as a secondary invader in association with infections such as pneumonia, sinusitis, or a severe form of meningitis. *Hemophilus influenzae* apparently can cause a whooping cough which clinically is indistinguishable from pertussis. This organism is commonly called the "influenza bacillus." The name is unfortunate, as it does not cause the epidemic influenza, which is a virus disease of human beings. Pfeiffer, a German scientist, found the organism in the lungs of many persons who died of influenza in the pandemic of 1893 and for some time it was regarded as the cause of influenza. More recent work has proved that it is a secondary invader, but the name survives as a reminder of a bacteriological mistake. Like most gram-negative rods, *Hemophilus influenzae* is relatively resistant to antibiotics. Recent reports, however, indicate that mortality rates from influenzal meningitis can be markedly decreased if patients are treated early with sulfadiazine and streptomycin, and specific antiserum. Aureomycin and chloramphenicol have also proved useful.

SUMMARY

A variety of microorganisms are transmitted by the secretions of the respiratory tract. Of these, the gram-positive cocci (streptococci and pneumococci) and the gram-negative cocci (meningococci) are susceptible to many antibiotics. In contrast, the relatively resistant gram-negative organisms (*Hemophilus pertussis* and *Hemophilus influenzae*) are susceptible to some of the newer antibiotics such as chloramphenicol and aureomycin.

REFERENCE

1. Dubos, R. J.: Bacterial and Mycotic Infections of Man. 2d ed. Philadelphia, J. B. Lippincott Co., 1952.

SUPPLEMENTARY READINGS

BOOKS:

American Public Health Association: The Control of Communicable Disease. 7th ed. New York, An Official Report of the American Public Health Association, 1950.

Burrows, W.: Jordan-Burrows Textbook of Bacteriology. 15th ed. Philadelphia, W. B. Saunders Co., 1949.

Dubos, R. J.: Bacterial and Mycotic Infections of Man. 2d ed. Philadelphia, J. B. Lippincott Co., 1952.

Maxcy, K. F.: Rosenau Preventive Medicine and Hygiene. 7th ed. New York, Appleton-Century-Crofts, Inc., 1951.

Report of the Committee on Immunization and Therapeutic Procedures for Acute Infectious Diseases of the American Academy of Pediatrics. Evanston, Ill., American Academy of Pediatrics, 1951.

Smith, D. T., and Conant, C. F.: Zinsser's Textbook of Bacteriology. 10th ed. New York, Appleton-Century-Crofts, 1952.

PERIODICALS:

Cohen, P., and Scadrons, S. J.: The Effects of Active Immunization of the Mother upon the Offspring. J. Pediat., *29:* 609–617, 1946.

Eldering, G., and Kendrick, P. L.: Incidence of Parapertussis in Grand Rapids Area as Indicated by 16 Years' Experience with Diagnostic Cultures. Am. J. Pub. Health, *42:* 27–31, 1952.

Gordon, J. E., and Hood, R. I.: Whooping Cough and Its Epidemiological Anomalies. Am. J. Med. Sc., *222:* 333–359, 1951.

Hedrich, A. W.: Recent Trends in Meningococcal Disease. Pub. Health Rep., *67:* 411–420, 1952.

Miller, C. P., and Schad, D.: The Resistance of Meningococci to Drying. J. Bact., *47:* 71–77, 1944.

Perkins, J. E., and others: Field Study of the Prophylactic Value of Pertussis Vaccine. Am. J. Pub. Health, *32:* 63–72, 1942.

Reimann, H.: The Changing Nature of Pneumonia. Ann. Int. Med., *33:* 1246–1253, 1950.

Strallerman, G. H.: Prophylaxis against Streptococcal Infections in Rheumatic Rever Patients. J.A.M.A., *150:* 1571–1575, 1952.

Wanamaker, L. W.: Prophylaxis of Acute Rheumatic Fever by Treatment of the Preceding Streptococcal Infection with Various Amounts of Penicillin. Am. J. Med., *10:* 673–695, 1951.

CHAPTER 26

Bacteria Transmitted by Respiratory Secretions (Continued)

BACTERIA: *Corynebacterium diphtheriae; Mycobacterium tuberculosis; Mycobacterium leprae*

CORYNEBACTERIUM DIPHTHERIAE

THE DIPHTHERIA organism is a slender rod which is often curved or club-shaped. With methylene blue, some of the bacteria stain irregularly so that deep-staining bars or granules are often visible within the cells. This hardy organism grows well on laboratory medium containing blood serum or in milk at any temperature ranging from 15 to 40° C. (59 to 104° F.), but is easily killed by heat and chemicals. When protected by body secretions, it is very resistant to cold and to drying, and in dried membrane the organisms have remained alive for days.

The diphtheria organism produces an exotoxin as it grows in animal tissues or in laboratory medium. This exotoxin is a potent stress agent capable of destroying cells of the mucous membrane and capillaries, followed by inflammation, leakage of blood proteins, and clotting of blood within capillaries. The toxin, which is readily absorbed, causes damage to internal organs. Recent investigations reveal that diphtheria toxin prevents the host cells from forming certain essential respiratory enzymes (cytochromes).

On the basis of cultural characteristics, diphtheria organisms can be divided into three groups: (1) the *gravis* (grave), (2) the *intermedius*, and (3) the *mitis* (mild). By agglutination tests the gravis group can be subdivided into 13 types, the intermedius into 4, and the mitis into 40 types. This procedure is relatively new and will undoubtedly be of value in tracing epidemics caused by this organism.

Serious and fatal infections can be caused by any strain but are more commonly associated with the gravis or intermedius types. For example, during the Copenhagen epidemic in 1944–1945, mortality rates for gravis diphtheria in unvaccinated persons were 19.2 per cent as compared to 6.8 per cent for mitis diphtheria, and 8.2 per cent for intermedius.

Infection   Diphtheria occurs when toxin-producing organisms* reach the mucous membranes of susceptible persons and find conditions favorable for growth. The signs of the disease become apparent after two to five days. The organisms seldom invade the deeper tissues but grow near the surface, producing toxin that destroys the underlying skin or mucous membrane. The local lesion usually occurs in the respiratory tract but may infrequently be found in wounds or on the lip, nose, or vagina. These dead cells serve as a suitable medium for further growth and more toxin production. The bacteria, the dead cells, and the coagulated lymph form the gray, foulsmelling, diphtheria membrane. This membrane may be small or absent, or it may extend throughout the nasal passages, the larynx, the trachea, and bronchi. A large membrane favors the production and absorption of toxin. In diphtheria of the respiratory tract, this membrane occurs in one of three areas: the nose, the pharynx, or the larynx. *Nasal diphtheria* is often mild because the toxin is not readily absorbed from the nose. This type of infection is accompanied by little or no fever and may resemble a head cold with a mucoid discharge which is blood-tinged. *Pharyngeal* (faucial) *diphtheria* has a high fatality because the toxin is readily absorbed from the mucous membrane of the throat. *Laryngeal diphtheria* is more difficult to recognize and is apt to obstruct breathing and thus cause death by suffocation. The toxin which is rapidly absorbed causes destruction of cells in the heart muscle and nerves supplying the heart as well as in the liver, kidney, lymph nodes, spleen, and nervous system. Death is commonly caused by toxemia, suffocation, heart failure, or bronchopneumonia due to secondary invaders such as pneumococci or streptococci.

---

* There is evidence that some so-called nonvirulent strains release an endotoxin (closely related to the exotoxin) which is capable of producing clinical diphtheria. Apparently both endotoxins and exotoxins contribute to the disease process but not necessarily to the same extent.

The host responds to diphtheria toxin by forming circulating antibodies (antitoxin) to neutralize the poison. If the toxin is formed faster than the antitoxins which neutralize them, the poisons attack the cells causing renal or circulatory failure or paralysis. This can often be prevented by the early administration of large doses (10,000 to 80,000 units) of diphtheria antitoxin. To be of value, the antitoxin must be given early and in adequate amounts. Antitoxin can prevent injury to the cells by combining with the toxin, but it cannot restore damaged cells. Antitoxin may be supplemented by intravenous glucose, cortisone, and penicillin.

Susceptibility   Susceptibility to diphtheria can be determined by the *Schick test*—named for Bela Schick, who developed the test. Diphtheria toxin injures living cells; but if antitoxin is present no injury occurs. One skin-test* dose of toxin is injected into the skin of the forearm. If the person possesses enough antitoxin to neutralize the toxin, no injury results (a negative reaction to the Schick test). When no antitoxin is present, the irritant poison causes local redness and edema followed by a brown discoloration. This constitutes a positive reaction and indicates that the person is susceptible to diphtheria. A control test is made by injecting 0.1 cc. of diphtheria toxoid or toxin that has been inactivated by heat. Redness of the control area indicates that the person is sensitive to substances other than toxin.

The reaction to the Schick test is considered positive when (1) the site of injection shows a reddened area in twenty-four to thirty-six hours, which continues red for several days and is followed by a persistent brown discoloration, (2) the control shows no sign of irritation or shows a red area in the first twenty-four hours and fades before the fifth day. Susceptibility to diphtheria varies with age. It is low in the first six months of life because of a passive immunity acquired from an immune mother. It is high in children from one to five years of age, but tends to decrease during the school years. Schick tests

* One skin-test dose is 0.1 cc. or 1/50 of a minimal lethal dose or M.L.D. A minimal lethal dose is the smallest amount of diphtheria toxin that will kill a guinea pig weighing 250 gm. four days after a subcutaneous injection of toxin.

are commonly given three to six months after inoculation with toxoid and are recommended also for persons twelve to fourteen and sixteen to eighteen years of age.[1]

The change in susceptibility occurs in many persons who have not had the disease and who have not been protected by inoculation. Susceptibility is higher in northern states than in the South, and is higher in rural populations than in urban areas. (Diphtheria rates, however, may be higher in southern communities where little attention has been paid to the inoculation of infants.) Susceptibility to the disease is likely to vary in any person, especially in the young. After inoculations with toxoid, a high percentage of children will become "Schick negative" but, a few years later, some of these will again give a positive Schick reaction. With the decline of the disease there occurs an increase in the number of susceptible adults in the community.

Immunity It is now recognized that both exotoxins and endotoxins play a part in the disease-producing ability of diphtheria organisms. It is therefore not surprising that at times diphtheria toxoid and diphtheria antitoxin fail to give full protection. Recovery from the disease, when the patient has been treated with antitoxin, may or may not confer immunity. It is thought that repeated inapparent (subclinical) infections with organisms of low virulence provide a higher degree of immunity because they afford opportunities for the cells to develop a sensitivity to the endotoxin as well as to form antitoxin. Diphtheria endotoxin (somatic antigen) as an immunizing agent is being used experimentally. Inoculation with diphtheria toxoid increases the resistance of the person for several years, thereby decreasing the risk of a diphtheria infection. A temporary immunity which lasts two or three weeks can be induced by giving diphtheria antitoxin.

When diphtheria organisms reach an immune person, they are likely to be engulfed by phagocytes or carried into the stomach; in either case they will leave no evidence of their presence. If the specific defenses are less adequate, the bacteria may multiply moderately in the nose or throat without producing injury; in other words, potentially dangerous organisms may live as harmless parasites for days or even months. The person who harbors these bacteria, the healthy carrier, may transfer the organisms to other persons, especially during the course of colds or other respiratory infections.

Control   Carriers and persons with unrecognized infections make the control of diphtheria difficult. However, the following important steps should be taken: (1) recognition and reporting each case to the health officer; (2) isolation of the sick person; (3) passive immunization of susceptible contacts, especially infants and young children who have been exposed to the disease; (4) quarantine of such children and of adults who work with children or with food until bacteriological examination shows that they are not carriers; (5) investigation of the possible sources of infection (previous cases, carriers, raw milk). It is customary to isolate the infected person until two negative cultures from the throat and two from the nose are obtained on two successive days. When carriers are discovered, it may be desirable to determine the toxin-producing power of the organisms carried. This can be done by animal tests (see page 336). The carrier of nonvirulent organisms can be freed from the restrictions placed upon those who carry organisms capable of producing disease. Carriers and persons who have been in contact with infection are commonly treated with penicillin or aureomycin.

Prevention   Epidemic diphtheria can usually be prevented in the community when children are adequately protected against the disease. This can be accomplished by inducing an artificial active immunity in children. The antigen in common use is a preparation of toxin which has been modified by chemical treatment to form the relatively harmless *toxoid*. In adults and older children who may be sensitive to diphtheria proteins, toxoid sometimes causes unpleasant local and general reactions. A skin test can be used to reveal those who are sensitive to the toxoid mixture and the unpleasant symptoms can be minimized by giving multiple doses of diluted toxoid. Diphtheria toxoid should never be given to persons over ten years of age without first doing a skin test to detect sensitivity.

The following schedule is commonly recommended:

1. Inoculate all infants two or three months of age with three doses of combined alum-precipitated or aluminum hydroxide absorbed

diphtheria and tetanus toxoids containing *Hemophilus pertussis* (whooping cough) vaccine. This antigen is given intramuscularly at intervals of not less than one month and is usually begun at the age of three months. Give a stimulating dose of toxoid (recall or booster) injection at the age of one year and every three years thereafter.

2. Inoculate preschool children (not immunized in infancy) and susceptible school children.

3. Inoculate susceptible adults who may be exposed to diphtheria, e.g., teachers, nurses, doctors, laboratory workers.

Diphtheria is much less common in the United States today than it was fifty years ago. The decline in illness and death from this disease is due undoubtedly in part to artificial immunization, although the sharp decline before these methods became available indicates that other factors have contributed to this trend. Diphtheria is characteristically a disease of children under fifteen years of age.

Recent experience emphasizes the fact that diphtheria is still a serious disease with mortality rates which are often above 5 per cent. The epidemics in Europe and the occasional serious outbreaks in the United States point to the need for continuing diphtheria control programs. Many health officers advocate immunizing at least 70 per cent of the children under five years of age as a means of preventing diphtheria epidemics in this country. While outbreaks have occurred in communities in which 90 per cent of the children had been inoculated (as, for example, in Medford, Oregon, in 1949), these are rare.

MYCOBACTERIUM TUBERCULOSIS

The tubercle bacillus (*Mycobacterium tuberculosis*) is a moldlike organism which can be recognized by its appearance and its *acid-fast* staining reaction. It is unique in behavior as well as in appearance. It is thought by some authorities that the waxy outer surface of the cell slows its exchange processes; hence, it is hard to stain, hard to decolorize, and very resistant to most disinfectants. For example, phenol, 5 per cent, requires twelve hours to kill tuberculosis organisms in sputum, while ethyl alcohol varies in its effectiveness.[2] (See page 164.) The waxy composition of the cell protects it against drying. In dried sputum, these organisms have survived for periods of two to eight months. They have been known to resist direct sunlight for more than twenty hours. They are, however, susceptible to heat and are readily destroyed by boiling.

The organism grows slowly in laboratory media and in the animal body. In the body its growth is characteristically within phagocytic cells. It may require from three to six weeks incubation to produce visible evidence of growth. Two new methods for growing tuberculosis organisms have been developed. In one the organisms are grown in the yolk sac of a fertile egg; in the other, on a glass slide inoculated and placed face down on a nutrient medium. These methods are reported to reveal organisms in six or seven days instead of the usual three weeks. Virulent strains grow in long, twisted cords which tend to spread over the surface of the medium. Recent investigations reveal that virulent organisms when engulfed inhibit further movements by the phagocyte whereas avirulent organisms appear to have no effect on the engulfing cells. There is considerable evidence that leukocytes carry virulent bacteria to the lymph nodes without destroying the parasites. The invader may on occasion cause an acute local or general infection but more commonly it gives rise to a low-grade chronic infection. The word *slow* perhaps gives the best description of the life activities of this parasite. It grows slowly; it stains slowly; it produces its disease and kills its victims slowly. Also it dies slowly, except where heat is used as the destructive agent. The ability of this organism to survive drying for long periods makes it essential to collect tuberculosis sputum in cleansing tissues that can be burned promptly after use. Contaminated dishes and linens may be disinfected by submerging them in boiling water for ten minutes or more.

Some strains of tuberculosis organisms are adapted to growing in cold-blooded animals. Of those capable of growing in warm-blooded animals, three are important to man. They are:

1. *Mycobacterium tuberculosis* variety *avian*
2. *Mycobacterium tuberculosis* variety *bovis*
3. *Mycobacterium tuberculosis* variety *hominis.*

Tuberculosis in man is caused by either the human or the bovine strain and only very rarely by the avian. In bovine tuberculosis, the organisms are commonly present in the lungs, intestines, or udder of the cow. From any of these sources the organisms are readily carried to man by raw milk. In man, the organisms may be found in sputum, urine, feces, and in fluids from lesions. Because the organism is resistant, the transfer may be indirect. However, the prolonged contacts of family life are especially effective in transferring the parasites from tuberculous to well persons. The bacteria may enter the lung tissue directly or they may be carried from the nose, tonsils, or intestine to nearby lymph nodes by the leukocytes. The exact route traveled is a debated point. In the bovine tuberculosis in man, inhalation seems improbable because 95 per cent of these infections occur outside of the lungs. Some of the organisms may escape from the primary focus to nearby or distant lymph glands or bones to remain inactive or to set up a tuberculous infection. The bovine type of infection has become rare in the United States since improved dairy methods have led to the eliminating of tuberculous cows and to the pasteurization of milk. The disease is still common in countries where raw milk is used.

Host Responses   Tuberculosis organisms growing in lung tissue give rise to two types of lesions: the exudative and the productive. The *exudative* type is an acute inflammation which resembles a bacterial pneumonia in that the invading organisms are surrounded by a wall of exudate and phagocytes. The invaded area may be microscopic in size or may extend to an entire lobe. After a few days the injured area may heal without scars, or become necrotic, or (as often happens) develop into a productive lesion. The *productive lesion* is formed when the tissues respond as they would to any foreign body. First a large number of phagocytes (neutophils, lymphocytes, monocytes) surround the invaders. Then these phagocytes and bacteria are surrounded by giant cells—large epithelial-like cells containing several nuclei. The giant cells in turn are enclosed by a wall consisting of an inner layer of epithelial cells and an outer layer of fibrous connective tissue. When the host's resistance is high there is a tendency to form a small discrete mass called a *hard tubercle,* which becomes smaller as time passes. Usually bacteria within a hard tubercle are killed, the soft center becomes filled with calcium deposit, and the wall is reinforced with fibrous connective tissue forming a healed tubercle. This process often occurs without symptoms.

When the relative resistance is low or the bacteria are numerous and highly virulent the tubercles that are formed tend to be large and soft and are surrounded by an ill-defined wall. As bacteria multiply within a soft tubercle the tubercle enlarges and extends to nearby tissue. The center of this mass, which is soft and cheeselike, ruptures and gives rise to a cavity in the lung. The tubercle may rupture into a bronchial tube, a lymph vessel, or a vein and thereby scatter organisms to the lung and other organs.

The human strain of *Mycobacterium tuberculosis* commonly causes pulmonary tuberculosis. While the organism is capable of growing in many areas of the body, most infections are secondary to a lung infection. Pulmonary tuberculosis in man gives rise to two distinct types of infection: the primary and the post-primary or secondary types. These are sometimes referred to childhood and adult types. The terms are misleading because the type of response is not related to the age of the individual. The primary or first infection may occur at any age.

Primary (First) Infection   The primary or first infection is commonly acquired by inhaling droplets containing tuberculosis organisms. It often occurs in children but may occur in adults who escaped early exposure to the organism. It is an acute disease involving some portion of the lung and one or more of the bronchial lymph nodes. As a rule the disease lasts for a few days and usually goes unrecognized. The lesions are of the exudative type and may heal without scars or may form tubercles which later become calcified. If the resistance is low, as in infants, the organisms may multiply and scatter through the lymph and blood giving rise to a fatal generalized infection of the viscera, spinal cord, and brain. Usually the infection is mild and tends to be local and the whole process occurs without symptoms. The only visible evidence of the infection is the healed tubercle which can be discovered by x-ray examination. Since the host becomes sensitive to the proteins of the invading cells, reaction to the *tuberculin* test becomes positive.

Tuberculin Reaction   During the primary infection, bacterial proteins have been freed and carried to the cells of the body, which are so changed that they respond vigorously whenever they come in contact with this protein. This "sensitivity" can be detected by a skin test (the tuberculin test), similar to those used to detect food and pollen allergies.

The Tuberculin Test
  A. Kinds of tuberculin
     1. *Old tuberculin*—obtained by culturing tubercule bacilli in alkaline glycerin broth for six to eight weeks. After killing the culture, the fluid is concentrated and filtered. The resulting brown fluid contains the bacterial proteins as well as a variety of other substances.
     2. *Purified protein derivative* (P.P.D.)—obtained from cultures of tubercle bacilli grown on synthetic protein-free medium which is later concentrated and filtered. Purified protein derivative is distributed in white tablets (0.00002 mg. and 0.005 mg.) which are dissolved just before the test is made. This preparation contains one hundred or two hundred times as much tuberculin as the old tuberculin. As the name indicates, it is relatively free from extraneous matter.
  B. Types of tuberculin tests
     1. Mantoux test: the intradermal injection of
        a. Old tuberculin
           First dose: 0.1 cc. (1/100 milligram of tuberculin)
           Second dose: 0.1 cc. (1.0 milligram of tuberculin)
           or
        b. Purified protein derivative
           First dose: 0.1 cc. (1:50,000 dilution of 1 per cent)
           Second dose: 0.1 cc. (1:200 dilution of 1 per cent)
     2. Patch test (Vollmer) consists of an adhesive tape which supports three pieces of filter paper. The two end-papers are embedded with tuberculin in lanolin while the one in the center (the control) contains lanolin alone. The strip of adhesive is applied to an area of clean, dry skin and left in place for forty-eight hours.
     3. Other tests: There are many ways of administering tuberculin. In addition to the methods mentioned above, the test material may be applied to the scarified skin or it may be dropped into the eye. The latter method is used more frequently for cattle than for human beings.

A small amount of the bacterial protein, tuberculin, is injected into or applied to the skin. Tuberculin, though harmless to the nontuberculous, is poison to the person who is sensitive to it. The person who has an *active* or *healed* tuberculous lesion responds by developing fever and local redness and swelling at the site of inoculation. The reaction is usually positive if the person is or has been infected with the tubercle bacillus. The reaction is negative in the absence of tuberculosis, and also may be negative in the very early and very late stages of the disease. Since as many as 90 per cent of adults living in cities react positively to tuberculin, the test has little diagnostic value for adults but is more significant for children.

According to some authorities, the sensitivity, indicated by a positive reaction to the tuberculin test, represents a slight but definite resistance to a second infection. Under ordinary circumstances, 80 per cent of the well persons who have a positive tuberculin reaction will develop no further infection. Many authorities agree that the risk of acquiring an active tuberculosis infection is greater for well adults who have a negative tuberculin reaction than for those with a positive reaction. Obviously, the fact that most persons suffering from tuberculosis give a positive tuberculin reaction shows that it is no guarantee against the disease.

Experimental Infection   Experimental infections in laboratory animals afford some clues regarding the influence of heredity, dosage, and tuberculin sensitivity. Well-controlled experiments indicate that it is possible to breed rabbits which are very resistant to tuberculosis, as indicated by their ability to form small, discrete, hard tubercles. In contrast, other rabbits may show little ability to localize the infection and therefore succumb readily. In experimental tuberculosis as in other infections, the number of organisms which enter the body influences the character and outcome of the infection. Massive doses of organisms will produce overwhelming infections in both susceptible and resistant animals.

The response of the normal rabbit or guinea pig differs from that of the sensitive animal. The injection of living tuberculosis organisms into the leg of the normal animal causes little or no local inflammation. However, in three to five weeks, the animal dies of tuberculosis and autopsy reveals tubercles in many parts of the body. In contrast, injection of living organisms into a sensitive animal results in prompt local inflammation with profuse suppuration. This suggests that tuberculin-sensitive animals are more effective in localizing the invading or-

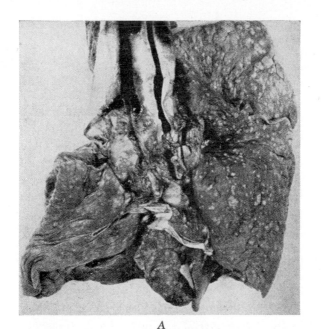

A

B

Figure 66   *A,* Multiple tubercles (nodules) in the lungs of a dog.
B, Tubercle near periphery of lung of dog (same as *A*). (× 70.)
(Hull, T. G.: Diseases Transmitted from Animals to Man. Courtesy of
Charles C Thomas, Publisher.)

419

ganisms. Furthermore, there is some evidence that the phago-cytic cells, especially the lymphocytes, of the sensitive animal release substances which inhibit the growth of the tuberculosis organism. There is, however, no evidence of any specific pro-tective antibody globulin in the blood or lymph.

Second Infection   Reinfection (adult type) may be caused either by organisms from without the body or by organisms developing in a partially healed tubercle. The cell response giving rise to a positive tuberculin reaction changes the character of the second infection. Characteristically, a slow, chronic, local infection develops in the lung tissue. This limiting factor is an advantage to both parasite and host in that it permits both to live for a very long time. For society, it is a distinct disadvantage because it maintains a focus of in-fection from which the parasites may be transferred to others.

During the early months, the infection produces no symp-toms and can be recognized only by x-ray examination. Later, the absorption of bacterial products results in fever, loss of weight, and weakness. The destruction of lung cells and the accumulation of fluid are followed by abnormal breath sounds (rales) and production of thick sputum containing the bacteria.

Treatment of clinical tuberculosis aims to do one of three things: to maintain the nutrition of the body, to rest the whole body, or to rest the diseased part. For instance, the affected lung is rested by collapsing the organ. This method of treat-ment usually prevents the escape of the tubercle bacillus in the sputum. As in any other infection, the outcome of the disease depends upon the ability of the host to overcome and destroy the invading parasites and to heal the diseased tissues. Diets abundant in protein, calcium, and vitamin C are essen-tial to the healing process. Streptomycin alone or in combina-tion with para-aminosalicylic acid is of value in the treatment of certain forms of tuberculosis. (In general, bacteriostatic drugs tend to be ineffective in disease processes that involve large areas of necrotic tissue.) Various isonicotinic acid com-pounds alone and in combination with streptomycin are being used experimentally. Early reports seem promising although the tuberculosis organisms tend to become resistant to both streptomycin and to isonicotinic acid. Vaccines and antiserums have proved ineffective as a means of treatment.

Susceptibility   Susceptibility to tuberculosis infection is general and eventually nearly everyone develops a primary infection and thereby becomes sensitive to tuberculin (protein from the tubercle organism). Susceptibility to disease (clinical tuberculosis) varies with age and is greatly influenced by environmental factors. Children under three and young adults are highly susceptible, while older children, before the age of puberty, are less likely to develop tuberculosis; after puberty they become highly susceptible. Negroes actually have less tuberculosis than whites, but once infected, they are prone to develop a rapidly fatal form of the disease.[3] As a rule, death rates for Negroes are three or four times those of the corresponding white group. In the United States, tuberculosis is the leading cause of death in the group from twenty to forty years of age, and has been called a disease of young women and of older men. The rates are always high among unskilled laborers and others in the low-income group. Dubos points out that tuberculosis rates are highest among peoples at the times when they are changing from a rural to an industrial economy and at times when they are subjected to stresses (wars, migrations) which lead to physiological misery.

Control   BCG Vaccine   BCG (*Bacillus of Calmette-Guérin*) vaccine containing living attenuated tuberculosis organisms of the bovine strain has been tried in many parts of the world. Recent studies indicate that the vaccine is safe and that it affords some protection for persons not sensitive to tuberculin who live or work in an environment where they are exposed to tuberculosis. Extensive studies now in progress are designed to test the value of this product. A new irradiated tuberculosis vaccine made from killed organisms is reported to be stable and as effective as BCG and to have the advantage of containing a preservative which inhibits possible contaminants.

Other Control Measures   Until the preventive powers of BCG vaccine are determined, control measures center upon the person who transmits the disease, which is communicable

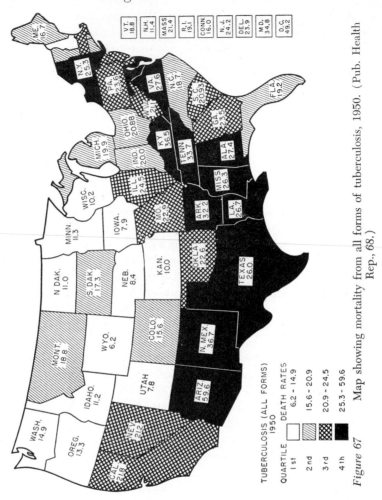

Figure 67   Map showing mortality from all forms of tuberculosis, 1950. (Pub. Health Rep., 68.)

as long as there is an open lesion discharging organisms. This may occur for long periods before the person knows that he is ill. Community control measures, therefore, must include the search for early infections that are without symptoms. This is best accomplished by the x-ray examination of large groups of adults suspected of having the infection (high school and college students, nurses, medical students, and industrial groups). When persons with beginning infections are found, they should be isolated to prevent the transfer of parasites to others, and these precautions should be continued until body discharges remain free from the tubercle bacillus. The prevention of tuberculosis is largely a matter of improving the general health of the population. The disease is always more prevalent among the undernourished and ill-housed groups.

A variety of stresses such as psychological insecurity, malnutrition, low income, crowding, and poor housing are some of the social factors which predispose to tuberculosis. Any effective control measures, therefore, must be directed toward the social factors which influence the disease as well as toward the organism itself. Although deaths from tuberculosis are on the decline, the disease is still a health problem. As of June, 1952, the National Tuberculosis Association estimated that there were 250,000 known active cases, 150,000 unknown active cases, and that 115,000 new cases of tuberculosis could be expected annually.

MYCOBACTERIUM LEPRAE

Mycobacterium leprae (*Bacillus leprae*), the organism that causes leprosy, is a slender, acid-fast organism similar to the organism that causes tuberculosis. It has not been cultivated on artificial media or in laboratory animals, and for that reason little is known about this organism. Its staining reaction suggests that it may be similar in behavior to the tubercle bacillus.

Leprosy   Leprosy is undoubtedly a very old disease. While exact information is lacking, the disease seems to be less common and also less virulent than it was a few centuries ago. Today it is found chiefly in tropical or subtropical areas of Asia and Africa and is endemic in Louisiana, Texas, Florida, and California, and also in Hawaii, the Philippines, and Puerto

SUMMARY

ORGANISM	DISEASE	DIAGNOSTIC PROCEDURES	SITE OF INFECTION	ACTIVE IMMUNIZATION	PASSIVE IMMUNIZATION	CHEMOTHERAPY
Corynebacterium diphtheriae	Diphtheria	Nose and throat cultures Virulence tests	Mucous membranes or wounds	Toxoid	Antitoxin	Penicillin with antitoxin
Mycobacterium tuberculosis	Tuberculosis	Acid-fast stain of discharge Cultures Inoculation of guinea pig or rabbit Tuberculin test	Lungs, bones, glands, skin	BCG vaccine (experimental)	None	Streptomycin Para-amino-salicylic acid Isonicotinic acid
Mycobacterium leprae	Leprosy	Acid-fast stain of discharges	Skin, mucous membranes, nervous system	None	None	Chaulmoogra oil Sulfones Streptomycin

Rico. The disease has been introduced into several midwestern states by immigrants, but does not appear to spread to the native population. It has been estimated that there are approximately 750 lepers in the United States.

Little is known concerning the method of transmission or about the incubation period of the *Mycobacterium leprae*. The organisms are present in discharges from lesions on the skin and mucous membranes. They are sometimes found on areas revealing little or no evidence of infection as well as in ulcerated areas. Long and intimate contact is usually required to transmit the infection from one person to another. After an incubation period of one or several years, the organisms may invade the skin and mucous membranes or the nerves or both. It is thought that the destructive action of the organism on human tissues is due to injurious proteins, fats, and waxes, which make up the cells, rather than to toxins. This slow, chronic disease is amenable to treatment by chaulmoogra oil and is seldom fatal although it may make the victim more susceptible to tuberculosis and other infections. Recent reports indicate that certain sulfones (Promin, Diasone, and Promizole) are of value in the treatment of leprosy. Since these drugs act slowly, it is hoped that they may be replaced by other drugs which act more quickly.

PREVENTION AND CONTROL   Until more is known about the disease, control measures will probably be limited to the following:

1. The recognition and investigation of the source of infection.
2. The isolation of the person in a leprosarium or at home. The United States Marine Hospital in Carville, Louisiana, is the only leprosarium in the United States.
3. The disinfection of discharges by methods which would be suitable for the tuberculosis organism.
4. The separation of infants from leprous parents at birth.

REFERENCES

1. Report of the Committee on Immunizations and Therapeutic Procedures for Acute Infectious Diseases of the American Academy of Pediatrics. Evanston, Ill., Academy of Pediatrics, 1951, p. 8.

2. Frobisher, M., and Sommermeyer, L.: A Study of the Effect of Alcohols on Tubercle Bacilli and Other Bacteria in Sputum. Am. Rev. Tuberc., *68:* 419–424, 1953.
3. Smillie, W. G.: Preventive Medicine and Public Health. New York, The Macmillan Co., 1946, p. 270.

SUPPLEMENTARY READINGS

BOOKS:

American Public Health Association: The Control of Communicable Disease. An Official Report of the American Public Health Association. 7th ed. New York, 1950.

Burnet, M.: Natural History of Infectious Disease. 2d ed. Cambridge, Mass., Harvard University Press, 1953.

Burrows, W.: Jordan-Burrows Textbook of Bacteriology. 15th ed. Philadelphia, W. B. Saunders Co., 1949.

Dubos, R. J.: Bacterial and Mycotic Infections in Man. 2d ed. Philadelphia, J. B. Lippincott Co., 1952.

Dubos, R., and Dubos, J.: The White Plague—Tuberculosis, Man and Society. Boston, Little, Brown and Co., 1952.

Frobisher, M.: Fundamentals of Microbiology. 5th ed. Philadelphia, W. B. Saunders Co., 1953.

Maxcy, K. F.: Rosenau Preventive Medicine and Hygiene. New York, Appleton-Century-Crofts, Inc., 1951.

Meyers, J. A.: Tuberculosis among Children and Adults. Springfield, Ill., Charles C Thomas, 1951.

Rich, A. R.: The Pathogenesis of Tuberculosis. Springfield, Ill., Charles C Thomas, 1944.

Smillie, W. G.: Public Health Administration in the United States. 3d ed. New York, The Macmillan Co., 1947.

Smith, D. T., and Conant, N. F.: Zinsser's Textbook of Bacteriology. 10th ed. New York, Appleton-Century-Crofts, Inc., 1952.

PERIODICALS:

Aronson, J. D., and Aronson, C. F.: Appraisal of Protective Value of BCG Vaccine. J.A.M.A., *149:* 334–343, 1952.

Bartz, Q. R.: Viomycin, a New Tuberculostatic Antibiotic. Am. Rev. Tuberc., *63:* 4–6, 1951.

Corper, H. J.: Analysis of the Value of Chemotherapeutic Agents in the Treatment of Tuberculosis. J.A.M.A., *151:* 1475–1478, 1953.

De Lien, H., and Dahlstrom, A. W.: An Ethnic Reservoir of Tuberculosis. Am. J. Pub. Health, *41:* 528–532, 1951.

Doane, E. A., and Boger, E.: Streptomycin Dependent Tubercle Bacilli. Am. Rev. Tuberc., *64:* 191–195, 1951.

Dubos, R. J.: Biologic and Epidemiologic Aspects of Tuberculosis. Am. Rev. Tuberc., *68:* 1–8, 1953.

Ebert, R. H.: In Vivo Observations of Effect of Cortisone on Experimental Tuberculosis Using the Rabbit Ear Chamber Technique. Am. Rev. Tuberc., *65:* 64–74, 1952.

Editorial: Serum Test for Active Tuberculosis. J.A.M.A., *143:* 1489, 1950.

Editorial: Infectiousness in Tuberculosis. J.A.M.A., *145:* 1070, 1951.

Editorial: Irradiated Tuberculosis Vaccine. J.A.M.A., *146:* 931, 1951.
Editorial: Yolk Sac Technic in Diagnosis of Tuberculosis. J.A.M.A., *150:* 1604, 1952.
Editorial: Slide Cultivation of Tubercle Bacilli. J.A.M.A., *151:* 1199, 1953.
Editorial: Incidence of Tuberculosis among American Medical Students. J.A.M.A., *152:* 922–923, 1953.
Editorial: Allergy to Diphtheria Toxoid. Ann. Allergy, *10:* 65–66, 1952.
Frobisher, M., Jr., and Parsons, E. I.: Studies on Type Specific Immunization with Somatic Antigen of *C. Diphtheriae.* Am. J. Hyg., *52:* 239–246, 1950.
Horton, R.: Epidemic of Tuberculosis in a High School. J.A.M.A., *149:* 331–343, 1952.
Lees, H. D.: Tuberculosis in Medical Students and Nurses. J.A.M.A., *147:* 1754–1757, 1951.
Levine, M. I.: Deficiencies in Our Knowledge of BCG Vaccine. Pediatrics, *7:* 862–863, 1951.
Lurie, M. B., and others: On the Response of Genetically Resistant and Susceptible Rabbits to Quantitative Inhalation of Human Type Tubercle Bacilli. J. Exper. Med., *95:* 119–134, 1952.
Maillard, E. R.: Further Studies of a New Serologic Test in Tuberculosis. Am. J. Pub. Health, *42:* 175–181, 1952.
Merkel, E. A.: An Outbreak of Diphtheria in Medford, Oregon, 1949. Am. J. Pub. Health, *41:* 522–527, 1951.
Meyers, J. A.: Prevention of Tuberculosis among Children without Use of BCG. Pediatrics, *7:* 793–805, 1951.
Pappenheimer, A. M., Jr.: The Diphtheria Toxin. Scient. Am., *187:* 32–36, 1952.
Pappenheimer, A. M., Jr., and Williams, C. M.: The Effects of Diphtheria Toxin on the Cecropia Silkworm. J. Physiol., *35:* 727–740, 1952.
Pitts, F. W., and others: Isoniazid and Streptomycin in the Treatment of Pulmonary Tuberculosis. J.A.M.A., *152:* 886–890, 1953.
Riggins, H. M.: Tuberculosis Control in Hospital Personnel. Am. Rev. Tuberc., *67:* 74–84, 1953.
Sandage, C., and others: Erythrocyte Destruction in Tuberculous Animals Following Tuberculin Injection. J. Infect. Dis., *88:* 9–16, 1951.
Scott, N. B., and Smith, D. T.: A Simple Modification of the Middlebrook and Dubos Hemagglutination Test for Serum Antibodies to Products of Tubercle Bacilli. J. Lab. & Clin. Med., *35:* 503–507, 1950.
Van Deinse, F.: Vaccination against Tuberculosis with Freeze-Dried BCG Vaccine. Am. J. Pub. Health, *41:* 1209–1214, 1951.
World Health Organization: World Incidence of Diphtheria during Recent Years. Chronicle of World Health Organization, *6:* 303–306, 1952.
World Health Organization: Prevalence of Leprosy in the World. Chronicle of World Health Organization, *6:* 308–311, 1952.

CHAPTER 27

Viruses Transmitted by
                       Respiratory Secretions

VIRUSES: *Chickenpox; Common Cold;
Influenza; Measles; Mumps; Rubella;
Smallpox*

THERE are a number of infections which are not associated
with the visible parasites, but are caused by ultramicroscopic
forms, called filtrable viruses, many of which enter and leave
the body in respiratory secretions and are then inhaled or
ingested by a second person. Some of these viruses may also
leave the body by way of skin lesions. Viruses show a definite
preference for certain tissues. Viruses are so small that they are
visible only when observed with the aid of the electron microscope. They can be recognized by what they do and may be
studied by growing them in suitable laboratory animals or in
developing chick embryos. Animal-protection tests and serological tests (precipitation, complement-fixation) may also be
used. Since these procedures are too time-consuming and
expensive for routine work, virus infections are usually recognized on the basis of clinical symptoms without laboratory
aids. In this chapter, the description of the structure of ultramicroscopic parasites will be omitted. Since viruses are known
by what they do, they will be discussed in terms of the infections which they produce. These diseases differ from one another in the site of infection, and in regard to the degree of
immunity and the persistence of the virus.

CLASSIFICATION OF VIRUS DISEASES

The virus diseases of man fall into three groups:* (1) those
in which infection persists with little immunity (Group I);
(2) those in which neither immunity nor infection persists

* Francis[1] includes a fourth group in which both infection and immunity persist, a condition which occurs in certain animal diseases such
as mouse cancer.

(Group II); and (3) those in which immunity persists but the infection does not (Group III).

Group I   This group of diseases includes lymphogranuloma (page 463), psittacosis, and ornithosis (page 489). The acute phase of infection is usually followed by a long latent period during which the person may infect others or may suffer periodic relapses. Some of the viruses of this group are susceptible to the action of sulfonamides, penicillin and other antibiotics.

Group II   This group includes the common cold, influenza, rabies (page 487), poliomyelitis (page 364), and herpes simplex.* These diseases, with the exception of rabies, are characterized by a short incubation period and by the invasion of tissues which are not readily reached by circulating antibodies. Immunity to these diseases tends to be transient.

Group III   This group includes certain mosquito-borne infections, such as dengue (509) and yellow fever (page 507), mumps, and the pox diseases. It has been suggested that second infections of yellow fever and dengue do not occur because the viruses are inactivated by the antibody globulin before they can reach and invade the susceptible cells. In contrast, the viruses causing the pox diseases invade superficial cells before they reach the blood stream. These viruses are transmitted by persons with clinical infections, not by carriers. Relapses do not occur and second attacks are very rare. It is possible that the viruses may invade the mucous membranes a second time, causing only a local infection since the presence of circulating antibodies would prevent further invasion. Such local infections, if they do occur, would undoubtedly stimulate antibody formation.

MUMPS—INFECTIOUS PAROTITIS

The virus which causes mumps is present in the mouth and, possibly, the nasal secretions and is transmissible before as well as after the development of the disease. This virus is especially adapted to living in gland tissue. It multiplies within cells causing damage with resulting leakage of blood proteins

---

* Some authorities would place the herpes virus in Group I, and poliomyelitis may be intermediate to Groups II and III.

into the intracellular spaces. After an incubation period of twelve to twenty-six days, the parotid glands (sometimes the submaxillary and sublingual also) become swollen and tender. Subclinical infections associated with little or no swelling are thought to be common. In adults, the virus may invade the gonads, causing cell destruction and sterility. Less frequently the virus may invade the brain causing an encephalitis with or without producing noticeable swelling of the salivary glands. Various other organs—ovary, pancreas, kidney, mammary glands—may at times be invaded.

All persons who have not had the disease are susceptible to it. One attack, involving one or both glands, usually confers a lasting immunity. As a rule, mumps is a disease of school children, and also occurs among those recruits in the army who have come from rural areas. It is probably desirable to acquire this disease between the ages of five and ten years because one then develops an immunity without the risks that attend the infection in infancy and after puberty.

A vaccine composed of attenuated mumps virus is being used experimentally. Persons who have been vaccinated or have had the infection usually develop complement-fixing antibodies and a sensitivity to mumps antigen as indicated by a positive skin reaction. Irradiated convalescent serum or serum from vaccinated donors is sometimes used in the treatment of mumps. It appears to have some value in preventing the virus from infecting the testes—a frequent complication in males after the age of puberty.

THE COMMON COLD

Everyone is familiar with the characteristics of the common cold. The symptoms are due largely to changes in the blood supply to the nose associated with changes in the character and amount of mucus secreted. These changes occur in response to many stress agents. Sinus infection, hay fever, fear, frustration, exhaustion, or hormone imbalance may produce any or all the signs and symptoms of a cold. It is well to remember that a number of the communicable diseases of childhood begin with the symptoms of a cold. While many "colds" (some estimate 75 per cent) are incited by nonliving stress agents, others are caused by the invasion of microorganisms—usually viruses.

The virus or viruses that cause the common cold are widely distributed and easily transmitted. Apparently they may be transferred before as well as for two or three days after the symptoms occur. Following a short incubation period (two to three days), the symptoms appear. A cold is an acute self-limited infection of the upper respiratory tract, accompanied by nasal congestion, a profuse watery nasal discharge associated with headache, malaise, weakness, exhaustion, and sometimes fever. The virus tends to lower the resistance of the affected tissue to secondary infection due to bacterial parasites. These secondary invaders increase the inflammation of the respiratory tract and give rise to a thick, purulent discharge in the later stages of the illness. Colds are frequently followed by complications such as bronchitis, sinusitis, and infections of the middle ear. The self-limiting character of the disease is evidence of the development of immunity. However, this immunity lasts for a short time—usually from six weeks to three or four months.

The factors which determine susceptibility are not completely understood. Some people are highly susceptible while others are somewhat more resistant. However, it is the unusual person who is free from a cold for even a year. Some interesting observations have been made on the transfer of the infection among isolated populations. The people of certain areas of Alaska and Spitzbergen are free from colds for several months during the winter when there is no communication with the outside world. The cold virus apparently arrives with the first steamer in the spring and is quickly acquired by and transferred from native to native. Since this process repeats itself every year, it would seem to indicate that the virus causing the cold comes from an outside source. The disease is endemic in cities and tends to become epidemic during the cold months. City populations are constantly exposed to the cold virus and other organisms that cause infections of the respiratory organs. That such infections are the chief cause of absence from work and school is a significant fact and one that is often overlooked.

Present knowledge is inadequate to prevent the disease or to control its spread. So-called remedies are numerous but generally unreliable. One method of bacteriological interest is the *cold vaccine* which consists of a suspension of killed bacteria: micrococcus, pneumococcus, streptococcus, Friedländer's bacillus, and influenza bacillus. It contains no virus. Some authorities consider it of some value in controlling the secondary infection which occurs in the later stages of a cold, but observations made on 272 vaccinated and 276 unvaccinated persons showed no significant difference in the number of colds developed by the members of the two groups. A new cold vaccine[2] consisting of virus grown in the chick embryo is being used experimentally on human volunteers. The preliminary reports seem promising but not conclusive. In view of the large number of nonspecific stress agents which may disturb the function of the nasal mucosa, one cannot be too optimistic about cold vaccines.

Isolation of the person who has a cold is desirable for the protection of both the victim and his associates. A person with a cold is also more susceptible to bacterial infections. By staying at home, he limits his contacts with other people from whom he might acquire virulent pneumococci and streptococci. Experiments on animals and human volunteers indicate that the virus is present in the respiratory secretions. Therefore, care should be taken to prevent these discharges from reaching others. Many persons are careless about this and too often neglect measures that have protective value such as covering the mouth and nose while sneezing and coughing, washing the hands after using a handkerchief, washing the hands before handling food or dishes, and using individual equipment.

INFLUENZA

Influenza is a disease which periodically becomes epidemic and at times even spreads rapidly over large areas of the world. Usually it takes a toll of lives among the very young and the very old. The epidemic of 1918, however, behaved like a new disease in that it attacked and killed an unusual number of young adults. The smaller outbreaks of the disease seen before and after 1918 caused relatively few deaths among young adults.

The Infection   During the last decade, the influenza viruses have been extensively studied. To date, three distinct types,* A, B, and C, have been found. Viruses A, B, and C will grow in chick embryos and will cause infection in ferrets and mice. The viruses may be cultured from nose and throat washings. Blood specimens taken during the acute and convalescent stages may be used for determining the type and amount of antibodies formed during the infection.

The viruses invade and destroy ciliated epithelium of the trachea, bronchi, and bronchioles. Inflammation promptly follows with the appearance of mucus, phagocytes, and blood proteins from the damaged tissues. The illness that appears after a short incubation period (twenty-four to seventy-two hours) is characterized by a sudden onset, fever, prostration, aches and pains, and the local symptoms of a cold. Bacterial pneumonia is a common complication and cause of death. The lack of clear-cut clinical features makes influenza very hard to recognize during periods when the disease is not prevalent. In general, the infections of the respiratory tract in which the systemic symptoms predominate are termed "influenza" while those that are more local are called "colds." In influenza, convalescence is slow and may be prolonged for weeks or months, whereas recovery from colds is usually more rapid.

Susceptibility   Susceptibility to influenza tends to decrease with age; the attack rate is highest in childhood although mortality is very low. In contrast, the incidence of infection in adults is relatively low but the mortality rates are higher than in children. During widespread epidemics, from 25 to 75 per cent of the population escape the infection. One attack of the disease confers an immunity of short duration against the invading virus. A vaccine composed of influenza virus A and B may confer an immunity which lasts for several months.

Control   Influenza is a highly communicable disease which occurs in epidemic form. These epidemics may be re-

* Each type may be subdivided into several subtypes—an obvious handicap to those who would prepare vaccines.

stricted to a small area or may spread across a continent. There is some evidence that virus A epidemics occur about every three years and the virus B epidemics occur about every four to six years. Both types appear to be spread by close direct contact. To date, none of the usual methods, e.g., the closing of schools and theaters or the wearing of masks by the general population, have prevented the spread of the disease. Nevertheless, the crowding of human beings together, always an undesirable practice, is especially to be avoided during epidemics. Although there is no sure way of avoiding the disease, the risk is minimized if the victim goes to bed as soon as the symptoms appear. The isolation of patients and the wearing of masks by attendants are indicated for the protection of the patient and his associates. Influenza vaccine, containing strains A and B, has proved effective in some epidemics and useless in others. For example, its ineffectiveness in the epidemic of 1947 was due to the fact that the virus strain present at that time was antigenically different from the viruses in the vaccine. The increased resistance conferred by influenza vaccine lasts about five months.

VIRUS PNEUMONIA

Primary atypical pneumonia is a disease of the lower respiratory tract which, in contrast to bacterial pneumonias, may be caused by any one of a large number of viruses or rickettsias as well as by certain fungi.* Viruses which may cause pneumonia include the psittacosis-granuloma viruses, influenza A and B viruses, the lymphocytic choriomeningitis virus, and, possibly, others. The rickettsia of Q fever (*Coxiella burnetii*) also causes a pneumonia.

Virus pneumonia has an incubation period of two to three weeks and is transmitted by secretions from the nose and throat. Mild cases occur and are likely to go without recognition. More severe cases are characterized by fever, malaise, fatigue, muscle pain, and cough. The respiratory symptoms may be absent even though x-ray gives evidence of extensive invasion of lung tissue. Control measures are similar to those

---

* Similar symptoms are caused by the fungi responsible for coccidioidomycosis, histoplasmosis, and blastomycosis (page 466).

used for the common cold. As would be expected, penicillin and sulfonamides are of no value in this type of infection. The acute phase of the disease appears to be shortened by treatment with aureomycin.

SMALLPOX—VARIOLA

The virus of smallpox is present in the blood and in the lesions of the skin and mucous membranes. It is resistant to drying and may be transmitted by air or by contact with contaminated clothing or fomites, as well as by contact with the infected person. When the virus reaches a susceptible person, it invades the epithelial cells of the respiratory tract and then extends through the blood to the entire body. It invades epithelial cells causing degeneration followed by swelling and edema of the tissues. The fluid separates the layers of the skin forming a blister-like lesion called a *vesicle*. Later the vesicle becomes filled with pus. On mucous membranes and in internal organs these lesions appear as open ulcers whereas the skin lesions tend to be covered by a membrane.

From eight to sixteen days after exposure, the person develops an illness which progresses through several different stages. These stages are:

GENERAL SYMPTOMS	RASH	DURATION
1. Fever	None	1–5 days
2.	Papules on face, extremities, external surfaces, rare in groin, armpits	1–4 days
3.	Vesicles	1–4 days
4.	Pustules	2–6 days

The pustular lesions, which are deep and inflamed, form crusts. From ten to forty days after the onset of the disease the crusts fall off leaving deep, pink scars. The virus is present and is transmissible until all scabs and crusts have disappeared. The disease varies in severity, the mortality rates ranging from 30 per cent to less than 1 per cent. In recent years, many of the cases of smallpox have been mild in character.

Control   All persons are susceptible unless they have had the disease or have been vaccinated successfully. One attack confers immunity which lasts for a few years, but not necessarily for life. Since inoculation with vaccine virus gives an immunity which lasts for one year or more (see Chapter 16), it is quite unnecessary for anyone to have this disfiguring disease.

Inasmuch as there are no carriers of the virus, the sick person is the source of the infection. He should be isolated in a room that is free from flies and vermin. Linens and equipment should be boiled and all discharges should be disinfected. When smallpox breaks out, all persons in the community who have not been vaccinated within a year and those who have been exposed to the disease should be promptly inoculated. Vaccination within four days of the exposure may protect because the incubation period for vaccinia is eight days while that of smallpox is usually about fourteen days. Persons who have been exposed are usually quarantined until the vaccination reaction is well developed or, when the vaccine is given late, for sixteen days after the last exposure. Vaccinations which do not "take" should be repeated because immunity is dependent upon the multiplication of the virus. The outbreak in Brighton, England, in 1951 serves as a grim reminder that smallpox can occur following direct and indirect contacts. There were twenty-nine cases with ten deaths. Six infections occurred among workers at the laundry where the original patient sent his clothes. Of the ten patients who died seven had never been vaccinated and three had been vaccinated in infancy only.

CHICKENPOX—VARICELLA

Chickenpox is a highly contagious disease of childhood. The virus that causes it, like that of smallpox, is transmitted by direct or indirect contact with the discharges from the respiratory tract or from the skin. After an incubation period of two or three weeks, it causes a mild disease characterized by fever and skin eruption. Large or small areas of the skin develop a raised (maculopapular) rash which quickly changes to vesicles or blisters. These lesions tend to occur on the exposed parts of the body and remain for three or four days. They heal promptly by forming a granular scab. The disease is mild and seldom causes death. It is usually limited to children, but in adults the infection is likely to be more severe and may be confused with smallpox.

All persons are susceptible until they have developed an immunity by having the disease. About 90 per cent of the population acquire the disease before they are fifteen years old. Because this infection is extremely contagious, persons who have the disease should be excluded from school and kept from contact with susceptible individuals. Quarantine is not necessary when infected persons remain at home.

MEASLES—RUBEOLA

The measles virus invades the endothelial cells of the capillaries of the skin and mucous membranes. Fluid leaks from the damaged capillaries and in turn injures the epithelial cells of the skin and mucous membranes. Brain tissue too may at times be damaged. After an incubation period of ten days, the patient develops a fever, other signs of a cold, together with bluish white spots in the mouth; the latter are called "Koplik's spots." Four days later, a blotchy skin rash appears which fades after two or three days. The injured cells are then shed as branlike scales. The virus is readily transmitted during the time when the abnormal respiratory secretions are present, that is, for four days before the rash appears and until the rash fades.

The infection itself is mild, but, like most virus diseases, it lowers the resistance of the person to a variety of bacterial infections such as sinusitis, pneumonia, and otitis media. The mortality is high in infants under two years of age. Because of the danger of secondary infections, it is advisable to isolate patients with measles from one another.

Susceptibility and Immunity   Susceptibility is general after the first six months of life, and one attack usually confers a lasting immunity. A passive immunity of short duration can be induced by giving convalescent serum or gamma globulin. The antiserum prevents the disease when it is given within the first four or five days after exposure. Given later, it modifies the disease by decreasing the severity of symptoms and often by increasing the incubation period to seventeen to nineteen days. Passive immunization is desirable for sick children and for infants, but it is not necessary for older children. As a rule, gamma globulin is given five days after exposure so that a milder infection occurs and at the same time confers an active immunity to the disease.

Measles virus grown in chick embryos has been used to cause experimental infections.

Control   Community efforts to prevent the spread of measles have met with very little success. About 90 per cent of the adults have had the disease before they reached the age of twenty. Since the infection carries little risk for older children, there is a growing tendency to focus the attention on the protection of infants and young children. Isolation of the sick child is desirable for his own protection as well as for that of others.

The Disease Pattern   Measles is a typical example of an endemic disease which confers a lasting immunity. The virus attacks children; 75 per cent of the persons who acquire measles are under ten years of age. This is to be expected, since adults and older children have already had the disease and are, therefore, immune. Periodic outbreaks of epidemic proportions occur when the population contains a large number of susceptible persons. In large cities, every second or third year is usually a "measles" year; in smaller communities, where the virus is not always present, the period between epidemics may be longer. In isolated communities, where the virus has been absent for generations, the whole population is susceptible. When the virus is introduced into such a community it causes severe and often fatal infections among adults as well as children.

RUBELLA

Rubella, or German measles, is a mild disease of childhood caused by the virus of rubella. After an incubation period of fourteen to twenty-three days the infected person develops a rash which may resemble that of measles or of scarlet fever. Lymph nodes in the back of the neck (postauricular and suboccipital) are characteristically enlarged. There may be a slight fever at the time the rash appears. The disease is characteristically mild and lasts for one to three days. The virus is present in nasal secretions for about four days after the

SUMMARY

DISEASE	SITE OF INFECTION	IMMUNITY AFTER INFECTION	ACTIVE IMMUNIZATION	PASSIVE IMMUNIZATION	CHEMO-THERAPY
Chickenpox	Skin and mucous membranes	Lasting	None	None	None
Common cold	Respiratory tract	Transient	Virus vaccine (experimental)	None	None
Influenza	Respiratory tract	Transient	Virus vaccine (A and B)	None	None
Measles	Skin and respiratory tract	Lasting	None	Gamma globulin	None
Mumps	Parotid and other glands	Lasting	None	Gamma globulin	None
Rubella	Skin and mucous membranes	Lasting	None	Gamma globulin	None
Smallpox	Skin and mucous membranes	Lasting	Vaccine virus	None	None

onset of symptoms. All persons are susceptible unless they have had an attack of the disease. One attack usually confers immunity. The disease is of importance only because it is recognized that infection occurring during the first four months of pregnancy results in virus invasion of the embryo. A high percentage of the infants born of mothers who have had rubella during the first three months of pregnancy show congenital defects of the brain, heart, eyes, or ears. It is therefore desirable that girls be infected with rubella before puberty. Pregnant women should if possible avoid exposure to rubella unless they have previously had the infection. Gamma globulin may be given to protect a pregnant woman who has been exposed to the disease.

REFERENCES

1. Francis, T.: Mechanisms of Infection and Immunity in Virus Diseases of Man. Bact. Rev., *11:* 147–156, 1947.
2. Pollard, M., and Caplovitz, C. D.: Immunological Studies with the Common Cold Infection. Am. J. Hyg., *47:* 106–112, 1948.

SUPPLEMENTARY READINGS

BOOKS:

Burnet, F. M.: Virus as Organism. Cambridge, Mass., Harvard University Press, 1945.

Magill, T. P.: Reactions of the Cells of the Respiratory Tract to Virus Infections. In: Kidd, J. G.: The Pathogenesis and Pathology of Viral Diseases. New York, Columbia University Press, 1950.

Maxcy, K. F.: Rosenau Preventive Medicine and Hygiene. 7th ed. New York, Appleton-Century-Crofts, Inc., 1951.

Rivers, T. M.: Viral and Rickettsial Infections in Man. 2d ed. Philadelphia, J. B. Lippincott Co., 1952.

Smillie, W. G.: Preventive Medicine and Public Health. New York, The Macmillan Co., 1950.

PERIODICALS:

Benenson, A. S., and others: Problems in Maintaining Immunity to Smallpox. Am. J. Pub. Health, *42:* 535–541, 1952.

Editorial: Patent Ductus Arteriosus and Maternal Rubella. J.A.M.A., *150:* 419, 1952.

Editorial: Smallpox Vaccination and Pregnancy. J. Pediat. *43:* 229–231, 1953.

Foreign Letters: Smallpox in Brighton. J.A.M.A., *145:* 1002, 1951.

Henle, G., and others: Studies in the Prevention of Mumps. J. Immunol., *66:* 535–578, 1951.

James, D. G.: Primary Atypical Pneumonia. J.A.M.A., *151:* 810–813, 1953.

Osmun, P.: Are You Sure You Have a Cold? Am. J. Nursing, *52:* 168–169, 1952.

Salk, J. E., and others: Direction of Research on Vaccination against Influenza—New Studies with Immunologic Adjuvants. Am. J. Pub. Health, *41:* 669–677, 1951.

Wheeler, R. E., and Benenson, A. S.: Criteria of Immunity to Mumps in Young Adults. Am. J. Pub. Health, *41:* 1238–1239, 1951.

Winslow, T. G., and others: Studies on the Prevention of Mumps. V. The Development of a Neutralization Test and Its Application to Convalescent Sera. J. Immunol., *71:* 66–75, 1953.

Yeager, C. F.: The Value of Influenza Virus Vaccination in Industry. Am. J. Pub. Health, *42:* 723–725, 1952.

CHAPTER 28

Bacteria Transmitted by Contact with Wounds

NONSPORE-FORMING: *Micrococcus; Streptococcus; Colon-Aerogenes-Proteus Group; Pseudomonas aeruginosa; Chromobacteria*

SPORE-FORMING: *Clostridium tetani; Clostridium perfringens*

WOUNDS in the skin or mucous membranes invite the entrance of bacteria—either parasites from the body surfaces or saprophytes coming directly or indirectly from the soil. The former are usually more dangerous because they are adjusted to living in body fluids. The common sources of infections are the skin, the secretions from the nose and throat, the hands of attendants or the patient himself, air, dressings and instruments, and the soil. As a rule cuts and scratches are not heavily contaminated at the time of injury. However, since they are susceptible to infection until they are completely healed, it is important to protect them from bacteria. The first principle in caring for such wounds is to protect them from immediate and subsequent contamination* from outside sources. A second principle is to

---

* The following recommendations for the care of wounded patients in a hospital were made by a committee of experts[1] after an extensive study of the problem of preventing wound infections:

1. Dressings should be done *not less* than one hour after bed linen has been changed and floor swept.

2. All dirty linen should be bagged as it is removed from the bed. Under no circumstances should it be put on the floor.

3. Windows should be closed and ward traffic reduced to a minimum while wounds are dressed.

4. Surgeons and all assistants should be adequately gowned and masked during the dressing period.

5. Soiled dressings should be placed in covered containers immediately after removal.

6. All containers, utensils, instruments, and apparatus should be sterilized immediately after use.

foster those conditions that favor the natural antibacterial action of the cells; it is therefore important to avoid irritant drugs, mechanical injuries, tight bandages, and other factors that injure cells. With care, these relatively clean wounds often heal with little or no evidence of infection.

In contrast, war wounds and others characterized by crushing injury provide favorable conditions for the growth of both parasitic and saprophytic bacteria. Wounds of this type are often infected by as many as five or ten different kinds of organisms. The presence of dead tissues, blood clots, and foreign bodies encourage the growth of microorganisms. Hence, an important part of the treatment of such wounds is the surgical removal of such debris and the applications of sterile dressings to provide protection and gentle pressure to the wound.

The bacteria which can be recovered from wounds fall into three groups:

(1) *Systemic pathogens*—organisms which produce toxins or are capable of invading, or are both toxin-forming and invasive, such as *Micrococcus pyogenes* (Group A), *Streptococcus pyogenes* (Group A), *Clostridium tetani* (toxin only), and *Clostridium perfringens*.

(2) *Wound pathogens*—organisms which retard repair by secreting enzymes capable of digesting tissue proteins. Examples are various clostridia, *Proteus vulgaris*, *Pseudomonas aeruginosa*, various micrococci, and various streptococci.

(3) *Nonpathogens* (sometimes called *commensals*)—organisms which grow in wound fluids without producing apparent injury. Examples are aerobacter, escherichia, various micrococci, and various streptococci.

It will be noted that some wound pathogens form spores and

---

7. All crusts, pus, pieces of tissue, or foreign bodies removed from wounds should be placed in a covered container and disposed of in a manner which will kill the microorganisms present.

8. Plaster casts, if contaminated, should be changed because the surface of the cast cannot be sterilized.

9. Physicians, nurses, and others suffering from infections of the respiratory tract or of the hands should be relieved of their duties until they have completely recovered.

others do not. The more important members of both groups will be discussed here.

NONSPORE-FORMING BACTERIA

Micrococcus   The genus *Micrococcus* includes a large and varied group of bacteria. They are alike in that they are gram-positive cocci which appear singly or in grapelike clusters. They are all hardy organisms that will grow on almost any laboratory medium at a temperature range of from 15° to 40° C. (59° to 104° F.). Pigment formation on solid medium divides them roughly into three classes: *Micrococcus citreus*—lemon yellow; *Micrococcus pyogenes* var. *aureus*—golden yellow; and *Micrococcus pyogenes* var. *albus*—no pigment. The pigment-forming *Micrococcus pyogenes* (commonly known as *Staphylococcus aureus*) is usually more virulent and is often found in the pus from boils, carbuncles, and wounds. The albus strains sometimes cause minor infections, such as stitch abscesses. Pigment formation is a variable characteristic, since an organism may lose its ability to form pigment after it has been grown on artificial medium. These organisms are among the more resistant of the nonspore-formers. Many strains can resist a temperature of 60° C. (140° F.) for one-half hour and can survive drying for long periods. Various micrococci are present on the skin and on the membranes of the nose and mouth at all times. Most of these organisms have little ability to produce disease, but other strains form potent exotoxins and possess considerable ability to invade the tissues. On the basis of antigen-antibody tests, *Micrococcus pyogenes* var. *aureus* may be divided into two groups: A—virulent pathogens, and B—nonvirulent organisms. The toxic materials present in cultures of virulent micrococci may produce one or more of the following injurious effects when observed in the laboratory:

ACTION OF FILTRATE	COMMON NAME
Destruction of red blood cells	Hemolysin
Destruction of white blood cells	Leukocidin
Destruction of skin cells	Necrotizing toxin; skin-reddening (erythrogenic) toxin
Coagulation of citrated plasma	Coagulase
Solution of fibrin	Fibrinolysin

ACTION OF FILTRATE   COMMON NAME

Stimulate vomiting center in brain ....Enterotoxin (food-poison-
                                                           ing toxin)
Increase in tissue permeability ....Spreading factor

INFECTION   Micrococci cause many infections in human
beings, either by initiating the process or by acting as secondary invaders. Wounds are frequently invaded by them.
There is some evidence that these organisms can also penetrate
skin which is apparently intact. Boils and carbuncles have
been produced by rubbing cultures of virulent staphylococci
on apparently normal skin. These local infections are characterized by inflammation and pus formation. When the organisms escape to the lymph or blood stream they may set up
secondary infections in other parts of the body. *Micrococcus
pyogenes* may be associated with a variety of infections in
various areas of the body:

1. Skin ....Wounds, acne, boils, carbuncles
2. Blood stream ....Septicemia, with or without rash
                              (scarlet fever)
3. Bone ....Osteomyelitis, mastoiditis
4. Mucous membranes ....Otitis media, conjunctivitis, tonsillitis,
                              sinusitis
5. Heart valves ....Endocarditis
6. Lungs ....Pneumonia
7. Central nervous system ......Meningitis
8. Intestines ....Dysentery (usually following pro-
                              longed antibiotic therapy)

Certain persons appear to be very susceptible to micrococcus
infections since they develop one boil after another. It has been
suggested that the pathogenic micrococcus may establish itself
as a part of the flora of the skin as healing takes place. Then
when local resistance is lowered by trauma or irritation, the
organisms may again invade and cause infection. Originally
most strains of *Micrococcus pyogenes* were susceptible to antibiotics. Today more and more strains are resistant to one or
more antibiotics. As a result they may appear as important
secondary invaders following the inhibition of other pathogens
by antibiotics. For example, there have been cases of micrococcal scarlet fever in patients undergoing antibiotic therapy
for burns. Likewise there have been cases of micrococcal
dysentery following the treatment of salmonella infections with
aureomycin and Terramycin.

It is important that the person with an infected wound, pimple, or boil be instructed concerning its care. The infected area is surrounded by a wall of phagocytes and fibrin. Rough handling, squeezing, pinching, or improper incision may easily break the wall and introduce the invaders to surrounding tissues and to the lymph and blood vessels. Boils should never be squeezed. Infections of the nose or upper lip should receive especially gentle handling, as they often give rise to a generalized infection.

Streptococcus   The appearance and behavior of the large and varied group called streptococci have been discussed in Chapter 25. These parasites resemble the micrococci in that they are potent toxin-formers and may cause a variety of local and general infections. Streptococci of the viridans type often cause focal infections of the teeth, tonsils, and sinuses, from which the organisms may spread to the blood stream and to distant organs such as the heart valves and joints. Hemolytic streptococci (Group A) may cause or complicate a variety of disease processes including upper respiratory infections, bronchopneumonia, enteritis, erysipelas, puerperal sepsis, wounds, and burns, as well as scarlet fever and septic sore throat.

Streptococci are often responsible for serious infections in wounds and burns. Therefore, great care should be taken to prevent the transfer of microorganisms from the wounds or respiratory secretions of one person to open wounds on his own body or on that of another. Most strains of streptococci are susceptible to sulfonamides, penicillin, and other antibiotics.

The Enteric (Intestinal) Organisms—The Colon-Aerogenes-Proteus Group   Many enteric bacteria seem to live with almost equal success as parasites or as saprophytes and are found in the intestines of man or animal, in sewage, and in decomposing materials. They resemble one another in many respects. They are small, gram-negative, motile rods that grow readily at room temperature or body temperature on any common medium. *Proteus vulgaris* may prolong or delay wound healing by its ability to destroy body proteins. *Escherichia coli* and *Aerobacter aerogenes* are commonly present in mixed wound infections.

These organisms, though similar, can be differentiated on the basis of enzyme action. For example, *Proteus vulgaris* differs from the other two organisms in that it liquefies gelatin and fails to ferment lactose.

Usually, the colon bacillus and others of this group live in the body as harmless intestinal parasites. It is thought that they sometimes enter the portal circulation; if they do, it is unlikely that they escape the phagocytes of the liver. They are important, probably as secondary invaders, in abdominal or perineal wounds. The colon bacteria frequently invade the urinary tract where they produce infections that are often chronic and persistent. Apparently the parasites are so well adapted to living in the body that they fail to stimulate the host defenses. Members of this group of organisms are very resistant to antibiotics and may persist after more susceptible organisms have been suppressed.

Pseudomonas aeruginosa — Bacillus pyocyaneus
Pseudomonas aeruginosa resembles the enteric organisms in that it is a small gram-negative rod that grows readily on common laboratory media and is easily killed by heat and chemicals. However, it is easily distinguished from them by the fact that it produces a blue-green pigment as it grows in medium or in the pus of infected wounds. It is often present in the air or on the skin. It is a normal inhabitant of the human intestine. Here it is usually present in small numbers but often increases markedly when coliform organisms are suppressed by antibiotics. As a wound pathogen, it is relatively nonvirulent and is commonly found as a secondary invader in wounds, burns, and infections of the urinary tract especially when antibiotics have suppressed the normal flora and primary invaders. It is a common cause of chronic infections of the middle ear in malnourished children. Like other gram-negative rods, *Pseudomonas aeruginosa* is resistant to the action of most antibiotics. Many strains are reported to be sensitive to polymyxin B.

Chromobacteria   The chromobacteria are a group of gram-negative, aerobic, nonspore-forming bacteria which form pigment when grown in suitable media. Ordinarily they are saprophytes found in soil, air, and water. Recently three strains of chromobacteria (*Chromobacterium violaceum, Chromobacterium prodigiosum* [*Serratia marcescens*], and *Chromobac-*

terium aquatilis) have been recovered from the urine or blood of patients who have experienced catheterization, cystoscopy or genitourinary surgery. The chromobacteria are highly resistant to antibiotics.

ANAEROBIC SPORE-FORMING BACTERIA

The clostridia are large spore-forming anaerobic rods which are native to the soil. They are frequently ingested by man and animals. While they are essentially saprophytes, some of them may live as parasites in the digestive tract. *Clostridium perfringens* is usually present and *Clostridium tetani* is less frequently present in the feces of human beings, as well as in feces of domestic animals. Clostridia may also be found in dust, soil, milk, and sewage. Like other true saprophytes, they are chemically active and also may produce potent toxins. Since they are obligate anaerobes, they will grow only in media containing no free oxygen. Wounds containing dead tissue and blood clots are essentially anaerobic, and therefore provide ideal conditions for the growth of organisms which require little or no oxygen. The vegetative cells are not unusually hardy but in spore form they are very resistant. Tetanus spores will resist 80° C. (176° F.) for six hours and live steam for eight minutes, and may survive in 5 per cent carbolic for twelve to fifteen hours.

These organisms can be ingested without danger of disease, but when introduced into deep or mangled wounds, they may grow and produce their toxins. It is thought that the decomposing tissue and invading aerobes, such as the micrococcus, provide the required anaerobic conditions. In wounds, they live as saprophytes on dead tissue and excrete the toxins which produce the disease.

Clostridium tetani   *Clostridium tetani* is a large gram-positive rod which forms terminal spores. It can be cultured by excising a piece of tissue from the infected wound and transferring it to a suitable anaerobic medium. In media, it produces two toxins: the first, a nerve toxin (*tetanospasmin*), and the second, a substance which dissolves red blood cells (*tetanolysin*). The former is responsible for the characteristic symptoms of the disease. From eight to twenty-four hours after the injection of a small dose of the toxin, a laboratory animal will develop muscular contractions and die.

Tetanus, or lockjaw, is an old disease, often associated with soldiers and babies. Hippocrates (b. 460 B.C.) described a typical case of tetanus in a wounded Greek soldier. In the tropics, where sanitary measures and the practice of obstetrics are primitive, tetanus infection of the umbilicus is a leading cause of death in the newborn. The disease is likely to follow injuries sustained in war or in street and highway accidents, and is especially prone to occur in persons with deep or puncture wounds. The disease has, however, occurred after slight injuries such as pinpricks, frostbites, burns, insect bites, and smallpox vaccination. These injuries have one thing in common—that is, each may introduce tetanus spores into the tissues. Lay people often associate tetanus or lockjaw with a rusty nail. Obviously, neither the rust nor the nail is of itself important; the essential factor is that tetanus spores are introduced.

The invasion of the wound by aerobes, such as the micrococci, set up anaerobic conditions while the dead cells serve as food for the *Clostridium tetani.* The spores may lie dormant in the wound for a long period or they may promptly begin to grow. They do not invade but continue to grow in the wound and excrete the toxins. After an incubation period of from two to fifty days, the absorbed toxin unites with motor nerve endings and anterior horn cells of the spinal cord and produces symptoms.* The disease is characterized by painful contractions of the face and neck and also of the trunk and limbs. In rare instances, the contractions may be limited to the area around the wound. Tetanus following a short incubation period has a high fatality rate—70 to 80 per cent.

The treatment of tetanus which is often very unsatisfactory usually includes the removal of infected tissue from the wound, sedation, and the administration of penicillin and tetanus antitoxin intravenously and intramuscularly around the wound. A

---

* There is no general agreement regarding the route by which toxin reaches the central nervous system. Some assert that the toxin passes by way of nerve pathways while others are sure that it is transported by the blood.

high degree of protection can be conferred by administering tetanus antitoxin at the time when the injury is treated. It is of little use after the toxin has been formed. Soldiers in the United States Army are actively immunized with tetanus toxoid. At the time of injury, a stimulating dose of toxoid may be given to increase their resistance to tetanus.

PREVENTION OF INFECTION   The early treatment of the wound to remove dead tissue and foreign bodies makes conditions less favorable for the growth of the tetanus organism. The administration of two or three doses of toxoid as well as tetanus antitoxin provides a means of preventing the disease. The passive immunity conferred by antitoxin alone lasts about ten days, during which time the organisms may remain dormant and then cause the disease after the antibodies have disappeared. In the case of a soldier who has already been actively immunized, one dose of the toxoid at the time of the injury is desirable to increase his active immunity to tetanus. The fact that tetanus was rare in the United States Army during World War II emphasizes the value of active immunization in preventing this infection. Active immunization with tetanus toxoid is advocated for all children and is often given with inoculations for diphtheria and pertussis.

The Gas Gangrene Group   Gas gangrene is a condition that develops in some wounds incurred in war, or in highway or street accidents. It is definitely a mixed infection that is due to various combinations of aerobes and anaerobic saprophytes (clostridia). The presence of dead tissue appears to be necessary for the development of gas gangrene, and further destruction is effected by the organisms which produce toxins and rapidly invade the area. The production of gas by the fermentation of muscle sugar and the extensive destruction of cells are both suggested in the term "gas gangrene." The disease is often severe and mortality in patients not treated by chemotherapy may be as high as 60 per cent.

The saprophytes associated with gas gangrene fall into two groups: (1) proteolytic organisms that digest and liquefy tissues; e.g., *Clostridium sporogenes, Clostridium histolyticum*, and (2) saccharolytic organisms that ferment sugars forming acid and gas; e.g., *Clostridium perfringens, Clostridium septi-*

cum, Clostridium fallax. The proteolytic group may be considered wound pathogens, since they possess feeble powers of invasion; however, in the presence of other organisms, they may prevent the healing of wounds. *Clostridium perfringens* is the most important member of the gas gangrene group and will be discussed in some detail.

Clostridium perfringens   This organism is a short, thick gram-positive rod, a strict anaerobe normally found in soil and in the intestines of man and animals. It is an active fermenter which changes the common sugars to lactic and butyric acids, large quantities of gas being formed in the process. In milk, this "stormy fermentation" results in the formation of a clot which is rapidly torn to pieces by gas bubbles. The organism forms several toxins, some of which destroy tissues when they are injected into the skin of laboratory animals. One of the toxins is an enzyme (lecithinase) which destroys lecithin, an important constituent of most tissues. Most strains secrete the enzymes (fibrinolysin and hyaluridonidase) which split the cement that holds cells together (hyaluronic acid). After an incubation period varying from five hours to seven days the invading organisms cause a rapidly spreading infection characterized by edema and the presence of gas bubbles in the tissues. Potent enzymes secreted by the organisms rapidly destroy both connective tissues and muscle.

Clostridium perfringens can be isolated from wounds in about 75 per cent of the patients with gas gangrene. However, it may be present in wounds without causing the gangrene. It is thought that disease production depends upon the presence of dead tissue, the absence of oxygen, and the ability of the organism to form toxins. Treatment usually consists of radical surgery and large doses of penicillin and a polyvalent gas gangrene antitoxin.

The early removal of dead tissue and foreign bodies from wounds is important. A mixture of antitoxins against the common toxins formed by the gangrene group is also available. This polyvalent serum is sometimes combined with tetanus antitoxin and given in one dose. Active immunization by means of toxoids is still in the experimental stage, but a preparation of alum precipitated gas gangrene toxoids (*Clostridium per-fringens* and *Clostridium novyi*) is available. It is, of course, important that instruments and equipment used in caring for the infected person be sterilized in the autoclave to insure the killing of spores.

SUMMARY

ORGANISM	COMMON SOURCE	ACTIVE IMMUNI-ZATION	PASSIVE IMMUNI-ZATION	CHEMO-THERAPY
Enteric group	Intestines	None	None	Uncertain—
Pseudomonas				many re-
aeruginosa	Wounds	None	None	sistant
Micrococcus				strains
pyogenes	Skin, wounds, boils, respiratory secretions	None	None	
Streptococcus pyogenes	Wounds, respiratory secretions	None	None	Sulfonamides Penicillin
Clostridium tetani	Feces of animals and man, soil	Toxoid	Tetanus antitoxin	
Gas Gangrene group	Feces, soil	Toxoid (experimental)	Polyvalent gas gangrene antitoxin	Penicillin

REFERENCE

1. Report of Committee on Chemotherapeutic and Other Agents and the Committee on Surgery of the Division of Medical Sciences of the National Research Council: Prevention of Infection of Wounds and Burns. War Med., 2: 488–496, 1942.

SUPPLEMENTARY READINGS

BOOKS:

Burrows, W.: Jordan-Burrows Textbook of Bacteriology. 15th ed. Philadelphia, W. B. Saunders Co., 1949.
Dubos, R.: Bacterial and Mycotic Infections of Man. 2d ed. Philadelphia, J. B. Lippincott Co., 1952.
Frobisher, M.: Fundamentals of Microbiology. 5th ed. Philadelphia, W. B. Saunders Co., 1953.

Recognition of Infection   The infection can be recognized in the early stages by finding the organisms and in the later stages by finding complement-fixing antibodies in the serum. In the primary and secondary stages of the disease, the organisms are present in large numbers in the lesions and can be demonstrated by darkfield examination of the fluid. It requires, however, a person with great skill to distinguish the *Treponema pallidum* from other more or less harmless spirochetes found in the mouth.

In the later stages of the disease it is usually impossible to find the spirochetes. Diagnosis then depends upon the history, the physical signs and symptoms, and complement-fixation and precipitation reactions. When properly made these tests have an accuracy of 90 or 95 per cent. (See Chapter 21.) It is well to remember that reactions to these tests are negative in the early stages of the disease and also in a few persons who are definitely known to have the infection. Still more confusing is the fact that positive serological reactions occur in a few persons who do not have the disease and have never had it. For example, the blood serums of persons who have recently been vaccinated against smallpox or have had an attack of malaria or certain other infections* may give a false positive precipitation or complement-fixation reaction. For this reason, the results of serological tests must be considered in the light of the medical history and the clinical findings. Whenever mass testing is done, one may expect to encounter a small number of false positive or false negative results. Furthermore, these serological reactions change from positive to negative in response to adequate treatment.

Transmission   Acquired syphilis is a slow, chronic infection which may appear to be latent for long periods. The organisms are present in the lesions of the first and second stages of the disease and are also present in the blood stream and viscera. They are usually transmitted by sexual intercourse

---

* Infections which may give rise to positive reactions to flocculation tests include: leprosy, tuberculosis, pneumococcal pneumonia, bacterial endocarditis, scarlet fever, rheumatic fever, typhus, leptospirosis, relapsing fever, atypical pneumonia, measles, and chickenpox.

or other intimate contact.* The organisms have also been transferred by blood transfusion. Likewise, spirochetes in the blood
of the mother may penetrate the placenta to infect the developing fetus. Indirect transmission by means of clothing, towels,
drinking cups, and bathtubs seldom occurs because the parasite is too fragile to live long without the host. In fact, such
transmission is possible only when contact is made with the
organisms in moist secretions. The risk of transmitting the
disease is greatly lessened after the infection has progressed
for two years.

Early Syphilis   First Stage   The *Treponema pallidum,* after penetrating the skin or mucous membrane, multiplies and invades the tissues and the blood stream. From three
to six weeks later, after sensitization has occurred, a hard
painless ulcer appears at the point of entry. This slow-healing
sore, called a *chancre,* contains innumerable spirochetes. Chan-
cres usually form on the genitalia, but they may occur on the
lips, mouth, or fingers. Sometimes the lesion may be quite
insignificant or it may be located in areas that are not readily
visible. Without treatment, the chancre will usually heal in
four to six weeks, after which the patient is without symptoms.
During this time the organisms continue to multiply freely.

Second Stage   Four to eight weeks later, as host sensitization and resistance increase, numerous inflamed areas appear throughout the body. Symptoms of second stage syphilis
include: fever, joint pains, enlarged lymph nodes, skin rash,
sore throat, and mucous patches on mucous membranes of the
mouth and genitalia. Spirochetes are present in the lesions and
can be transferred to others by contact or by the immediate
use of common utensils or linen. The skin rash and mucous
patches may remain for a few days or months. Relapses are
common during the first year. The inflammatory reaction tends
to destroy many spirochetes and thus establish an equilibrium
between host and parasites.

Late Syphilis   The infection may remain latent for

* In certain primitive communities of Europe and Asia, syphilis
(bejel) occurs as an endemic, nonvenereal disease of childhood. Since
the early lesions occur on the skin and mouth the organisms are readily
transmitted from child to child. Late syphilis in these areas is similar to
that which occurs with the venereal form of the disease.

many years before there is further evidence of disease. As years go by, certain cells become increasingly allergic and respond to the presence of the organism by tissue destruction and scar tissue formation. These lesions may rupture forming a syphilitic ulcer (gumma) or may heal with distortion and scarring. These processes may occur in any part of the body but are especially serious when they involve the liver, the heart, the blood vessels, or the brain and spinal cord.

Congenital Syphilis   Spirochetes from the blood of the mother invade the placenta and fetus, thickening blood vessel walls and thus interfering with nutrition of the fetus. The child may die or may be born with evidence of early congenital syphilis. This disease is characterized by general malnutrition and underdevelopment of various body structures. For example, internal organs may be enlarged by excessive growth of connective tissue and degenerative changes may occur in the brain, spinal cord, auditory nerve, eyes, bones, teeth, skin, or mucous membranes. Fortunately this disease is rare because many syphilitic women receive treatment during pregnancy. If the treatment of the mother is inadequate, the disease may become apparent in the infant at some later time.

The diagnosis of congenital syphilis is often difficult because the clinical signs are indefinite and serological tests are unreliable in infants and young children. At the time of birth, the spirochetes can often be seen in a darkfield examination of scrapings made from the umbilical cord. Likewise, x-ray examinations of the long bones made two weeks after birth may reveal significant signs of disease.

Susceptibility to Syphilis   The human host is highly susceptible to syphilis. Second attacks may occur but not during the course of the initial infection. No satisfactory vaccine or antiserum has been developed against the spirochete.

Prevention and Control of Infection   Obviously the disease can be prevented by avoiding contacts with persons in the infective stages of the disease. Congenital syphilis can be controlled by treating the syphilitic mother during each pregnancy. Prompt treatment of every infectious case with penicillin or arsenic and bismuth compounds will decrease the reservoir of infection in the community. Adequate treatment

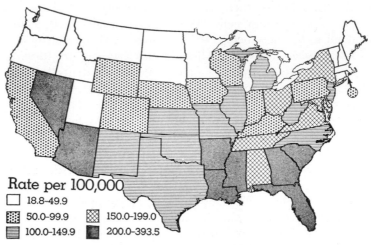

Figure 68   Reported syphilis rates per 100,000 civilian population, fiscal year 1951. (Pub. Health Rep., *64*.)

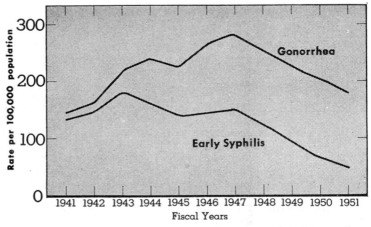

Figure 69   Trend in early syphilis and gonorrhea reported case rates, continental United States, civilians, fiscal years 1941–51 (includes primary, secondary, and early latent). (Pub. Health Rep., *64*.)

will also benefit the patient by preventing the degenerative changes of late syphilis.

Syphilis should be one of the easiest of diseases to control; in practice, however, it is one of the most difficult because the chronic character of the disease does not impress the victim with the need for continued treatment. Furthermore, psychological attitudes make it difficult to find the sources of infection. Because of incomplete reporting the prevalence of syphilis is not known. It is significant, however, that in the year 1951 a total of 198,640 cases (132 per 100,000 population) were reported to the United States Public Health Service. Data from the same source reveal a decrease in early syphilis infections since 1947. (See Figures 68 and 69.)

Prophylaxis   Prophylactic treatment of persons exposed to syphilis, though of some value in military groups, has been less successful in civilian use. Prophylaxis usually includes thorough washing of the genitalia with soap and water, and the local application of mercury ointments or solutions. To be of value, such treatment must be instituted before the spirochetes have penetrated into the tissues. If the hands of the physician or nurse become contaminated with discharges from the syphilitic person, they should be washed promptly and thoroughly with soap and hot water.

NEISSERIA GONORRHOEAE

The gonococcus—*Neisseria gonorrhoeae*—is a small, gram-negative coccus appearing in pairs. It is often called an intracellular diplococcus because it is found in pus within the cytoplasm of the body phagocytes. The organism has little resistance to heat, light, or complete drying, and is very sensitive to silver salts and other chemicals. It is killed by a temperature of 55° C. in five minutes and 42° C. in five to fifteen hours.

The organism, which can be isolated from the discharges from the genitourinary tract or eyes of infected persons, is a strict parasite adapted to living in certain human tissues (columnar and transitional epithelium). In the body the organism produces marked cell damage which is followed by severe inflammation. This process tends to localize the infec-

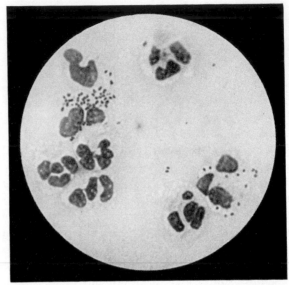

Figure 70   *Neisseria gonorrhoeae* (gonococcus). Note the coffee-bean shaped cocci, most of which are within phagocytes. (Therapeutic Notes. Parke Davis.)

tion by preventing its spread through blood and lymph. The gonococcus grows well in the laboratory media containing body fluids but does not produce typical gonorrhea when inoculated into laboratory animals.

Infection   The infection, gonorrhea, occurs in the columnar epithelial tisues of the eye or the genitourinary organs. The eyes of the newborn may be infected during passage through the infected birth canal and the resulting inflammation of the cornea and conjunctiva may cause blindness. Silver solutions such as silver nitrate, 1 per cent, are commonly required by law to be used in the eyes of the newborn to prevent infection. Recent studies show that some antibiotics dropped in the eyes are safe and effective. Some states now permit the use of antibiotics instead of silver salts.

The eyes of the person with a genitourinary infection may be infected by the person himself touching his eyes with his own contaminated hands. Persons caring for patients with gonorrhea must be careful to protect their eyes from contamination with the gonococcus.

In adults, the gonococcus may be transferred by intimate contact to the mucous membranes of the urethra and other parts of the genitourinary tract. An incubation period of from one to eight days is followed by an acute inflammation with pus formation. The process usually remains local or spreads to nearby organs, but sometimes the organisms invade the blood stream causing chronic systemic infections involving the heart valves, the joints, or the meninges.

The host response to the infection varies with the individual. In some cases, the body defenses may effectively localize the invader and kill the organisms. More frequently, the opposing forces are so well balanced that a latent or chronic infection occurs. Persons with chronic infections may be carriers for years. Gonococci are usually susceptible to treatment with penicillin alone or combined with sulfonamides. Since many strains of gonococci have become sulfonamide resistant, these drugs (sulfonamides) are not likely to be effective if used alone.

The acute gonorrheal infection can often be recognized on the basis of the clinical signs alone. In the male, the disease is characterized by an acute inflammation of the urethra which may extend to the prostate gland and to the seminal vesicles. In the female, the infection involves the bartholin glands, the vagina, the cervix, the uterine tubes, rectum, and possibly the peritoneal cavity. In some cases, the organisms invade the blood stream, giving rise to secondary infections such as gonorrheal arthritis or endocarditis.

In the acute stage, the organisms may be detected by a direct examination of the pus in which they appear as biscuit-shaped diplococci within the phagocytic cells. The organisms can be isolated by culturing on special serum-agar media. Positive cultures are valuable in confirmation of the diagnosis and determination as to whether or not further treatment is required. Negative cultures are less significant because they indicate only that the bacteria were not found. It is difficult to determine when the disease is cured, because the person may still have a residual infection even when the cultures are negative. The reaction to the complement-fixation test may become positive several weeks after the beginning of the infection. The test is, therefore, of more value as a diagnostic aid for chronic infections than for those that are acute.

Susceptibility to Gonorrhea   It appears that all persons are susceptible and that one infection does not confer immunity. It is obvious, therefore, that serums and vaccines will be practically useless. Little girls before puberty are highly susceptible to gonococcus vulvovaginitis, an infection that is sometimes epidemic in institutions caring for children. Fortunately, this infection responds to treatment with penicillin.

Prevention of Gonorrhea   Gonorrhea is an important cause of sterility in both males and females. The prevalence of the disease is not known but is thought to be three or four times that of syphilis. The disease is widespread in the age group of twenty to thirty years. It is more common in men than in women, also more common in Negroes than in members of the white race. The attack rates for rural groups are lower than for urban groups. Prostitutes and other persons with acute, chronic, or latent disease maintain a large reservoir of infection in the community. During times of war, the rate of infection increases in both civilian and military populations. Community efforts have centered on education of the public concerning the disease, and finding and treating infected persons. As a result a marked decline in gonorrhea infections has occurred since 1947. (See Figure 69.)

HEMOPHILUS DUCREYI

Ducrey's bacillus (*Hemophilus ducreyi*) is a short gram-negative rod that can be grown on blood agar. This microorganism is the cause of *chancroid* or *soft chancre*. It is usually transmitted by sexual contact but is sometimes transferred by towels or other fomites. After an incubation period of four to eight days, the organism invades the genitals causing irregular spreading ulcers and swelling and suppuration of the inguinal lymph nodes. The infection tends to be chronic, but responds to treatment with the sulfonamides.

THE VIRUS OF LYMPHOGRANULOMA VENEREUM

Lymphogranuloma venereum is a virus infection of the genitals, characterized by ulceration and enlargement of the inguinal and pelvic lymph glands. Like the other infections in this group, it is transmitted by sexual contact and is commonly found in persons who are infected with syphilis or gonorrhea. The virus apparently persists in the tissues. Therefore, relapses occur and the person may be infectious even though there are no clinical symptoms. This is one of the few virus diseases which responds to treatment with penicillin and the sulfonamides.

Infection causes the person to become sensitive to the virus protein (obtained from a chick embryo culture). This sensitivity can be detected by a skin test (Frei test) which resembles the tuberculin test.

SUMMARY

The summary is located on page 464.

REFERENCES

1. Smith, D. T., and Conant, N. F.: Zinsser's Textbook of Bacteriology. 10th ed. New York, Appleton-Century-Crofts, Inc., 1952, p. 588.
2. Smith, D. T., and Conant, N. F.: Zinsser's Textbook of Bacteriology. 10th ed. New York, Appleton-Century-Crofts, Inc., 1953, p. 335.

SUPPLEMENTARY READINGS

BOOKS:

Burrows, W.: Jordan-Burrows Textbook of Bacteriology. 15th ed. Philadelphia, W. B. Saunders Co., 1949.

Dubos, R.: Bacterial and Mycotic Infections of Man. 2d ed. Philadelphia, J. B. Lippincott Co., 1952.

Greenberg, M., and Matz, A. V.: Modern Concepts of Communicable Disease. New York, G. P. Putnam's Sons, 1953.

Rivers, T. M.: Viral and Rickettsial Infections of Man. 2d ed. Philadelphia, J. B. Lippincott Co., 1952.

Smillie, W. G.: Preventive Medicine and Public Health. 2d ed. New York, The Macmillan Co., 1952.

PERIODICALS:

Akrawi, F.: The Primary Sore in Bejel. Tr. Roy. Soc. Trop. Med. & Hyg., 46: 77–80, 1952.

SUMMARY

ORGANISM	DISEASE	SITE OF INFECTION	DIAGNOSTIC PROCEDURES	ACTIVE IMMUNI-ZATION	PASSIVE IMMUNI-ZATION	CHEMO-THERAPY
Treponema pallidum	Syphilis	Local and general	*Early:* Darkfield examination *Late:* Complement-fixation and precipitation tests	None	None	Arsenic compounds Penicillin
Neisseria gonorrhoeae (gonococcus)	Gonorrhea	Eyes Genitourinary system	*Early:* Smears, cultures	None	None	Sulfonamides with penicillin
Hemophilus ducreyi	Chancroid (soft chancre)	Ulceration of genitalia and regional lymph glands	Culture	None	None	Sulfonamides
Specific virus	Lymphogranuloma venereum	Ulceration of genitalia and regional lymph glands	Frei (skin) test for determining sensitivity	None	None	Sulfonamides Penicillin

Arnold, R. C., and others: Studies in Penicillin Treatment of Syphilis. Pub. Health Rep., *67:* 78–89, 1952.

Bauer, T. J.: Venereal Disease Control Program in Transition. Pub. Health Rep., *67:* 17–20, 1952.

Davidson, H. H., and others: Penicillin in the Prophylaxis of Ophthalmia Neonatorum. J.A.M.A., *145:* 1052–1055, 1951.

Editorial: Congenital Syphilis. J.A.M.A., *146:* 256–260, 1951.

Moore, J. E., and Mohr, C. F.: Biologically False Positive Serological Tests for Syphilis. J.A.M.A., *150:* 467–473, 1952.

Rake, G., and Oskay, J. J.: Cultural Characteristics of *Donovania granulomatis.* J. Bact., *55:* 667–675, 1948.

Wilkcockson, T. H., and Cox, C. D.: Studies in Newborn Using Terramycin, Polymyxin B and Silver Nitrate. South Dakota J. Med. & Pharm., *6:* 147–148, 1953.

World Health Organization: Endemic Syphilis in Bosnia. Chron. World Health Organ., *7:* 4–12, 1953.

Wright, J. J.: Venereal Disease Control. J.A.M.A., *147:* 1408–1411, 1951.

CHAPTER 30

*Fungi Transmitted by
                     Contact with Spores*

YEASTS: *Monilia; Cryptococcus;
        Coccidioides*

MOLDS: *Microsporum; Trycophyton;
       Epidermophyton; Sporotrichum;
       Histoplasma*

ACTINOMYCETES

ALTHOUGH most fungi are nonparasitic, certain actinomycetes, molds, and yeasts are capable of causing disease in man and animals. Fungous diseases called *mycoses* naturally fall into two groups: those which occur on body surfaces, and those which attack internal organs. Ringworm, athlete's foot, and thrush are examples of superficial fungous infections. They are caused by yeast or moldlike parasites which grow on the upper layers of the skin or mucous membrane, or on the hair or nails. As a rule, they do not invade the deeper tissues, and are transferred from host to host by direct or indirect contact. Characteristically, they produce persistent chronic infections which do not endanger health, although parasites acquired from animals may be somewhat more virulent for man. Fungous growth causes redness and scaling of the skin and may cause destruction of the hair or nails. Such infections induce tissue sensitivity which in the skin has some protective value in that it tends to limit the spread of infection.

In contrast, deep-seated fungous infections are usually caused by free-living organisms which enter the body through wounds or by inhalation. They are seldom transferred from man to man, but constitute occupational hazards for persons who are repeatedly exposed to the spores of certain fungi. It is thought that upon entry into the tissues, the organisms persist but do not multiply or invade. The body responds by develop-
466

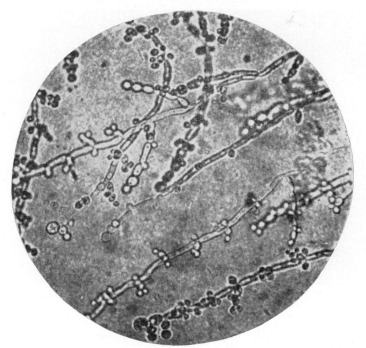

Figure 71   *Candida albicans* (*Monilia albicans*), unstained, showing
mycelium, spores, and yeastlike cells. (Benham.)

ing sensitivity to the cell proteins and often walls off the foreign body by tubercle formation. Then further contact with
the fungus results in progressive injury and, especially in lung
tissue, leads to extension of the disease. In time, the organisms
adapt themselves to life within the body and begin to grow,
slowly liberating metabolic products which induce more sensitivity and more tissue destruction. These infections resemble
tuberculosis and leprosy in that they are usually associated
with tubercle formation and tissue destruction. Generalized
fungous infections are chronic, progressive, and usually fatal.
The pathogenic fungi closely resemble the free-living yeasts,
molds, and actinomycetes.

PATHOGENIC YEASTS
Three groups of disease-producing yeasts will be considered

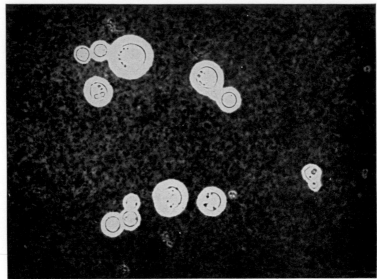

Figure 72   *Cryptococcus neoformans* in pus. (Courtesy Dr. Donald
S. Martin, Duke University.)

briefly; they are the monilia, the cryptococcus (torula), and
coccidioides.

Monilia   The monilia are fungi that are difficult to
classify because they resemble both yeasts and molds; they are
characterized by large, thick-walled yeast cells that form
threads or filaments like the hyphae of molds. (See Figure 71.)
Some of these organisms are commonly present in the mouth,
intestines, and vagina without producing injury. When the resistance of the host is low, however, the *Candida albicans*
(*Monilia albicans*), or other varieties, may invade the tissues
of the mouth, the intestine, the vagina, or the skin, nails,
bronchi or lungs. The disease, commonly known as *thrush,* is
characterized by the formation of white or cream-colored
patches on the infected tissue. The diagnosis is based on the
appearance of the lesions and the observation of yeastlike cells
in tissue from the lesion, or is made by culturing the fungi.
Since the organisms are present in the lesions in large numbers,
care should be taken to prevent the transfer of the fungi to
other persons. However, pathogenic strains of *Candida albicans*

can often be recovered from the skin, mucous membranes, and stools of normal persons. Monilia infections of the intestine have been reported following prolonged administration of antibiotics which suppressed the normal flora of the bowel.

Cryptococcus (Torula) The cryptococcus is a yeast-like organism which reproduces by budding. (See Figure 72.) This fungus may cause a skin infection characterized by the formation of pustules, ulcers, and subcutaneous tumors. It also invades the central nervous system or lungs, producing chronic lesions that may be confused with those of tuberculosis or syphilis. The method of transmission is not definitely known, nor is there any specific treatment available. The diagnosis is made by examining pus from the lesions in which the yeast cells are seen as large ovoid cells surrounded by a large gelatinous capsule. Mortality from this infection is high, but fortunately the disease is a rare one.

Coccidioides immitis The coccidioides are yeastlike cells that reproduce by budding or by forming endospores. In tissue and pus, the fungus appears as a granular, spherical cell with a double-contoured capsule. (See Figure 73.) On solid medium, the mycelium forms a pattern that looks like frost or snowflakes. The spores, which may be present in dust, soil, or vegetation, enter the body through contact with abrasions or by inhalation, and attack the skin, bone, or lung tissue. The organism is found in certain areas of California, Texas, and Arizona. It is associated with two forms of disease: (1) *valley fever*, a benign pulmonary infection characterized by malaise, chills, fever, pleural pain, cough, and headache; and (2) *coccidioidal granuloma*, a highly fatal disease characterized by the formation of tumors that suppurate. The latter may be confused with tuberculosis or syphilis. Infection with the coccidioides causes the person to become sensitive to the protein *coccidioidin*. This sensitivity can be detected by a skin test similar to the tuberculin test. Recent studies show that at least 60 per cent of coccidioidal infections produce no symptoms, or symptoms so mild and atypical that they are not recognized. Discharges from skin lesions, sputum, and necrotic lymph nodes contain the spores and should, therefore, be disinfected. The infection does not appear to spread from man

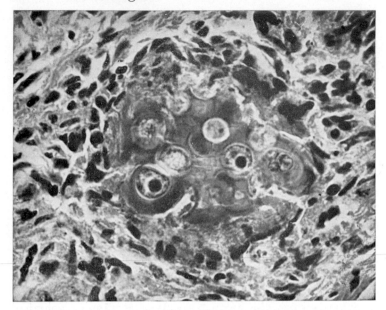

Figure 73   *Coccidioides immitis.* Round, nonbudding spores in section of granulomatous lesion. (Mackie, T. T., et al.: Manual of Tropical Medicine.)

to man, although such discharges cause infection in experimental animals. Measures designed to control dust (paving of roads and runways, planting of lawns, etc.) have proved of some value in decreasing the risk of infections in Army personnel stationed in areas where the disease is common.

PATHOGENIC MOLDS

The saprophytic molds have been discussed in Chapter 6. The parasitic molds resemble them in appearance; that is, they are multicellular plants that grow in long, branched filaments or hyphae that tend to form a network of threads called a mycelium. Like the saprophytes, they multiply by producing relatively resistant reproductive bodies called spores. Some species are capable of living in body tissues and there produce characteristic signs of injury. As a rule, they, like the yeasts, have a low degree of virulence and invasiveness and cause infections that are more or less chronic and persistent. Suscepti-

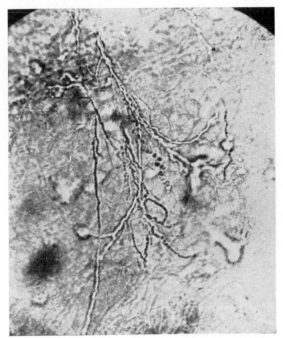

Figure 74   Mycelium and spores in hydroxide preparation of scales from ringworm of foot. (Courtesy, Miss Rhoda W. Benham.)

bility to mold infections varies greatly and appears common among persons whose general resistance is low. A large group of molds, called dermatophytes, literally skin plants, are adapted to living in epithelial tissues. They include *Microsporum,* the *Trichophyton,* and the *Epidermophyton,* the fungi that cause tinea or ringworm.

Microsporum   The microsporum, or small-spored molds, form threads of unbranched septate mycelium containing small rounded spores. On solid artificial medium, they grow as tangled filaments that form a matlike growth which is often white and downy. These organisms are capable of invading and growing within the strands of hair as well as in the skin.

One member of this genus, *Malassezia furfur,* grows in the superficial layers of the skin, causing a benign skin condition called *tinea versicolor* which is characterized by the appearance

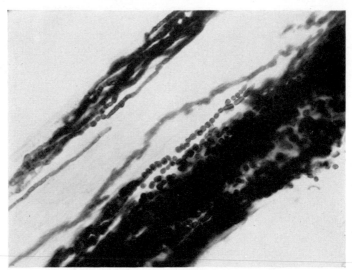

Figure 75   A hair infected with ringworm fungus (*Trichophyton tonsurans*). Note the threadlike mycelium and chains of spores growing within the hair. (Courtesy of Mycology Laboratory, P.H.S., Communicable Disease Center, Atlanta, Georgia.)

of fawn-colored, scaling patches. The fungus is virtually a saprophyte living on the dead skin cells, and causes no destruction, inflammation, or discomfort. This condition is not transmissible and thus differs from the ringworm infections.

Two other members of the genus microsporum, *Microsporum audouini* and *Microsporum canis* (*Microsporum lanosum*), are pathogenic since they invade and multiply within the hairs of the scalp or beard. The former causes ringworm in man, while the latter causes the disease in dogs and cats as well as in human beings. The organisms appear as tightly packed spores within the infected hair or skin cell. Most epidemics of ringworm of the scalp are due to *Microsporum audouini* and occur in children before puberty. The infected hairs fluoresce and can be seen with the aid of a Wood's (ultraviolet) lamp.

Trichophyton and Epidermophyton   The trichophyton, literally hair plants, are fungi adapted to growing within the hair. They cause the infected hair to break off leaving bald patches surrounded by inflamed scaling vesicles. The epidermophyton, or skin plants, are a group of fungi that invade the epidermis causing ringworm of the hand, foot, or body. Like the microsporum, these organisms can be identified by culturing them on artificial media and by examining suitable preparations of the infected hair and skin through the microscope. (See Figures 74 and 75.) The infections caused by these organisms are similar in many respects and therefore can be considered as a group.

Ringworm   Skin infections due to the fungi are common and widespread and are known by the names *tinea, ringworm, or athlete's foot.* The infection may be transmitted by direct contact with the lesion or by contact with clothing or damp floors that are contaminated with the spores. In general, the ordinary indoor activities of home and school favor the transfer of the fungus. The spores may persist for long periods on contaminated articles such as gloves, shoes, and purses, It is quite possible for lesions that are entirely healed to become reinfected by contact with these articles. During the course of the disease, wearing cotton clothing is desirable because it can be disinfected by boiling. Leather goods may be disinfected by exposing them to formaldehyde gas for twenty-four hours. Fungous infections may be acquired from infected dogs and cats as well as from human beings.

Ringworm of the foot is so prevalent that it is impractical to exclude carriers and persons with mild infections from school or swimming pools. Therefore, it is important that people use individual equipment and that they wear sandals when using public showers or swimming pools. Cleanliness and thorough drying of the feet after bathing are desirable since fungi require moisture for growth. Prompt and continuous treatment for ringworm infection is necessary for the protection of the patient as well as for his associates.

Sporotricha   The sporotricha are hardy molds that are widely distributed in nature and live as saprophytes on many kinds of vegetation. When grown in media, they form interlacing, septate hyphae that show branching. The spores of this mold are very resistant to drying, sunlight, and low temperatures, but are killed by high temperatures. The spores are thought to enter the tissues by contact with thorns, briars,

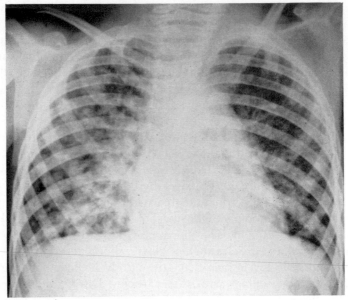

Figure 76   Benign histoplasmosis. Chest x-ray of child, four and one-half years of age showing calcified tubercles (fuzzy mottled infiltration) scattered through both lungs. The reaction to the tuberculin test was negative; the reaction to the histoplasmin test was positive in a dilution of 1:1000. Reaction to the complement-fixation test for histoplasmosis was also positive. (Miller and Grossman: J.A.M.A., *147.*)

or by bee stings or insect bites. The infection is found among people who work with plants. In tissue, the fungi often appear as oval or cigar-shaped cells that are present within large phagocytic cells. They commonly invade the skin, subcutaneous tissues, and lymph vessels, and sometimes the bones or the central nervous system where they form deep ulcers that resemble the lesions of syphilis. Spontaneous cure seldom occurs; however, treatment with iodides has proved very effective.

Histoplasma capsulatum   *Histoplasma capsulatum* attacks the lungs, causing a rare chronic fatal disease and a mild acute infection which resembles influenza. The latter is seldom recognized but is of importance in that it is characterized by tubercle formation. In x-ray photographs, these tubercles, which are often calcified (see Figure 76), are readily confused

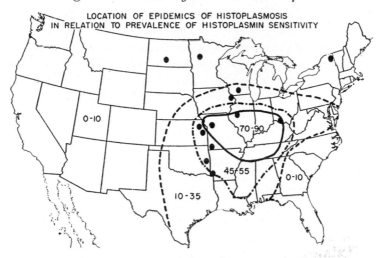

LOCATION OF EPIDEMICS OF HISTOPLASMOSIS
IN RELATION TO PREVALENCE OF HISTOPLASMIN SENSITIVITY

Figure 77   The areas of histoplasmin sensitivity are shown schematically by the approximate per cent of young adults reacting to histoplasmin. Note that histoplasmin sensitivity is rare in the western and northern states and relatively more common in the eastern and central states. (Am. J. Pub. Health, *43*.)

with those of tuberculosis. Sensitivity tests are useful in differentiating between the two infections, since persons infected with *Histoplasma capsulatum* react to histoplasmin (a protein obtained from the mold) but not to tuberculin. Outbreaks of histoplasmosis have been reported in widely scattered areas in the eastern half of the United States. Seventy per cent or more of the adults living in southern Illinois, Indiana, Kentucky, and Missouri are sensitive to histoplasmin. (See Figure 77.) *Histoplasma capsulatum* can be isolated with some regularity from certain moist soils such as those found in unused silos and storm cellars. In areas where mild infections are common, cattle, horses, and sheep as well as children are sensitive to histoplasmin. This suggests that both domestic animals and man acquire the infection from the soil. At present there is no evidence of person-to-person transfer of the fungus.

ACTINOMYCES

The actinomyces are microorganisms intermediate between the bacteria and the molds in structure. They are moldlike in that they produce a septate branched mycelium and reproduce by forming spores, although in size they resemble bacteria. The group contains many saprophytes that are present and active in producing changes in soil and water. A few species are pathogenic and are capable of invading tissues. The source of this type of infection has not been definitely determined; in all probability these organisms are normal inhabitants of the oral cavity and intestine and they become pathogenic only when the local or general resistance of the host is lowered.

The disease known as *actinomycosis* or *lumpy jaw* is usually a local, chronic infection of the cheek or neck, characterized by the formation of large or small tumors. When the disease spreads to bone or viscera, it causes symptoms that may be confused with syphilis, tuberculosis, sarcoma, or carcinoma. General infections progress very slowly but are usually fatal. Sulfonamides, penicillin, and Terramycin have been reported to be useful in the treatment.

SUMMARY

FUNGUS	INFECTION	SITE OF INFECTION	PREVALENCE	MORTAL-ITY
Yeasts				
Monilia	Moniliasis (thrush)	Ulceration of mucous membranes of mouth, intestine, skin, or vagina	Uncommon except in debilitated individuals	Low
Cryptococcus	Cryptococcosis (torulosis)	Ulcers of the lungs or central nervous system	Uncommon	High
Coccidioides	Valley fever	Lungs	Uncommon except in southwestern states	Low
	Coccidioidal granuloma	Ulcers of skin, bone, lungs, central nervous system	Uncommon	High
Molds				
Microsporum	Ringworm	Scalp and beard	Common	Low
Trichophyton	Ringworm	Scalp and beard	Common	Low
Epidermophyton	Ringworm	Smooth skin	Very common	Low
Sporotrichum	Sporotrichosis	Skin, subcutaneous tissue, lymphatics	Uncommon	Low
Histoplasma	Histoplasmosis			
	Acute	Lungs	Common	Low
	Chronic	Lungs, liver, spleen	Uncommon	High
Actinomyces	Actinomycosis (lumpy jaw)	Skin, subcutaneous tissue, bone, viscera	Uncommon	Low

SUPPLEMENTARY READINGS

BOOKS:

American Public Health Association: The Control of Communicable Diseases. 7th ed. New York, The American Public Health Association, 1950.

Conant, M., and others: Manual of Clinical Mycology. Philadelphia, W. B. Saunders Co., 1944.

Dubos, R. J.: Bacterial and Mycotic Infections of Man. 2d ed. Philadelphia, J. B. Lippincott Co., 1952.

Frobisher, M.: Fundamentals of Microbiology. 5th ed. Philadelphia, W. B. Saunders Co., 1953.

Greenberg, M., and Matz, A. V.: Modern Concepts of Communicable Disease. New York, G. P. Putnam's Sons, 1953.

Smith, D. T., and Conant, N. F.: Zinsser's Textbook of Bacteriology. 10th ed. New York, Appleton-Century-Crofts, Inc., 1952.

PERIODICALS:

Georg, L. K.: Tricophyton tonsurans Ringworm—A New Public Health Problem. Pub. Health Rep., 67: 53–56, 1952.

Grayston, J. T., and Furcolow, M. L.: The Occurrence of Histoplasmosis in Epidemics—Epidemiological Studies. Am. J. Pub. Health, 43: 665–676, 1953.

Kunstadter, R. H.: Mycotic Endocarditis Due to Candida Albicans. J.A.M.A., 149: 829–832, 1952.

Miller, I. R., and Grossman, S.: Benign Histoplasmosis in Siblings. J.A.M.A., 147: 753–755, 1951.

Zeidberg, L. D., and others: Some Factors in the Epidemiology of Histoplasmin Sensitivity in Williamson County, Tennessee. Am. J. Pub. Health, 41: 80–89, 1951.

CHAPTER 31

Organisms Transmitted by Contact with Animals

BACTERIA: *Bacillus anthracis; Malleomyces mallei; Mycobacterium tuberculosis; Brucella; Leptospira; Spirillum minus; Pasteurella tularensis*

RICKETTSIAS: *Coxiella burnetii*

VIRUSES: *Rabies; Ornithosis (Psittacosis); Cat Scratch Fever*

BOTH DOMESTIC and wild animals have their own varieties of parasites, many of which are unable to adapt themselves to life in the human body. Others can multiply when chance carries them to this new host. A World Health Organization committee lists eighty-six different diseases which can be transferred from vertebrate animals to man. In these diseases the animals in question maintain the parasites while man is an accidental host. For example, the dog, fox, and skunk serve as a reservoir of infection for the rabies virus. Some of the diseases are transmitted by the bite of a common parasite, while others are spread through contact with the infected animal or his secretions.

BACTERIA ACQUIRED FROM ANIMAL SOURCES

Bacillus anthracis The anthrax bacillus is a large, spore-forming rod (see Figure 78) which grows readily on laboratory media, forming large rough colonies. Its spores are very resistant and may remain alive for years in the soil or in the wool, hair, or hides of infected animals. A recent outbreak (1952) was traced to a shipment of bone meal which was contaminated with anthrax spores. This organism, which causes a serious blood stream infection in domestic animals (sheep, cattle, goats), is not highly infectious for man. Anthrax

479

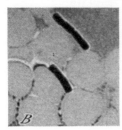 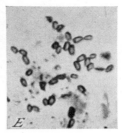 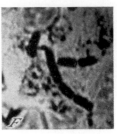

Figure 78   Stained anthrax bacilli and spores. (× 1700.) (Courtesy of Charles C Thomas, Publisher.)

is of historical interest because it was studied by Robert Koch and Louis Pasteur.

Man acquires this organism by direct contact with infected material or by inhaling dust that contains the spores or by ingesting the spores, as in working with hides from animals infected with anthrax. The organism may also be transferred by the bite of the deer fly or horsefly. When the anthrax bacillus invades the skin it forms an abscess or boil, the *malignant pustule*. The infection may remain local or may spread and become general. Inhalation of the organisms gives rise to pulmonary anthrax or *woolsorters' disease*—a rare disease. Intestinal anthrax may be acquired by eating when the hands are contaminated with the spores or by eating meat from infected animals. This type of infection is rare in man, although the alimentary tract is the usual portal of entry in animal infections. Penicillin is reported to be effective in the treatment of anthrax.

In caring for persons with anthrax infections, care must be taken to destroy the resistant spore-forming organisms which are present in large numbers in body fluids.

PREVENTION   Since the disease is an occupational hazard, most measures will need to be centered in the industries that use hides, hair, and wool. They should include the sterilization of bristles used in making brushes, the use of mechanical devices to remove dust from work rooms, the disinfection of water used for washing hides and wool, and prompt treatment for all skin abrasions. To prevent the spread of anthrax among farm animals, imported bone meal should be sterilized. Carcasses of animals that die of anthrax and straw or feed contaminated by them should be completely *burned to ash* to destroy all anthrax spores. If this is not done other animals may acquire the infection from soil contaminated with anthrax spores.

Malleomyces mallei   Glanders, or farcy, is a communicable disease of horses and various other mammals (mules, asses, cats, goats). It is caused by *Malleomyces mallei*, a small, gram-negative, nonmotile rod, which does not form spores. Its growth on artificial media is scanty and it sometimes stains unevenly. It is present in the pus or mucus in the nose, throat, or bowel of the infected man or beast. The organism may invade the skin or mucous membrane giving rise to an acute or chronic disease characterized by ulcers and nodules. In man, the infection is likely to be severe and may be fatal. One attack of the disease does not confer complete or lasting immunity. Since the disease is highly infectious and may be transferred from person to person, precautions must be taken to prevent the transfer of the bacteria to other persons.

The diagnosis can be made on the basis of (1) the complement-fixation test, (2) the agglutination test, (3) typical lesions in a guinea pig inoculated with pus, and (4) the *mallein* test. The latter is comparable to the *tuberculin* test for tuberculosis. The introduction of mallein (glycerol broth in which the organisms have grown) causes a rise in temperature and local inflammation in the sensitive animal. It may be applied to the skin or inserted into the eye. The ophthalmic test is used for horses but not for man.

The most effective means of preventing glanders is to destroy the reservoir of infection; i.e., those horses that react to the mallein test. Persons who work with horses should exercise care in handling infected animals.

Mycobacterium tuberculosis   Three strains of *Mycobacterium tuberculosis* cause infections in warm-blooded animals; the human, the bovine, and the avian. The avian causes disease in chickens and swine, while the bovine and human strains cause tuberculosis in man, cows, dogs, and swine. The infection may be transferred from tuberculous animals to man or vice versa. The cow is the important source of bovine tuberculosis in human beings.

The bovine strain of the tuberculosis parasite is essentially like the human strain (see page 413). The chief difference lies in the fact that the bovine type is pathogenic for rabbits and in man it seldom causes lung infections, whereas the human strain is less pathogenic for rabbits and commonly causes pulmonary lesions in man. Tuberculosis in cattle is usually a chronic infection involving the lungs and sometimes the udder and intestines. The organisms are transmitted to man by milk and may cause tuberculosis of the bones, joints, lymph glands, or intestine.

State-wide programs for killing tuberculous cattle provide an effective means of decreasing the reservoir of infection. Pasteurization is an effective way of destroying the parasites that may be present in milk. Meat inspection offers another means of protecting human beings against massive doses of tuberculosis organisms. The danger of transmission by meats is lessened by the fact that meats are usually cooked before being eaten.

Brucella   The brucella are small, gram-negative, non-motile rods that are pathogenic for goats, swine, and cattle. They were named for the British Army Surgeon, Robert Bruce, who discovered the organisms in the tissues of persons who died of Malta fever. There are three strains or types of the organisms, which can be differentiated by the use of suitable laboratory media: *Brucella melitensis* (goats), *Brucella abortus* (cattle), and *Brucella suis* (swine). These organisms cause infectious abortion in animals and are present in the tissues, blood, urine, feces, and milk. They may be transmitted to man by direct contact with the animal or indirectly by ingestion or inhalation. Brucella infections are, therefore, usually limited to those who work in meat-packing establishments, to farmers, and to those who drink raw milk. In addition, the infection is common among laboratory workers who handle the brucella.

The brucella are characteristically intracellular parasites. In man they enter through the intestinal or pharyngeal lymph nodes and invade the phagocytic cells of the liver and lymph nodes. It is thought that this intracellular position protects the organisms from the action of circulating antibodies and may in part account for the chronic nature of the disease. After an incubation period of from six to thirty days, a general infection occurs. The disease may be an acute one causing death, but more frequently it is subacute or chronic and lasts for months or years. The symptoms and the course of the disease are extremely variable. The symptoms often include anemia, an irregular (undulant) fever, chills, sweating, and pains in the joints and muscles. Frequently the patient will be up and about for a part of the day when he is free from fever. Furthermore, the disease often occurs in a mild chronic form which is difficult to recognize. Patients with chronic brucellosis may suffer ill health for years and are often considered neurotic by physicians and by their friends. In recent years, about 4000 cases of brucellosis have been reported in the United States each year. It has been estimated that the total number of brucella infections is 40,000 or more. In other words, the brucella infections recognized and reported are only a small fraction of the whole. Agglutinins appear in the blood after ten days, so reaction to the agglutination test is usually positive in the second or third week. However, in communities where raw milk is used, many persons who have no history of brucella infections will have positive agglutination reactions. Therefore, a positive agglutination reaction does not necessarily mean that the person has the infection; it merely means that he has antibodies against these organisms.

Infected persons become sensitive to the protein of brucella organisms. This sensitivity can be detected by a skin test (brucellergen test) which resembles the tuberculin test (page 417). A positive reaction indicates past or present infection.

As would be expected, susceptibility varies greatly. Certain persons appear to have an immunity, due, perhaps, to subclinical infections. To date, attempts to develop an active or passive immunity in man have failed, but chemotherapy with the sulfonamides and streptomycin or chloramphenicol, aureomycin, and Terramycin appears to have some value. Recent reports suggest that chloramphenicol given with small doses of slowly absorbed brucella antigen has resulted in decreased sensitivity and increased resistance and has given better results than those obtained when the antibiotic was administered alone. Theoretically, the disease may be transferred from man to man but this transmission is rare.

Leptospira   Leptospirosis is an infectious disease of domestic and certain wild animals. The infection in man is known as *hemorrhagic jaundice* or *Weil's disease*. It may be caused by any one of several species of leptospira. These organisms are tightly coiled spirochetes with a hooklike bend at one or both ends. The organisms are so small that they readily pass through a Berkefeld filter. They grow with reluctance on serum medium but multiply readily within the guinea pig. The organisms are primarily blood parasites and may be found in blood, urine, and tissues of infected animals.

The strains occurring in North America include:

ORGANISM	HOSTS
Leptospira bataviae	Mongooses, rats, mice
Leptospira pomona	Cattle, swine, horses
Leptospira autumnalis	Unknown
Leptospira ballum	Rats, mice
Leptospira canicola	Dogs
Leptospira icterohemorrhagica	Dogs, mongooses, rats, mice
Leptospira pyogenes	Rats, mice
Leptospira hebdomadis	Mice

These organisms are commonly transmitted to man by contaminated water or from contaminated working spaces.

The path by which the parasites invade the human host is not definitely known. After an incubation period of from four to nineteen days, the organisms appear in the blood; they invade all tissues but may persist in the kidneys for weeks. The usual signs of infection are fever, prostration, muscular pains, jaundice, and hemorrhage. Meningitis and transient paralysis have also been reported.

All human beings appear to be susceptible to the infection, which is an occupational hazard for men who come in contact with stagnant water that may have been contaminated with animal urine. Miners, bargemen, garbage workers, sewage workers, soldiers in trenches, rat trappers, and swimmers are prone to infection.

The extermination of rats and mice may be useful. It is obviously desirable that workmen and others protect themselves from contact with animal urine and from water that is contaminated with urine.

Spirillum minus   *Spirillum minus,* the cause of sodoku or rat-bite fever, is a short spiral organism found in the blood of infected animals such as rats, cats, weasels, ferrets, dogs, or bandicoots. The organisms can be grown in the laboratory by inoculating rats, mice, or guinea pigs and may be observed by a darkfield microscopic examination. The parasites usually reach man by the bite of an infected animal. After an incubation period of from one to three weeks, the injured area becomes inflamed, the lymph glands enlarge, and a fever develops. The disease, rat bite fever,* is usually limited to laboratory workers and others who have been bitten by rats. Like the spirochete of syphilis, *Spirillum minus* is sensitive to arsenic and penicillin.

Pasteurella tularensis   *Pasteurella tularensis* is a small, gram-negative rod that varies in size and shape. The organism is nonmotile and forms a capsule when growing in the animal body. It is a parasite of rodents that causes an epidemic septicemia among wild animals and is transferred either by contact, by ingestion, or by the bite of an arthropod vector. The organism has been isolated from many different kinds of animals, including rabbits, opossum, tree squirrels, skunks, deer, foxes, coyotes, ground hogs, muskrats, bull snakes, sage hens, quail, wood ticks, dog ticks, horseflies, and deer flies. Of these the wild rabbit is most frequently infected.

The disease in man is called *rabbit fever, deer fly fever,* or *tularemia;* the latter was derived from the name of Tulare County (California) where the organisms were first isolated from wild rodents. The parasite usually reaches man through contact with the carcass of an infected animal, or by a tick bite, or through eating inadequately cooked meat. The common form is characterized by a mild fever, a punched-out ulcer on the hand, and swollen glands that may suppurate. The organisms sometimes invade the conjunctiva or the lungs, or

---

* There have been recent reports of rat-bite fever associated with a microorganism called *Streptobacillus moniliformis.* This organism also is a rat parasite but differs in shape and in the fact that it can be grown on artificial medium.

they may invade the intestines and blood stream, causing an infection very similar to typhoid fever.

The diagnosis can be confirmed by inoculating a guinea pig or suitable artificial medium with body secretions. The infected person becomes sensitive to the organism, so that the reaction to a skin test using dead bacteria becomes positive early in the disease. Antibody formation can be detected within two weeks by an agglutination test. Tularemia antiserum and streptomycin have proved of some value in treatment. There have been conflicting reports regarding the value of aureomycin and chloramphenicol. A vaccine made from tularemia organisms treated with phenol is available and appears to be of value for protecting laboratory workers and others against the disease.

Susceptibility to tularemia appears to be general and one attack confers a high degree of resistance. The infection, which is neither prevalent nor severe, is usually limited to laboratory workers, hunters, butchers, and housewives who prepare rabbit for cooking. The disease has been recognized in the United States since 1904, although it was known in Siberia and Japan much earlier. Since the strains of the parasites found in the three countries are identical, it is thought that the disease spread from the rodents of Siberia to those of Japan and then to those of the United States. In tularemia, as in other animal diseases, man is an accidental host and therefore is not important in maintaining the parasite.

The following measures are useful in preventing the infection: (1) avoiding contact with ticks and blood-sucking flies; (2) avoiding contact with body fluids from ticks, flies, and rabbits; and (3) cooking rabbit meat thoroughly.

RICKETTSIAS ACQUIRED FROM ANIMAL SOURCES

Coxiella burnetii (Q fever)   The rickettsias of Q (query) fever (*Coxiella burnetii*) are small organisms which grow readily in chick embryos. They are found in various species of ticks, sheep, goats, and cattle. The disease in cattle is a mild blood stream infection which occurs without symptoms. It is thought that cattle are infected by tick bites or by inhaling infected dust. Many species of ticks are naturally infected and some, perhaps all, pass through the eggs so that each successive generation of ticks is infected. *Coxiella burnetii* is relatively resistant and may survive pasteurization procedures. Human infections of Q fever have been reported from Australia, Europe, Mexico, and the United States. In man the coxiella may be acquired by inhalation of infected dust, by drinking raw milk, or by direct contact with tissues or excreta of infected animals. The persons most commonly infected include those who work in slaughter houses, dairies, and laboratories and those who live near dairies or sheep barns. Man-to-man transmission is rare except when there is direct contact with infected materials.

After an incubation period of nineteen days (fourteen to twenty-six) the infected person develops fever, headache, backache, and chilly sensations. X-ray examination reveals patchy areas of consolidation in the lungs although the individual experiences few chest symptoms. Some individuals develop jaundice. After several weeks the fever leaves and the person recovers. Aureomycin, chloramphenicol, and Terramycin have proved of value in treating the infection. Q fever differs from other rickettsial infections in that it may be air-borne, it causes no skin rash, and the antibodies formed in response to it do not react with proteus organisms. (See page 497.)

Coxiella burnetii may be isolated by injecting infected blood, spinal fluid, or urine into a guinea pig. Ten days after the onset of illness antibodies can be detected by agglutination or complement-fixation tests. Control measures include a vaccine for persons who cannot avoid exposure. Pasteurization of milk and milk products is important because it will kill many if not all rickettsias present.

VIRUSES ACQUIRED FROM ANIMAL SOURCES

The Virus of Rabies   Rabies is a fatal infection caused by a specific filtrable virus. It is essentially a disease of dogs, foxes, and skunks, but may be transmitted to other wild and domestic animals. The virus, which is present in the saliva, is carried to living tissue by the bite of the rabid animal. It invades the nerve trunks and finally the central nervous system. The infected cells of the brain or spinal cord show characteristic inclusion bodies called Negri bodies. This fatal infection presents several distinguishing features which vary with the species of the host.

IN THE DOG   The disease is characterized by three stages: irritability, fury, and paralysis. In the first stage, after an incubation period of twelve days, the dog runs wildly, bumping into objects as though it were blind. This stage lasts from fifteen to twenty-four hours. In the second phase, which lasts for three or four days, the dog froths at the mouth and snaps viciously at any object in its path and sometimes barks hoarsely as if it were in pain. The animal fails to recognize its home or its master and refuses food and water. During this period it may wander far from home. In the final stage, before the dog dies, it becomes weak and exhausted and may develop paralysis or convulsions. In some dogs, the excitement stage fails to appear. This form of the disease, sometimes called *dumb rabies,* is more likely to occur in pets than in stray dogs.

IN MAN   Rabies in man is transmitted by the bite of a rabid animal. The incubation period is long (two to eight weeks), except when the bite is on the face or neck. The disease begins with tingling at the site of the bite, loss of appetite, insomnia, headache, mental depression, and irritability which may be followed by a period of excitement and mental confusion. The sight of water stimulates spasms of the muscles of the pharynx and larynx, thereby accounting for the name *hydrophobia,* literally "fear of water." After a period of irritability, the paralysis increases and coma and death follow.

PROPHYLAXIS   A biting dog should be placed under veterinary supervision for ten days. In that time, if the dog is rabid, it will develop the typical signs of the disease. It is unwise to kill the dog at once because, in the early stage of the disease, Negri bodies are not present in the brain cells. The diagnosis of rabies is made by finding the Negri bodies. However, if the dog has been killed, its head should be packed in ice and sent to a state laboratory for examination.

Any wound from a dog bite should be treated by a physician. The older treatment of cauterizing the wound with fuming nitric acid is being replaced by thorough cleansing with soap and water or with Zephiran. In man, the long incubation period makes it safe to delay the specific treatment until the dog is proved rabid. Then the Pasteur treatment of fourteen or more daily inoculations with attenuated virus may be given. In rare cases this vaccination is followed by a paralysis; it should, therefore, be given only when necessary. Mere contact of the skin with saliva does not transmit the infection, but any abrasion caused by an animal bite should be seen by a physician who will decide whether the vaccine treatment is necessary. The first-aid treatment for wounds caused by a dog bite consists of washing the abrasion with running water to remove the dog saliva that may be present. Rabies antiserum is available and may be used in conjunction with the vaccine. To be effective it must be given early, preferably within twenty-four hours after receiving the bite. The vaccine may be started later. Rabies vaccine has proved useful in protecting dogs from the disease.

CONTROL   In view of the large reservoir of infection in wild animals it seems probable that rabies will continue to be a problem in the United States. Rabies control aims to decrease the number of susceptible animals and to prevent contact between susceptible and infected subjects. In dogs this can be done by vaccinating and by requiring owners to keep the animals on leash or confine them to their own premises. With foxes, skunks, and vampire bats the number of susceptibles can be reduced by periodic hunting.

The Virus of Ornithosis (Psittacosis)   Ornithosis is a virus disease of birds which may be transferred to man by direct or indirect contact with birds. When associated with psittacine birds (parrots, parrakeets, parrotlets, cockatoos, etc.) the disease is called *psittacosis* or *parrot fever*. A related strain of the virus carried by domestic pigeons, chickens, ducks, turkeys, and other birds causes a disease (ornithosis) which closely resembles parrot fever but is less fatal to man. Ornithosis and psittacosis are caused by a specific virus which is present in the nasal secretions and droppings and also in the blood and tissues of infected birds. The virus is excreted by healthy carriers as well as by the diseased birds. Diseased birds may be recognized by the fact that they are thin and weak, and their feathers have a ruffled appearance. In human beings, infections have been contracted by bird handlers and by persons who cleaned cages previously occupied by infected birds.

Different strains of the virus appear to differ in their virulence for man; those carried by psittacine birds tend to cause more severe infections than those carried by domestic fowl. An incubation period of six to fifteen days is followed by a mild or severe illness that may be confused with pneumonia, typhoid fever, or influenza. Fortunately the virus, one of the lymphogranuloma group, is susceptible to penicillin and the broad spectrum antibiotics. Strict isolation is necessary because the virus is transmitted to those who care for the infected person. The wearing of gauze masks (8 layers of 40 to 48 threads to the inch or 16 layers of 20 to 24 threads to the inch) is advised by a Committee of the American Public Health Association in its report on "The Control of Communicable Diseases." All discharges should be disinfected.

The infection is common among parrots, love birds, and parrakeets; canaries, pigeons, and domestic fowl are frequently infected. Since apparently healthy birds may be infected, persons who work with birds should aim to avoid ingesting or inhaling the virus.

Cat Scratch Fever   Cat scratch fever is a disease which resembles tularemia. It is always preceded by the scratch or bite of a cat. After an incubation period of five to six days the individual develops fever, headache, and swollen painful lymph nodes. The causative agent is thought to be a virus but it has not yet been isolated. Aureomycin and Terramycin are said to be useful in controlling secondary infection. The virus (?) apparently does not cause illness in the cat.

SUMMARY

ORGANISM	DISEASE	SITE OF INFECTION	DIAGNOSTIC PROCEDURES	ACTIVE IMMUNIZATION	PASSIVE IMMUNIZATION	CHEMOTHERAPY
Bacteria: *Bacillus anthracis*	Anthrax	Skin, lungs	Cultures	Bacterial vaccine for animals	Serum therapy	Penicillin
Malleomyces mallei	Glanders	Skin or mucous membranes	Agglutination, complement-fixation, skin tests	None	None	None
Brucella	Brucellosis or undulant fever	General	Blood cultures, agglutination tests	None	None	Streptomycin Aureomycin Chloromycetin Terramycin
Leptospira	Hemorrhagic jaundice	General	Blood cultures	None	None	None
Spirillum minus	Rat bite fever	General	Darkfield examination of secretion of blood	Uncertain	Uncertain	Arsenic compounds Penicillin

SUMMARY—(Continued)

ORGANISM	DISEASE	SITE OF INFECTION	DIAGNOSTIC PROCEDURES	ACTIVE IMMUNIZATION	PASSIVE IMMUNIZATION	CHEMOTHERAPY
Pasteurella tularensis	Tularemia	General or local involving eyes, skin, glands, or intestines	Culture of blood or fluid from lesions, agglutination tests, skin tests	Bacterial vaccine (experimental)	Serum therapy	Streptomycin Dihydro-streptomycin
Rickettsias: *Coxiella burnetii*	Q fever	Lungs, general	Guinea pig inoculation Complement-fixation tests	Rickettsial vaccine	None	Aureomycin Terramycin Chloramphenicol
Viruses: Specific virus	Rabies	Central nervous system	Examination of brain of dog for Negri bodies	Attenuated virus vaccine	Antirabies serum	None
Specific virus	Psittacosis	General	Animal inoculation of secretions or blood complement-fixation test	None	None	Aureomycin Terramycin Chloramphenicol
Specific virus (?)	Cat scratch fever	Lymph nodes	None	None	None	Aureomycin (experimental)

SUPPLEMENTARY READINGS

BOOKS:

American Public Health Association: The Control of Communicable Diseases. An Official Report of the American Public Health Association. New York, 7th ed., 1950.

Dubos, R. J.: Bacterial and Mycotic Infections of Man. 2d ed. Philadelphia, J. B. Lippincott Co., 1952.

Maxcy, K. F.: Rosenau Preventive Medicine and Hygiene. 7th ed. New York, Appleton-Century-Crofts, Inc., 1951.

Rivers, T. M.: Viral and Rickettsial Infections of Man. 2d ed. Philadelphia, J. B. Lippincott Co., 1952.

Smith, D. T., and Conant, N. F.: Zinsser's Textbook of Bacteriology. 10th ed. New York, Appleton-Century-Crofts, Inc., 1952.

Webster, L. L.: Rabies. New York, The Macmillan Co., 1942.

PERIODICALS:

Corwin, W. C., and Stubbs, S. P.: Further Studies on Tularemia in the Ozarks. J.A.M.A., *149:* 343–345, 1952.

Editorial: Tularemia. J.A.M.A., *144:* 1468, 1950.

Editorial: The Problem of Brucellosis. J.A.M.A., *145:* 1136–1137, 1951.

Editorial: Prevention of Rabies. J.A.M.A., *149:* 1318–1319, 1952.

Evans, A. C.: Brucellosis in the United States. Am. J. Pub. Health, *37:* 139–151, 1947.

Foshay, L.: Tularemia. Ann. Rev. Microbiol., *4:* 313–330, 1950.

Fox, R. A.: So-Called "Cat Scratch Fever." Arch. Path., *54:* 75–83, 1952.

Frederickson, L. E.: Mass Immunization of Dogs against Rabies. Am. J. Pub. Health, *43:* 399–404, 1953.

Gauld, R. L., and others: Leptospiral Meningitis—Report of Outbreak among American Troops in Okinawa. J.A.M.A., *149:* 228–231, 1952.

Gochenour, W. S., and others: Leptospiral Etiology of Fort Bragg Fever. Pub. Health Rep., *67:* 811–813, 1952.

Irons, J. V.: Outbreak of Psittacosis (Ornithosis) from Working with Turkeys or Chickens. Am. J. Pub. Health, *41:* 931–937, 1951.

Koprowski, H., and Cox, H. R.: Recent Developments in the Prophylaxis of Rabies. Am. J. Pub. Health, *41:* 1483–1489, 1951.

Lange, H. L.: Cat-Scratch Fever. Am. J. Nursing, *53:* 832–833, 1953.

Leon, A. P., and others: Antibiotics and Immunodesensitization in the Treatment of Human Brucellosis. Science, *115:* 576–577, 1952.

Public Health Reports: Public Health in Veterinary Medicine. Pub. Health Rep., *67:* 977–988, 1952.

Spink, W. W., and others: Human Brucellosis. J.A.M.A., *136:* 382–387, 1948.

Steele, J. H., and Helvig, R. J.: Anthrax in the United States. Pub. Health Rep., *68:* 616–623, 1953.

Vinnard, R. T.: The Local Treatment of Dog Bites. Postgrad. Med., *10:* 322–326, 1951.

Yager, R. H., and others: Current Problems in the Field of Leptospirosis. Am. J. Pub. Health, *43:* 411–414, 1953.

CHAPTER 32

Organisms Transmitted by
Fleas, Lice, or Ticks

BACTERIA: *Pasteurella pestis*

RICKETTSIAS: *Rickettsia prowazekii;*
Rickettsia mooseri; Rickettsia
rickettsii

BACTERIA: PASTEURELLA PESTIS

THE PLAGUE bacillus, *Pasteurella pestis*, is a short, gram-negative rod which stains unevenly and grows readily on laboratory
media. It is easily killed by heat and chemicals, but may live
for weeks or months at low temperatures and within infected
tissues. It is capable of penetrating unbroken skin and grows
profusely in the animal body. As a stress agent it is highly
effective in producing extensive local and systemic destruction
of tissues. It is a parasite of rodents and may be found in rats,
squirrels, rabbits, mice, and prairie dogs. Epidemics of plague
occur periodically among rodent populations. The organism
causes a blood-stream infection in the rat and is transmitted
from animal to animal by the bite of the rat flea. When the rat
dies, the fleas leave and attach themselves to any warm-
blooded creature at hand.

When the flea transfers the parasites to man, the organisms
may cause a more or less local infection, a general infection,
or a fatal pneumonia. From a flea bite on the arm or leg the
bacteria multiply and invade the tissues, lymph stream, and
lymph nodes. *Pasteurella pestis* produces an endotoxin which
injures cells of lymphatic and blood vessels giving rise to
inflammation, hemorrhage, coagulation of body fluids, and at
times extensive destruction of tissue in lymph nodes, spleen,
liver, and lungs. The characteristic swollen, suppurating lymph
glands, called *buboes* (meaning groin), give the disease its
name—*bubonic plague*. When the organisms invade the blood
stream, they give rise to secondary infection, plague-boils, in
494

various parts of the body. These bacteria often have great invasive ability and produce injury to capillary networks, lymph nodes, liver, and spleen, and therefore may produce a form of disease that is severe and rapidly fatal. During the Middle Ages the infection was often accompanied by hemorrhages under the skin. This fact and the virulence of the infection explains why the disease was known as the *black death*. A mild form of the disease (*pestis minor*) occurs with little fever or toxemia; it is characterized by the formation of a bubo which may or may not suppurate.

The parasites may cause a primary or secondary pneumonia which is rapidly fatal. In this type of disease, the bacteria are present in the sputum in huge numbers and are so easily transferred from man to man that great care should be taken to protect persons who care for the victims of bubonic plague. These precautions include the wearing of a long gown and gloves, and covering the head and shoulders with a helmet of thick cloth fitted with transparent windows.

Prevention   Susceptibility appears to be general and one attack confers a lasting immunity. A passive immunity lasting three or four weeks can be conferred by an antibacterial serum. An active immunity of short duration (probably six months) can be induced by a bacterial vaccine. Plague vaccine, together with DDT (dichloro-diphenyl-trichloro-ethane), a delousing agent, proved of value in protecting United States Army personnel stationed in areas where plague was endemic.

Plague is epidemic in parts of Asia and Africa and is endemic in the rodent populations in many parts of the world. Early in the 20th century, plague-infected rats entered a California port and transmitted the infection to the ground squirrels and other rodents. As a result, there is now a relatively large reservoir of infection that is a potential threat, especially if the disease should spread to domestic rats and mice.

During periods when plague is not present in the human population its prevention depends largely upon flea and rodent control; that is to say, the extermination of rats on ships and in storehouses, the rat-proofing of buildings, and the protection of human beings from rats and their fleas are all-important

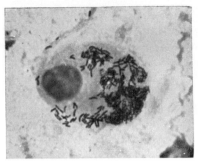

Figure 79   Rickettsias growing in the cytoplasm of a large serosal cell of the tunica vaginalis of the guinea pig. (U. S. Typhus Commission. In: Mackie, T. T., et al.: Manual of Tropical Medicine.)

factors. In the western states where plague is present, the wild rodents must also be exterminated. Persons engaged in rodent control should be vaccinated and should wear fleaproof clothing, including high boots and tight wristbands and collars. Plague epidemics can be stopped by dusting rat runs and rat harborages with DDT to kill fleas. Killing rats without first killing the fleas may actually favor the spread of the disease by forcing the rat parasites to find new hosts.

Early diagnosis is important because mortality in untreated plague is often from 50 to 90 per cent. Sulfadiazine, streptomycin, aureomycin, and plague antiserum are reported as valuable in treatment. When a person develops plague, great care must be taken to prevent the spread of the bacteria to man or to rats and fleas. When possible, plague victims are cared for in their homes or in emergency hospitals by teams of specially trained medical personnel. This is desirable because the patient is saved the stress of being transported to a distant hospital and often treatment can be begun earlier. The victim should be cared for in a room that is well screened and free from insects and rodents. All discharges should be disinfected or burned. Fomites also must be disinfected by the use of heat or chemicals. Every precaution must be taken in handling the bodies of those who die of plague because the pneumonic type spreads readily from man to man. Attendants, therefore, must protect themselves from infected droplets of sputum. Health authorities usually require a seven-day quarantine of persons who have been exposed to plague and a terminal *fumigation* of the premises to *kill insects and rodents* that might transmit the organisms. (Fumigation as a means of killing bacteria is an outmoded measure.) In addition, the walls, floor, and furniture should be thoroughly cleaned with soap and hot water, or 5 per cent cresol, and allowed to air for forty-eight hours.

RICKETTSIAS

Rickettsias are the common parasites of arthropods such as ticks, lice, fleas, and mites (Figure 79). Although most rickettsias are associated with animal hosts and their parasites, they sometimes cause severe infection in man. They characteristically cause severe stress by damaging capillary walls throughout the body, especially in the skin, muscles, and central nervous system. In this text, the discussion will be limited to typhus, Rocky Mountain spotted fever and Q Fever (see page 486).

European or Louse-Borne Typhus   Typhus is an old disease associated with famine, war, filth, rodents, and vermin. It has been known by many names, including *ship fever, jail fever,* and *camp fever.* It has been the curse of armies as well as of civilian populations. From the 16th to the 18th centuries, typhus was endemic in England, Ireland, and central Europe but now is usually limited to the Balkans, Asia, and Africa. Typhus commonly becomes epidemic during periods of war, famine, or forced migration, and is more common during the winter months when people crowd into shelters to escape the cold. Such conditions favor the transfer of infected lice from person to person. For example, typhus occurred frequently in Nazi concentration camps. Typhus, the scourge of armies, killed more soldiers than did enemy bullets in the Thirty Years' War and in Napoleon's disastrous Russian campaign. After World War I, there were great epidemics of typhus in Russia and Serbia. During World War II, there was an extensive outbreak of typhus in Naples which was effectively stopped by the use of DDT.

The typhus rickettsias (*Rickettsia prowazekii*) multiply in the intestine of the louse that has fed on an infected human being. After seven days, tremendous numbers of organisms are excreted in the feces and saliva. These may be introduced into man by the bite of the louse or by scratching the skin or conjunctiva that has been soiled by louse excretions, or by inhaling dried louse secretions from infested clothing. The rickettsias start to grow in the human tissues and, during an incubation period of twelve days, they invade and damage the blood vessels of the skin, heart muscle, and central nervous system, causing multiple small hemorrhages into the tissues and the formation of clots within the vessels. The infection is characterized by severe headache, stupor, fever, chills, and a rash which appears on the fourth or fifth day. The illness often ends by crisis on the twelfth day. Before antibiotics were available fatality rates among adults commonly ranged from 20 to 40 or even 90 per cent; in children, the infection is mild. Chloramphenicol, aureomycin, and Terramycin inhibit the growth of the rickettsias and markedly shorten the febrile period. Since these drugs do not kill the organisms, they are usually given intermittently until the body builds up its own immunity.

In endemic areas, typhus is usually recognized by the clinical symptoms. The diagnosis can be confirmed by the finding of antibodies as shown by positive Weil-Felix and complement-fixation tests and also by inoculation of guinea pigs. (See Figure 79.)

All persons are susceptible to typhus unless they have had the infection. Recovery from the disease confers lasting immunity. A vaccine is available and should be administered to persons before going to areas where typhus is endemic. The delousing of human beings and their clothing is essential for preventing outbreaks of typhus in endemic areas. Houses, vehicles, and clothing must be included in the delousing process because body lice may live in clothing for nine days, and their eggs may survive for forty days. DDT has been used with success for killing body lice and other arthropod vectors.*

Persons caring for typhus patients should wear clothing impregnated with DDT and should further protect themselves

---

* Recent reports (Editorial; King; Metcalf) indicate that various strains of arthropods are becoming resistant to DDT.

from lice and rickettsias by wearing gloves and gowns with close-fitting sleeves or coveralls which fit closely at the wrists and ankles. Adequate measures must be taken to free the patient and his clothing from the insects and their eggs. Since rickettsias may be present in louse feces in large amounts and may remain alive and infective for long periods, inhalation or contact with dust from infective materials should be avoided. Fomites, including hypodermic needles, should be handled with care and sterilized after use.

Murine or Rat Typhus Murine typhus, though milder, is similar to European typhus. It is an infection of rodents transmitted from rodent to rodent or from rodent to man by the rat flea or by the rat louse. The rickettsias (*Rickettsia mooseri*) can be transferred from man to man by body lice in the same manner as European typhus. The disease in man occurs in the summer and fall and is limited to sailors, longshoremen, and others who work where rats are numerous. Murine typhus is found in many parts of the world under varying names such as Toulon typhus, Moscow typhus, Manchurian typhus, and Malaya or shop typhus. The disease is found in the southern states and in Mexico where it is called *tabardillo*. The control of murine typhus, like that of plague, depends upon the eradication of fleas and rats.

Rickettsia rickettsii The rickettsias of Rocky Mountain spotted fever (*Rickettsia rickettsii*) are transferred to man by the bite of the wood tick, lone star tick, or the dog tick. The parasites develop in all the tissues of the tick, including the ovaries and eggs or the testes and spermatozoa, thereby infecting each succeeding generation of ticks. There is no evidence that the rickettsias injure the infected ticks. The organisms remain dormant during the long periods when the tick lives without feeding. However, when the insect comes in contact with a mammal, it attaches itself, burrows into the skin, and fills itself with blood. After an incubation period of six to eight hours, the rickettsias become active and multiply and if the tick remains attached, invade the tissues of the new host. Man is an accidental host for rickettsias and is quite unimportant in the life cycle of this parasite. Nevertheless, the organisms are capable of producing serious illness in man. As in typhus, they cause extensive damage to the lining of blood vessels.

ROCKY MOUNTAIN SPOTTED FEVER (AMERICAN SPOTTED FEVER, TICK TYPHUS)   From three to ten days after the bite by an infected tick the rickettsias invade the blood stream and blood vessels. The damage often gives rise to the formation of clots in vessels (thrombosis), to gangrene, and to hemorrhage into the skin. The disease has a sudden onset and is characterized by fever, intense headache, pains in the back, muscles and joints and a rosy rash. The infections vary from mild to very severe, although they seem to be less serious in children. Aureomycin, Terramycin, and chloramphenicol have been reported to be useful in checking the progress of the infection. The disease has been reported in forty-four states. In the Rocky Mountain area, it is transmitted by the wood tick, in eastern states by the dog tick, and in the south by the lone star tick. All human beings are susceptible to the disease. Recovery from infection confers a partial immunity. A vaccine is available for those who are exposed to ticks. Since this protection lasts for a year or less, the vaccine must be given each year.

Since rickettsias are not transferred from man to man, prevention depends upon avoiding contact with ticks. The most satisfactory method is to stay away from tick-infested areas. In such areas, picnickers and hikers should wear boots and protective clothing. After returning from the woods, they should bathe and search the body (especially the axilla, groin, the area behind the ears, and the hairline on the back of the neck) for the presence of ticks. When discovered, the ticks should be removed with forceps and burned and the hands should be carefully washed with soap and water. Similar precautions should be observed in removing ticks from dogs. Care should be taken not to crush the tick since the tissues and fluids may contain rickettsias.

SUMMARY

ORGANISM	DISEASE	SITE OF INFECTION	DIAGNOSTIC PROCEDURES	ACTIVE IMMUNITY	CHEMOTHERAPY
Pasteurella pestis	Plague	Local ulcer, lymph glands, general, or lungs	Cultures, inoculation of rats	Bacterial vaccine	Sulfadiazine Streptomycin Aureomycin (experimental)
Rickettsia prowazekii	Louse-borne typhus	General—especially blood vessels	Weil–Felix Complement-fixation	Killed rickettsial vaccine	Chloromycetin
Rickettsia mooseri	Murine typhus		Weil–Felix Complement-fixation	Killed rickettsial vaccine	Aureomycin
Rickettsia rickettsii	Spotted fever	General—especially blood vessels			Terramycin

SUPPLEMENTARY READINGS

BOOKS:

American Public Health Association: The Control of Communicable Diseases. An Official Report of the American Public Health Association. 7th ed. New York, 1950.

Burrows, W.: Jordan-Burrows Textbook of Bacteriology. 15th ed. Philadelphia, W. B. Saunders Co., 1949.

Dubos, R. J.: Bacterial and Mycotic Infections of Man. 2d ed. Philadelphia, J. B. Lippincott Co., 1952.

Greenberg, M., and Matz, A. V.: Modern Concepts of Communicable Disease. New York, G. P. Putnam's Sons, 1953.

Mackie, T. T., Hunter, G. W., and Worth, C. B.: A Manual of Tropical Medicine. 2d ed. Philadelphia, W. B. Saunders Co., 1954.

Rivers, T. M.: Viral and Rickettsial Infections of Man. 2d ed. Philadelphia, J. B. Lippincott Co., 1952.

Smillie, W. G.: Preventive Medicine and Public Health. 2d ed. New York, The Macmillan Co., 1952.

Smith, D. T., and Conant, N. F.: Zinsser's Textbook of Bacteriology. 10th ed. New York, Appleton-Century-Crofts, Inc., 1952.

Zinsser, H.: Rats, Lice and History. Boston, Atlantic Monthly Press, 1935.

PERIODICALS:

Bell, E. J., and Pickens, E. G.: A Toxic Substance Associated with the Rickettsias of the Spotted Fever Group. J. Immunol., *70:* 461–472, 1953.

Editorial: House Fly Resistance to Chemicals. J.A.M.A., *149:* 1635, 1952.

King, W. V.: DDT Resistant Houseflies and Mosquitoes. J. Economic Entomology, *43:* 527–532, 1950.

Metcalf, R. L.: Insects v. Insecticides. Scient. Am., *187:* 21–25, 1952.

Smadel, J. E.: Present Status of Antibiotic Therapy in Viral and Rickettsial Infections. Bull. New York Acad. Med., *27:* 221–231, 1951.

CHAPTER 33

Organisms Transmitted by Mosquitoes

PROTOZOA: *Malarial Parasites*

VIRUSES: *Yellow Fever; Dengue Fever; Encephalitis*

PROTOZOA: MALARIAL PARASITES

MALARIA parasites are small protozoa which develop in certain anopheline mosquitoes and then are transmitted to man or other vertebrates such as apes, monkeys, birds, or reptiles.

Human malaria is caused by four closely related protozoan parasites with similar life cycles. They are: (1) *Plasmodium vivax*, the common variety which is found in the Temperate Zone and in the tropics; (2) *Plasmodium malariae*, a type found in Asia and in the Mediterranean regions; (3) *Plasmodium falciparum*, a virulent organism found chiefly in the tropics; and (4) *Plasmodium ovale*, an uncommon species sometimes found in South Africa and New Guinea. These plasmodia have complex life cycles consisting of a sexual phase in the primary host (various species of anopheline mosquitoes) and an asexual development in the human host.

When an infected mosquito bites a human being, the infecting parasites located in the salivary glands of the mosquito are injected directly into a capillary by the biting mosquito. The plasmodia find their way to the cells of the reticuloendothelial system (liver, spleen, bone marrow, etc.). After multiplying in these cells for a period of four or five days, some of the parasites enter the blood stream and invade red blood cells. Lying on the surface of the cell, the plasmodium looks like a small, glassy signet ring. The parasite burrows into the cell and grows at the expense of the cell, using its hemoglobin and transforming it into pigment granules of hematin. During this process, both the red cell and the parasite increase in size. This stage is followed by segmentation which gives rise to rosette-like

503

masses of young parasites. Forty-eight hours* after the entry of the parasite, the damaged red cell disintegrates, liberating a new generation of parasites, each of which in turn invades another red blood cell and repeats the cycle. This process may continue for months or years. Eventually some of the parasites develop into sexual cells called *gametocytes*—the male cell (*microgametocyte*) and the female cell (*macrogametocyte*). The gametocytes are incapable of further development in man and will ultimately die unless they reach a suitable anopheline mosquito.

When ingested by a susceptible female mosquito, the gametocytes mature so rapidly that fertilization may take place within ten or fifteen minutes. The long, motile cell formed by the union of the male and female cells penetrates the gut wall of the mosquito and forms a cyst within the body cavity. Mosquitoes often have hundreds of such cysts developing within them. The cysts enlarge for two or three weeks until hundreds of spindle-shaped cells (*sporozoites*) mature and migrate to the salivary gland and to the other parts of the insect body. The mosquito is now infective, and each time she bites a human being will transfer parasites. The sexual phase of the parasite requires from ten to twelve days in a warm climate and a longer period when temperatures are low. Therefore, the mosquito becomes infective after an incubation period of at least ten days and remains infective for the rest of her life.

The cycle then is clear-cut—a period of development within the mosquito (ten days or more) followed by a period within a human host. The survival of the parasite obviously depends upon three events: (1) the infection of an anopheline mosquito by taking blood which contains the mature forms of the parasite; (2) the survival of the mosquito long enough to permit infection of its salivary glands; and (3) the survival of the mosquito long enough to infect a human being. In endemic areas, these events must take place with great regularity since it is not uncommon to find a high proportion of the human population carrying malaria parasites.

Malaria   Malaria affords a striking example of complex biological relationships involving the parasite and two hosts—

* Plasmodium malariae—seventy-two hours.

the human being and the anopheline mosquito. The development of the parasite in the mosquito occurs without harm to the host. In contrast, the human infection is often attended by acute or chronic illness and may, therefore, bring about far-reaching social consequences. Malaria was well known to the ancient Greeks and Romans and possibly played a part in the decline of both civilizations. The name *malaria*, meaning bad air, represents an early attempt to ascribe a cause for the malady. The infection is common in any area where the following are associated: (1) warmth and moisture (mean summer temperature of 75° F. and an annual rainfall of thirty inches or more); (2) anopheles mosquitoes; and (3) infected human beings. These conditions are uniformly present in many tropical and subtropical regions where the infection is endemic.

In temperate climates, the necessary circumstances may occasionally be present and give rise to epidemics among adults. During the 19th century, malaria was common in the settlements along the Ohio River and its branches. As living conditions improved, malaria progressively decreased until the Ohio valley became relatively free from the disease.

INFECTION   The symptoms of malaria commonly occur about fourteen days after the bite of an infected mosquito. The periodic disintegration of the red cells caused by the parasites gives rise to characteristic chills and fever. In the typical vivax infection, the fever occurs regularly every forty-eight hours with the progressive destruction of red cells causing anemia. The liver and spleen tend to enlarge under the burden of disposing of parasites and broken red cells. Infections by *Plasmodium malariae* are characterized by chills every third day, since that parasite requires seventy-two hours for its development. In the falciparum infection, the chills may occur every forty-eight hours or at irregular intervals. Falciparum, or malignant malaria, is often an acute disease characterized by massive destruction of red cells and consequent severe anemia. In this infection, the invaded red cells tend to stick together and to occlude the small vessels in the brain and other internal organs. Nausea, vomiting, deep coma, and the presence of hemoglobin in the urine are common symptoms in persons with severe infections of this type. As would be expected, mortality rates for falciparum malaria are high (about 25 per cent) as compared with those of vivax infections (3 to 5 per cent). Relapses are especially common in vivax malaria, and may be brought on by a variety of conditions such as fatigue, lack of food, exposure to cold, and gastrointestinal or other infections.

Repeated attacks of malaria undermine the health and interfere with the growth and development of children residing in regions where the disease is endemic. In tropical and subtropical countries, the high prevalence of chronic malaria with its attendant poor health presents tremendous social and economic problems.

Malaria may have been the first infection to be successfully treated by chemotherapy. Early records show that Peruvian bark, a crude form of quinine, was used by the Indians of Central and South America to treat this disease. Today, quinacrine (Atabrine), chloroquine, and chloroguanide (Paludrine) provide effective means of killing the asexual forms of the parasites as they are liberated into the blood stream. These are therefore useful in treating clinical infections and in suppressing attacks of malaria in military personnel. They decrease the number of active parasites but do not prevent infection or relapses. These drugs are useful in controlling the clinical infection but have little effect on the gametocytes which are able to infect the mosquito. The gametocytes can be killed by the administration of the synthetic drug, Plasmochin. A new drug, primaquine, has been reported to be effective in the early stage of the disease before the parasites invade the red blood cells.

SUSCEPTIBILITY   Susceptibility to the infection is general, but clinical malaria occurs chiefly in endemic areas in children and in persons, especially those of the white race, who have migrated from a nonendemic region. In endemic areas, malaria parasites may be found in the blood of as many as 90 per cent of the children and 70 per cent of the adults. Young children are likely to have repeated attacks, while adults and older children may be heavily infected without developing chills and fever. Older natives are often relatively immune and are also comparatively free from parasites. Immunity conferred by repeated malaria infections is highly specific and protects only against the strains that caused its formation.

PREVENTION   At present, there is no effective method of preventing malaria in the person who is exposed to an infected anopheles mosquito. However, the complexity of the life cycle of the parasite makes it possible to limit the spread of the disease by one of the following methods: (1) destruction of mosquito larvae, (2) destruction of adult mosquitoes, (3) protection of man from mosquitoes, or (4) provision of adequate treatment for infected persons.

Mosquito larvae may be destroyed by spraying oils or poisons on the surface of the water in which they grow, by the clearing of protective vegetation, and by changing the levels of impounded waters so that the larvae are periodically flooded or left high and dry. The introduction of natural enemies, such as minnows that feed on larvae, is sometimes helpful. Adult mosquitoes may be killed by insecticides. Both pyrethrum dust and DDT are satisfactory for this.

Human beings may be protected from mosquitoes by placing dwellings and camps more than a mile (the mosquito's flying distance) from malarious villages and breeding places of mosquitoes. The screening of dwellings likewise provides an effective barrier between the host and the parasite. Wearing protective clothing and the use of chemical repellents are also useful. Another important factor in malaria control is the provision of adequate treatment for all person who carry gametocytes in their blood because these persons constitute the reservoir of infection for the mosquitoes.

Malaria prevention has been successful in temperate and subtropical regions, but has been less successful in the tropics where environmental conditions favor the development of mosquitoes.

VIRUSES

The Virus of Yellow Fever   Yellow fever, a disease of man and of jungle animals, is caused by a filtrable virus that is transferred by the bite of the *Aedes aegypti* mosquito and also by other mosquitoes. The virus is present in the blood of the yellow-fever victim for the first three days of illness, and during this period is transmissible to the insect host. After an incubation period of twelve days, the infected mosquito carries the virus for life.

In man, the virus enters the blood stream, then invades and destroys cells of the liver, kidneys, and intestine. After an incubation period of three to six days, the victim develops an acute disease characterized by fever, prostration, headache, backache, black vomit, and jaundice. Severe infections associated with marked jaundice, hemorrhage, and suppression of urine, usually result in death between the fourth and seventh day. Although during epidemics, the mortality rates may be as high as 60 per cent, the disease sometimes occurs in mild form, especially in children.

All persons are susceptible unless they have survived one attack of the disease or have been inoculated with yellow-fever vaccine. The vaccine is prepared from virus that has been attenuated by passage through animals and through tissue cultures. As a result of this treatment, the virus loses its ability to destroy liver cells, but retains its ability as an antigen, which stimulates the development of a lasting immunity. Immunity after vaccination develops within a week and lasts for at least six years. Since yellow-fever vaccine deteriorates rapidly, it should be used within an hour after the dried concentrated vaccine is put into solution.

PREVENTION   The experiments of Carlos Finlay and Walter Reed opened the way to scientific methods of prevention by eradicating mosquitoes and by protecting men from mosquitoes. As a result, the disease virtually disappeared from Cuba and Panama. So promising were these early results that men were confident that yellow fever could be completely eliminated. However, that hope faded with the discovery of the virus in the blood of monkeys and other jungle animals. It is thought also that this jungle fever may be transmitted by several other mosquitoes as well as by the *Aedes aegypti*. Jungle fever is the name applied to yellow fever of animals. Men who work in the forests should be protected by vaccination, since mosquito control in the jungle is obviously impossible. Recent reports indicate that jungle fever is traveling northward in Central America.

As long as the United States was at least ten days' sailing distance from regions where yellow fever occurs, there was little danger of importing the virus because the infected person would develop the disease before he reached port. Since travel speed has increased, this protection no longer exists. Now any airplane from South America and Africa may bring with it infected mosquitoes or infected persons who may travel about before developing the disease, and, in the course of their travels, infect local mosquitoes with the virus. It is therefore important that all planes coming from the tropics be treated to kill mosquitoes.

Mosquitoes capable of transmitting yellow fever are present in many parts of the world. To prevent the spread of yellow fever, the following precautions are essential:

1. Destruction of the mosquito vectors—*Aedes aegypti* and others.
2. Destruction of mosquitoes carried by ships and airplanes.
3. Exclusion of nonimmune persons from areas where the disease occurs.
4. Vaccination of nonimmune persons, especially travelers.

The Virus of Dengue Fever The virus of dengue fever causes an acute infection characterized by fever, pain in the joints and muscles, severe headache, enlarged lymph nodes, and commonly a rash which appears on the third to the fifth day. Like malaria and yellow fever, it is found chiefly in tropical and subtropical regions including the Philippines. In the United States, dengue fever occurs in the states which border on the Gulf of Mexico.

The virus develops in human beings and in the *Aedes aegypti* and *Aedes albopictus* mosquitoes. It is transferred to man by the bite of an infected mosquito and is present in the blood of the infected person during the last part of the incubation period (four to fifteen days) and for the first four days of the disease. During this period, the virus may be transferred to the mosquito host where it develops for eleven days. After this period, the mosquito is capable of transmitting the infection during the remainder of its life. All persons appear to be susceptible to dengue fever. Recovery from the disease results in a specific immunity which lasts for several years. A second attack of dengue may be caused by another strain of the virus. A vaccine, prepared using virus grown in mouse brain, is being used experimentally.

It has been suggested that jungle animals may serve as a reservoir of infection for the virus of dengue as they do for yellow fever.

The methods for control are similar to those used in malaria. They include: protecting mosquitoes from persons infected with dengue fever; and protection of human beings against mosquitoes by screening and by eradication of insects.

Encephalitis Viruses   A large variety of living and nonliving stress agents are capable of disturbing the structure and function of the central nervous system giving rise to an inflammation of the brain (encephalitis) or of the brain and cord (encephalomyelitis). Encephalitis may occur as a result of chemical poisoning (alcohol, carbon monoxide, arsenic, diphtheria toxin) and may on occasion follow vaccination with rabies, smallpox, or pertussis vaccines.* In addition, a variety of infections—syphilis, measles, mumps, malaria, and typhus— may at times produce brain injury.

Encephalitis viruses transmitted by arthropods characteristically invade and injure the nervous system. There are at least twelve arthropod-borne viruses which are capable of producing encephalitis in man. The three types which occur in the United States are: (1) western equine (horse), (2) eastern equine, and (3) the St. Louis. The life cycles of these viruses are undoubtedly very complex. (See Figure 80.) Available information, though possibly incomplete, suggests that man and horse are accidental hosts and are really not essential to the survival of the virus parasite. The reservoir of infection apparently is a mite that feeds on various birds and transmits the virus to its offspring (through egg and sperm cells) and to various wild and domestic birds. Certain mosquitoes (Culex, Aedes, Culisata) also transmit the virus from bird to bird and from bird to horse or man. Birds, mites, and mosquitoes re-

* Encephalitis due to smallpox and pertussis vaccines is rare.

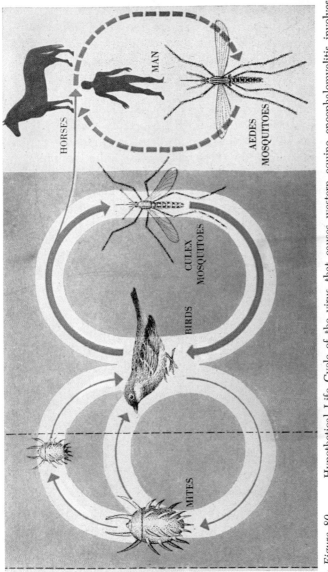

Figure 80   Hypothetical Life Cycle of the virus that causes western equine encephalomyelitis involves three lesser cycles. The possible reservoir of the virus (*left*) is mites, which pass it along to their young and to birds. The principal endemic cycle (*center*) circulates the virus among birds and Culex mosquitoes. The possible epidemic cycle (*right*) involves the infection of horses and men, who transmit virus through Aëdes mosquito. (Scient. Am., *181*.)

spond to infection by forming antibodies, but apparently suffer no injury from the virus. In contrast, the same viruses transmitted to horses or to man invade and injure large areas of the brain (thalamus, basal ganglia, gray and white matter of the cerebrum) and spinal cord. After an incubation period of five to fifteen days the infected person develops fever and various signs of disturbed nervous function (headache, drowsiness, insomnia, confusion, stupor, coma). Mortality varies with different strains (5 to 60 per cent) as does the degree of permanent damage suffered by those who recover from the infection. Complete recovery following infections of the western equine virus is more common than in the St. Louis and eastern types. However, mild and inapparent infections do occur because during epidemics many people can be found who have formed antibodies against the strain which at the time is causing disease in horses and man. Epidemics of viral encephalitis in man are often preceded by outbreaks of disease among horses.

CONTROL   These viruses are so well established in arthropod and bird populations that one cannot hope to eliminate them. Control measures are therefore directed toward decreasing the density of the mosquito vectors by the same methods that are used for controlling malaria-bearing mosquitoes. A vaccine has been developed and is being used to protect laboratory personnel, veterinarians, and horses. Since the virus is not transmitted from man to man, isolation of the infected individual is not necessary.

SUMMARY

ORGANISM	DISEASE	SITE OF INFECTION	DIAGNOSTIC PROCEDURES	ACTIVE IMMUNIZATION	PASSIVE IMMUNIZATION	CHEMOTHERAPY
Protozoa:						
Plasmodium vivax *Plasmodium malariae* *Plasmodium falciparum*	Malaria	Blood	Blood smears	None	None	Chloroquine, quinacrine, quinine, plasmochin, chloroguanide, primaquine
Viruses:						
Specific virus	Yellow fever	Liver		Virus vaccine	None	None
Specific viruses	Dengue fever	General		Virus vaccine (experimental)	None	None
Specific viruses	Viral encephalitis	Brain, spinal cord	Complement-fixation tests	Virus vaccine (experimental)	Specific antiserum (experimental)	None

SUPPLEMENTARY READINGS

BOOKS:

Burrows, W.: Jordan-Burrows Textbook of Bacteriology. 15th ed. Philadelphia, W. B. Saunders Co., 1949.

Greenberg, M., and Matz, A. V.: Modern Concepts of Communicable Disease. New York, G. P. Putnam's Sons, 1953.

Mackie, T. T., Hunter, G. W., and Worth, C. B.: A Manual of Tropical Medicine. 2d ed. Philadelphia, W. B. Saunders Co., 1954.

Maxcy, K.: Rosenau Preventive Medicine and Hygiene. 7th ed. New York, Appleton-Century-Crofts, Inc., 1951.

Rivers, T. M.: Viral and Rickettsial Infections of Man. 2d ed. Philadelphia, J. B. Lippincott Co., 1952.

Russell, P. F., West, L. S., and Manwell, R. D.: Practical Malariology. Philadelphia, W. B. Saunders Co., 1946.

PERIODICALS:

Alving, A. S., and others: Status of Primaquine. J.A.M.A., *149:* 1558–1568, 1952.

Aquilina, J. T.: Malaria in Returned Veterans of the Korean War. J.A.M.A., *149:* 834–838, 1952.

Editorial: Eradication of Malaria. J.A.M.A., *149:* 169–170, 1952.

Elton, N. W.: Sylvan Yellow Fever in Central America. Pub. Health Rep., *67:* 426–432, 1952.

Fritz, R., and Andrew, J. M.: Imported and Indigenous Malaria in the United States. Am. J. Trop. Med., *2:* 445–456, 1953.

Halverson, W. L., and others: Encephalitis Outbreak in California. Pub. Health Rep., *68:* 369–377, 1951.

Hammon, W. McD.: Encephalitis. Scient. Am., *181:* 18–21, 1949.

Public Health Reports: Insecticides and Rodenticides—1952. Recommendations for Use. Pub. Health Rep., *67:* 455–458, 1952.

Reeves, W. C.: The Encephalitis Problem in the United States. Am. J. Pub. Health, *41:* 678–686, 1951.

Russell, P. F.: The Present Status of Malaria in the World. Am. J. Trop. Med., *1:* 111–123, 1952.

Saxvik, R. O.: Mosquito Control in Water Resource Projects. Pub. Health Rep., *67:* 459–461, 1952.

Young, M. D.: Malaria during the Last Decade. Am. J. Trop. Med., *2:* 347–359, 1953.

Suggested Laboratory Experience for Unit IV

1. Demonstration of cultural methods for:
   (a) Enteric organisms
   (b) Diphtheria
   (c) Streptococci
2. Demonstration of serological test: (Note: It may be desirable to include some of these tests in the clinical courses instead of in the course in microbiology.)
   (a) Agglutination test
   (b) Precipitation test
   (c) Complement-fixation test
   (d) Neufeld typing
3. Preparation of an acid-fast stain of smears of tuberculous sputum that have been dried and fixed.
4. Examination of prepared slides of various pathogens.

Note to the Instructor: Since a license may be required for the handling of pathogens, it is wise to know the law of the state in which you reside before requesting pathological material containing living organisms. A permit is not usually required for receiving nonpathogens or commercial antigens and antisera.

MAN AGAINST PARASITES

CHAPTER 34 *Organization for Public Health*

THE RESEARCH of the past seventy years has provided a better understanding of the living cells of both host and parasite. As a result, it is now possible to control many diseases which were common in the past. Disease prevention and control for a community cannot usually be accomplished by individual effort alone. It requires an official organization to make and carry out an effective plan of action. In the United States this responsibility is delegated to the state and local health departments under the direction of medical health officers.

COMMUNITY RESPONSIBILITY FOR HEALTH IN THE UNITED STATES

In this country, community efforts to deal with health problems falls into four distinct periods:[1]

1. The colonial and pioneer period, until 1868.
2. The second period, 1869–1913.

3. The third period, 1914–1934.

4. The fourth period, 1935–.

The Colonial and Pioneer Period   During the colonial period, each isolated community dealt with its own problems as they arose. From time to time, temporary boards of health were appointed to check epidemics or to abate nuisances. These local boards eventually became a permanent part of the city government; they were organized long before the state departments. Environmental control was the chief concern of the local health boards. The citizens were offended by unsanitary and malodorous conditions, and medical opinion held that diseases might be due to inhaling vapors or miasmas given off by decaying animal and vegetable matter. Consequently, early health officials were expected to take measures against objectionable odors and thereby control disease. The health committee of New York City (1806) was concerned with: (1) pure water supplies; (2) construction of common sewers; (3) drainage of lowland marshes; (4) interment of the dead; (5) construction of walls at the water front; (6) planting trees and healthy vegetables; (7) habitation in dark cellars. No mention was made of vital statistics nor of regulations for the control of communicable disease. However, some attempts were made to control the spread of smallpox by isolation and quarantine. City records show expenditures for pest houses.

The end of the period, from 1800 to 1869, was marked by rapid growth of population. Immigrants came from all parts of Europe and both natives and foreigners moved westward. This shifting of human populations favored the transfer of microorganisms, and, since the cause of disease and the means of transmission were still unknown, epidemic followed epidemic. In 1850, Lemuel Shattuck published the *Report of the Sanitary Commission of Massachusetts,* in which he recommended the collection of vital statistics and the establishment of a full time state board of health. Later, in 1869, the first state board of health was organized in Massachusetts.

The Second Period (1869–1913)   Between 1869 and 1913, all states established boards of health. The larger cities also organized municipal boards of health with power to make and enforce rules for the control and prevention of disease. Often these official organizations, restricted in funds and personnel, failed to solve the problems of the community. Many voluntary health agencies, such as visiting nurses associations and Red Cross chapters, were organized to solve specific local health problems.

Not all voluntary organizations were small or local in their interests. The great foundations (Commonwealth, Cousens, Kellogg, Milbank, and Rockefeller) were established to promote public health. The Rockefeller Foundation, for example, sponsored an extensive study of the hookworm problem. During the same period, the United States Public Health Service investigated the cause of typhoid fever. Later, the Public Health Service and the foundations provided money and technical assistance to promote state and local health projects.

THE UNITED STATES PUBLIC HEALTH SERVICE   This organization started as the Marine Hospital Service, which was founded in 1798 to provide medical care for American sailors. The project was financed by a tax on the seamen's wages and was administered by the Collector of Customs, an official of the Treasury Department. The organization continued to grow and to take on new functions; the quarantine of ships coming from foreign ports was authorized by Congress in 1878, and funds for the establishment of the Hygienic Laboratories, now called the National Institute of Health, were provided in 1901. This new division of the service was organized so that laboratory and field studies in the cause and prevention of disease could be made. Under its direction, extensive studies were made on hookworm, typhoid, yellow fever, malaria, tularemia, Rocky Mountain spotted fever, typhus, dysentery, equine encephalitis, and Q fever.

In 1912, long after the organization had outgrown its original title, the name was changed to the United States Public Health Service. However, it remained in the Treasury Department until 1939 when it was transferred to the Federal Security Agency. The Public Health Service is concerned with national and international problems of health and disease. Its function may be stated as follows:

"Conduct and support of research and training in medical and related sciences, and in public health methods and administration;

[Provision] "of a full range of medical and hospital services to persons authorized to receive care from the Service, and aid in the development of the Nation's hospital and related facilities;

[Assistance] "to States in application of new knowledge to the prevention and control of disease, the maintenance of a healthful environment, and the development of community health services."*

Hereafter, the work of the Public Health Service† will be introduced only as it influences the progress of other organizations in the third and fourth periods.

The Third Period (1914–1934)   During the third period, interest centered in the development of local organizations. Federal and foundation funds were spent on rural health problems. As a result of grants-in-aid, full-time local health services on a county, township, or district basis, were increased from fourteen in 1915, to 963 full-time units operating under local authority providing service to 1400 counties and 276 municipal health departments in 1951. The minimum staff for a local health unit consists of a medical health officer, one or more public health nurses, a sanitarian, and a clerk. A well-developed local health unit aims to collect vital statistics, control communicable disease, prevent disease by immunization and environmental control, as well as to develop programs promoting the health of mothers, infants, preschool children, school-age children, and industrial workers. It will be seen that the original functions of sanitation and communicable disease control have been enlarged to include the protection and pro-

* Federal Security Agency: The Public Health Service Today. Washington, D. C., Federal Security Agency—Public Health Service Publication No. 165, 1952.

† Space does not permit a detailed discussion of the activities of the Public Health Service. A comprehensive outline is found in the pamphlet, *The Public Health Service Today, 1952.*

motion of individual health. Medical research, too, has recently been added to the duties of many official public health agencies.

The Fourth Period (1935–   )   In 1935, the first Federal Social Security legislation was passed. Title V of this bill allotted money to the Children's Bureau to aid state and local health work for maternal and child care and for the care of crippled children. Title VI provided funds, to be administered by the United States Public Health Service, to improve local and state health services. Since that time, federal funds have been provided for extensive research projects for the control of cancer (1937), venereal disease (1938), tuberculosis (1944), heart disease (1948), and for programs for mental hygiene (1946), for the development of hospitals and health centers (1947), and for dental research (1948). By 1951, 85 per cent of the people of the United States living in 1800 counties were provided with local health service, leaving about 15 per cent of the population without that protection.

The research of the last two decades has developed a better understanding of the relation of nutrition, infection, and emotional factors to the well-being of the individual. As a result, the emphasis is shifting from the prevention of disease to the promotion of optimum health. In fact, both aims and methods in the prevention of certain diseases are changing. For example, booster doses of diphtheria toxoid are advocated for older children. Furthermore, it is no longer considered either practical or desirable to prevent measles and mumps in children over five years of age. Although methods and emphasis change, the control and prevention of disease will continue to be an important duty of the public health official. Modern methods of transportation make this imperative since airplanes may import persons during the incubation period of a disease which may not be recognized at the time of entry; infected animals and insects, capable of transmitting parasites to man, may also travel by plane. Furthermore, as diseases transferred from man to man are brought under control the relative importance of infections transmitted by animals increases. Considerable space in current periodicals is devoted to animal diseases such as Q fever, leptospirosis, equine encephalitis, and trichinosis. These facts suggest that the struggle against parasites is still an unfinished battle—one which can be more successfully waged in time of peace than in war.

INTERNATIONAL RESPONSIBILITY FOR HEALTH

It has long been recognized that health problems are not confined by national borders. During the last fifty years, a number of international health organizations have been formed. These include the Pan American Sanitary Bureau, the International Office of Public Health, the Health Organization of the League of Nations, and the Health Division of UNRRA (United Nations Relief and Rehabilitation Administration). The latter was temporary and went out of existence in 1946. The functions of the first two have been taken over by the new World Health Organization.

World Health Organization   The San Francisco Conference (1945) made arrangements for the calling of an International Health Conference which convened in New York in June, 1946. This meeting was attended by delegates from fifty-one members of the United Nations and thirteen nonmember states. The main task of the conference was the writing of the constitution for the World Health Organization and the appointment of an Interim Commission consisting of eighteen states to carry on the work of the body until the permanent organization is completed. The objective of the Organization is "the attainment by all peoples of the highest possible level of health." Its activities include major projects for the control of malaria, tuberculosis, and venereal diseases as well as programs for the improvement of nutrition, maternal and child health, and environmental sanitation.

The work of the World Health Organization is carried out by three organs: (a) The World Health Assembly, consisting of delegates from member states which will be responsible for making final decisions; (b) The Executive Board, consisting of delegates from eighteen states; and (c) A permanent Secretariat, consisting of a Director General and Staff. He will act as the chief administrative officer of the World Health Organization.

SUMMARY

1. Community organizations in the form of local and state health departments were developed to assist in preventing disease and to promote health. The history of these organizations falls into four periods:

    a. The colonial and pioneer period when sporadic efforts were made to solve the health problems of the city or village;

    b. The second period when state health departments were organized in all states;

    c. The third period when many local health departments were organized and enlarged as a result of aid from the foundations and from the United States Public Health Service;

    d. The fourth period when the support of local and state health projects was strengthened by Federal funds.

2. The need for vigilance on the part of health officials has been increased by social conditions growing out of the war.

3. The World Health Organization has been organized to deal with the international aspects of health problems.

REFERENCE

1. Mustard, H. S.: Need of More Adequate Public Health Programs in Several States. Am. J. Pub. Health, 32: 957–964, 1942.

SUPPLEMENTARY READINGS

BOOKS:

    Castiglioni, A.: A History of Medicine. 2d ed. New York, Alfred A. Knopf, 1947.

    Chayer, M. E.: Nursing in Modern Society. New York, G. P. Putnam's Sons, 1947.

    Dublin, L. I.: Twenty-five Years of Health Progress. New York, Metropolitan Life Insurance Co., 1937.

    Dublin, L. I.: Health Progress, 1936–1945. New York, Metropolitan Life Insurance Co., 1948.

    Federal Security Agency: The Public Health Service Today. Public Health Service Publication No. 165. Federal Security Agency, Public Health Service. United States Government Printing Office, Washington, 1952.

    Matt, F. D., and Roemer, M. J.: Rural Health and Medical Care. New York, McGraw-Hill Book Co., 1948.

    Moutin, J. W., and Flook, E.: Guide to Health Organizations in the

United States 1951. Washington, D. C., Federal Security Agency—Public Health Service Publication 196, 1953.

Mustard, H. S.: An Introduction to Public Health. 3d ed. New York, The Macmillan Co., 1953.

Smillie, W. G.: Public Health Administration in the United States. 3d ed. New York, The Macmillan Co., 1947.

PERIODICALS:

Editorial: W.H.O. and You. Am. J. Pub. Health, *43:* 339, 1953.

Koos, E. L.: New Concepts in Community Organization for Health. Am. J. Pub. Health, *43:* 466–469, 1953.

Meyer, A.: A National Health Program—What the Public Expects and How to Organize It. Am. J. Pub. Health, *39:* 308–313, 1949.

Parran, T., and Boudreau, F. G.: The World Health Organization: Cornerstone of Peace. Am. J. Pub. Health, *36:* 1267–1272, 1946.

World Health Organization: Development and Constitution of W.H.O. Chron. World Health Organ., *1:* 1–43, 1947.

APPENDIX

THE MICROSCOPE

The Structure of the Microscope   The compound microscope is an expensive precision instrument which deserves to be handled with care. It consists of strong mechanical structures that support or control the lens systems. Multiple lenses are mounted in removable cases at either end of the long cylinder called the *body tube*. The lens system at the upper end of the tube is called the *ocular* or *eyepiece,* whereas the lenses at the lower end are referred to as *objectives.*

A good light is the first requisite for seeing through a microscope but direct sunlight should never be used because it may injure the lenses. Indirect daylight or light from an electric lamp with a frosted bulb may be used as a source of light. Proper illumination may be attained by adjusting the mirror so that it reflects light through the substage condenser— a device consisting of lenses that centers the light so that it travels through the objective and the eyepiece to the eye of the observer. The mechanical structures and the path of light rays through the microscope are shown in Figure 81. As the proper adjustment of the lens system depends upon the mechanical parts of the microscope, these structures will be considered first.

The Use of the Microscope
1. Clean the lenses with lens paper.
2. Place the low-power objective (16 mm.) in position.
3. Adjust the mirror so that an even white illumination is secured. If in doubt, remove the eyepiece and observe the light through the objective alone. Continue to adjust mirror until a circular area of white light is seen. The field should be free from shadows, dark spots, and glare. Replace the eyepiece.

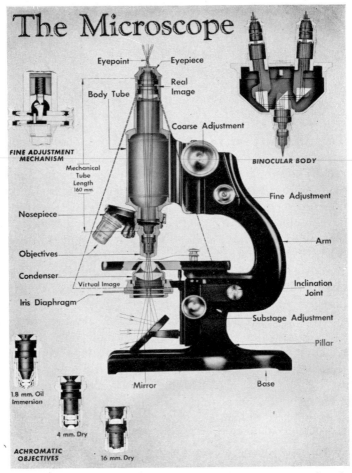

The Microscope

Eyepoint — — Eyepiece

Real
Image

Body Tube

Coarse Adjustment

FINE ADJUSTMENT
MECHANISM

BINOCULAR BODY

Mechanical
Tube
Length
160 mm.

Fine Adjustment

Nosepiece

Arm

Objectives

Condenser

Virtual Image

Inclination
Joint

Iris Diaphragm

Substage Adjustment

Pillar

Mirror

Base

1.8 mm. Oil
Immersion

4 mm. Dry

ACHROMATIC
OBJECTIVES

16 mm. Dry

Figure 81   The compound microscope showing parts and path of
light through the instrument. (American Optical Co.)

4. Place the slide on the microscope stage.
5. To focus the low-power objective (16 mm.):
   a. Lower the substage condenser.
   b. Lower the body tube with the course adjustment screw
      until the tip of the objective is about ¼ inch from the
      slide. Always keep the tip of the objective in plain
      view when lowering the body tube.

c. Keep both eyes open while looking in the microscope. Focus upward slowly until a clear image appears. *Never focus down when looking in the microscope.*

Table 29   THE LENS SYSTEM OF THE MICROSCOPE

PART	FUNCTION	REMARKS
1. Condenser	A series of lenses which increase illumination by focusing light rays from the flat mirror so that they enter the objective.	The condenser is required when using high-power or oil-immersion lenses. Use the flat mirror with the condenser.
2. Diaphragm	A shutter device for controlling the amount of light.	The size of the diaphragm is controlled by a sub-stage lever.
3. Eyepiece	Magnification 6 ×, 8 ×, or 10 ×.	
4. Mirror		
a. Flat	Reflect rays of light into the body tube.	For use with the low-power (16 mm.) lens and with the substage condenser.
b. Concave	Same.	For use with high-power (4 mm.) and without the substage condenser.
5. Objectives	*With 160 mm. tube length*	
a. Low-power (16 mm.)	Magnification 10 ×. Total magnification = (with 10 × eyepiece) 10 × 10 or 100 ×.	This objective is in focus when it is 7 mm. (about ¼ of an inch) from the object.
b. High-power (4 mm.)	Magnification about 45 ×. Total magnification = 45 × 10 or 450.	This objective is in focus when it is less than 1 mm. from the coverslip.
c. Oil-immersion (1.8 mm.)	Magnification about 95 ×. Total magnification = 95 × 10 or 950.	This objective must be immersed in oil. It is in focus when it is less than 1 mm. from the object.

6. To focus with the high-power objective (4 mm.):
   a. A coverslip must be used for observation with high power.
   b. Raise the substage condenser with the diaphragm open.
   c. Lower the body tube *slowly* until the lens almost touches the coverglass.

Table 30   THE MECHANICAL STRUCTURE AND FUNCTIONS OF
THE MICROSCOPE

PART	FUNCTION	DIRECTIONS FOR USE
1. Adjusting screws a. Coarse	Screw to raise or lower body tube.	When lowering tube, watch the objective to avoid crashing into the slide. *Always* focus upward when looking into the microscope.
b. Fine	Screw to bring the object into sharp focus.	During observation, keep the fine adjustment screw moving very slightly in either direction.
c. Substage	Screw to raise or lower the substage condenser.	Top surface should be parallel with stage when high-power or oil-immersion lenses are used. It should be lowered when the low-power lens is used.
2. Arm	Supporting structure.	To carry the microscope, grasp the *arm* firmly with one hand and support the *base* with the other hand.
3. Base	Supporting structure.	
4. Body tube	Supporting structure for lens system.	Control the position of the body tube by turning the coarse adjustment screw.
5. Nosepiece	Supporting structure for the objectives.	Watch the tip of the objectives while rotating the nosepiece when changing objectives to avoid contact with slide or stage.
6. Pillar	Supporting structure connecting the base and the arm.	
7. Substage mounting	Supporting structure for the condenser.	
8. Stage	Supporting structure for the object to be examined.	
9. Stage clip	A device for fixing the position of the glass slide.	

    d. Focus upward *very slowly* until the image appears. If rapid or jerky movements carry the objective out of focus repeat c and d until a successful focus is obtained. Remember that the high-power objective is in focus only when it is very near the object.

    e. Focus with the fine adjustment.

    f. If necessary, adjust light by partially closing the diaphragm with the substage lever.

7. To focus with the oil-immersion objective (1.8 mm.):

    a. Add a drop of immersion oil to the stained smear and place the slide on the stage of the microscope. The slide may be prepared with or without a coverslip.

    b. Raise the substage condenser and open the diaphragm.

    c. Lower the objective until it touches the oil and *almost* touches the slide or coverslip. *This objective must remain in contact with the oil,* i.e., *immersed in oil.*

    d. *Focus upward very slowly* until the image appears. If the contact between the front of the objective and the oil is broken, repeat c and d.

    e. Focus with the fine adjustment.

The Care of the Microscope

1. General directions:

    a. Protect the microscope from mechanical shocks when transferring or using the microscope. To carry the microscope, grasp the *arm* securely with one hand and support the *base* with the other hand. Place it on a firm supporting surface during use.

    b. Protect the microscope against extreme heat or cold and against rapid changes of temperature as they may cause the cement around the lenses to crack. Therefore, do not expose a microscope to the direct rays of the sun and do not place a microscope next to a gas flame or stove.

    c. Alcohol and other solvents, except xylol (xylene) should not be used on any part of the microscope. Lens paper moistened with xylol may be used to clean lenses on which immersion oil has been allowed to dry.

    d. Protect the lenses from dust and fingerprints. Before

and after use, clean the lenses with *lens paper* giving special attention to cleaning and polishing the oil immersion lens.

e. After use—

 (1) Clean lenses with lens paper.
 (2) Lower the condenser.
 (3) Place the lower-power objective in position and lower the draw tube.
 (4) Place the microscope in case or cover and place in cupboard or locker.

2. Special directions:

 a. Dust or lint may be removed from the lenses with a small camel's-hair brush.

 b. The care of the coarse adjustment:

  (1) Remove eyepiece.
  (2) Remove draw tube.
  (3) Clean pinion and rack with a soft cloth moistened with xylol.
  (4) Lubricate with a few drops of paraffin oil (mineral oil).
  (5) If the coarse adjustment screw becomes loose following a jar or after long use, it may be adjusted by tightening the small screws which hold it in place. Use a small screwdriver and hold the supporting structure of the microscope firmly during the procedure.

Darkfield Illumination   Microscopic examinations are usually made with brightfield illumination. That is, light rays are directed into the microscope so that the stained bacteria are seen on a field of white light. In contrast, the darkfield apparatus permits the observation of unstained cells against a black background. The darkfield system depends upon the use of a special substage condenser which blocks out all but the very oblique rays of light. (See Figure 82.) These slanting rays of light are so directed that they illuminate the organisms or other objects in the field without entering the microscope. Hence, the unstained cells appear as white, glistening bodies against a black field. This method is useful in demonstrating spirochetes and other organisms which do not stain readily.

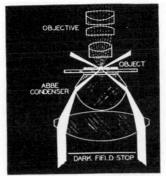

Figure 82 The path of light through an Abbe condenser with the darkfield stop. Observe that the light passes obliquely through the object but does not enter the microscope. The object therefore appears white against a black background. (Bausch & Lomb.)

Directions for the use of the darkfield apparatus can be found in books on the microscope and in catalogues and pamphlets prepared by the manufacturers of microscopes.

The Electron Microscope The electron microscope is a remarkable invention which promises to reveal new information concerning the structure of many small bodies. It is particularly useful for observing bacteria and viruses. The length of the waves of visible light limits the useful magnification of the ordinary compound microscope to approximately 1500 diameters. The new microscope which uses electronic waves, which are much shorter than light rays, magnifies objects 20,000; photographs of these objects may be further enlarged to 80,000 or 100,000 diameters. Electronic waves like those of light travel in straight lines and can be focused by electromagnets as light rays are focused by lenses. These invisible rays form visible images when they are focused on a fluorescent screen or a photographic plate. Objects are not seen through the electron microscope, instead, images are observed by projecting them on a screen or photographic plate. Gage points out three important differences between the light and the electron microscope:

1. The electron microscope costs thousands of dollars, while the compound microscope is valued in the hundreds of dollars.

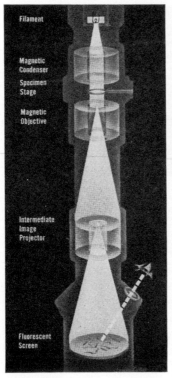

Figure 83   The electron microscope. The illustration shows how electrons are focused in the microscope. At right, Dr. V. K. Zworykin and James Hillier, of RCA, are working with the electron microscope which they helped to develop. (Science Illustrated.)

2. The parts of the electron microscope must be used in a vacuum, while the compound microscope functions in an ordinary room. (See Figure 83.)

3. The electron microscope can be used only for the examination of small, thin, dry objects which can be mounted in collodion on a fine wire screen. In contrast, the compound microscope can be used for the examination of relatively large objects mounted in air, water, or Canada balsam.

The electron microscope is, therefore, a research instrument which is not likely to replace the light microscope in the classroom laboratory. It is particularly useful for the study of viruses which are not visible in the compound microscope. Likewise, it reveals details of bacterial cells which are not visible with ordinary magnification. It is quite probable that the electron microscope will make possible many new discoveries in chemistry and biology.

SUPPLEMENTARY READINGS

Bausch, E.: Use and Care of the Microscope. Rochester, New York, Bausch & Lomb Optical Company.

Beck, C.: The Microscope. London, R. and J. Beck, 1938.

Frobisher, M.: Fundamentals of Microbiology. 5th ed. Philadelphia, W. B. Saunders Co., 1953.

Gage, S. H.: The Microscope. Ithaca, N. Y., Comstock Publishing Company, 1941.

INDEX

535